D1515419

INVESTIGATING CANADA

Front and back cover:

The Canadian Museum of Civilization in Hull, Québec, opened on 29 June 1989. The museum is located across the Ottawa River from Parliament Hill. According to Douglas Cardinal, the design architect, his design of curving walls and domed roofs is "evocative of a Canadian landscape sculpted by the natural erosion of glaciers, wind, and water."

The museum has four permanent halls that examine various aspects of Canadian life. For example, the History Hall displays 1000 years of Canadian history in geographic and chronological streetscapes.

The Architects:

Douglas Cardinal was born in Calgary, Alberta, in 1934. He came to prominence in the 1960s with his design of St. Mary's Roman Catholic Church in Red Deer, Alberta. Since then, he has designed buildings such as the Grande Prairie Regional College, the Ponoka Government Services Centre, the Edmonton Space Sciences Centre, and the St. Albert Civic and Cultural Centre. All of Cardinal's designs use wave-like shapes that suit the nature of the activities within.

Michel Languedoc, of Montréal, Québec, is an expert on the development of computer systems to aid design. Without the use of computers, the flowing curves of the museum would have been impossible to design.

GRAHAM DRAPER • GAIL RAPPOLT • WAYNE ANDREW • JOHN McLEAN • JOHN SMEES

INVESTIGATING CANADA

CONTRIBUTING EDITOR: RICHARD P. BAINE

Irwin Publishing
Toronto, Canada

Canadian Cataloguing in Publication Data

Main entry under title:

Investigating Canada

ISBN 0-7725-1619-7

1. Canada – Description and travel.   2. Anthrop-
geography – Canada.   3. Physical geography –
Canada.   I. Draper, Graham A.

FC75.I68 1990   917.1   C89-090569-X
F1017.I68 1990

COVER PHOTO: Bill Brooks / Masterfile
DESIGN: Brant Cowie / ArtPlus Limited
PAGE MAKE UP: Heather Brunton / ArtPlus Limited
FILM OUTPUT: Tony Gordon Ltd.
PROJECT EDITOR: Maryjean Lancefield
COPY EDITOR: Kate Revington
TECHNICAL ILLUSTRATION: ArtPlus Limited
MAPS: Catherine Farley
PHOTO RESEARCHER: Francine Geraci

This project has been supported by the Canadian Studies Directorate of the Department of the Secretary of
State of Canada.

1 2 3 4 5 FP 94 93 92 91 90

Printed and bound in Canada by D.W. Friesen & Sons Ltd.

Introduction

Investigating Canada was written by a group of geography teachers who wanted to create a book that would help students understand our country. Over the years we have learned a lot from our students, and this has helped us to write this book. We have learned that:

- all important learning involves change in the way people think, speak, and act. Many of us find change a bit frightening
- there are as many different ways of learning as there are people
- when we enjoy what we are doing, and it makes sense to us, we will remember it and make it a part of our way of thinking.

We hope that what we learned from our students will help you.

In the first three chapters of *Investigating Canada*, you will look at the human and physical resources of your classroom, school, neighbourhood, and province. This may seem like a simple approach, but the ideas and techniques that geographers use are best learned by studying that which is around you.

Chapters 4 to 13 examine the many different aspects of life in Canada, from the make up of our population, to the jobs we have, to the links that hold us together as a nation. Once again, human and physical resources play an important part in your understanding of the geography of the country.

The remaining two chapters are about your connections to the rest of the world. When you finish this part of the book, you should have a better sense of how Canadians fit into the global scene.

The Skill Builders (pp. 329-350) help you work through the Investigations in each of the chapters. Small marginal symbols (like the one in this margin) will point out the Skill Builders that are particularly helpful, but you should use this section of the book whenever you encounter difficulty. The Glossary (pp. 351-355) and the Index (pp. 357-363) will also be useful. Words printed in **bold type** appear in the Glossary.

Good luck to you as you set about *Investigating Canada*!

SKILL BUILDERS

COMPARATIVE THINKING

Acknowledgements

Many people have contributed to the preparation of this book. We would like to thank them all, but especially Gladys Neale, David Francis, Norma Pettit, Maryjean Lancefield, and Michael Davis. Dick Baine has been a font of wisdom throughout the project. Most of all, however, we would like to thank our families who have endured the process of book creation at our sides.

GRAHAM DRAPER
GAIL RAPPOLT
WAYNE ANDREW
JOHN MCLEAN
JOHN SMEES

Contents

CHAPTER ONE

Geography in Your Classroom and School

T O UNDERSTAND THE WAY something large works, it is usually best to start by investigating a small part of it in detail. If we begin by using the tools of geography to study the environment right around us, we can start to understand the whole world better. So, in this chapter, we are going to explore the resources of your school. Understanding these resources will help us see what our nation and world are like.

Geography

Some geographers say that geography is a way of looking at the world. Basically, geography tries to answer three questions:

WHERE is it?
WHY is it there?
WHAT is important about it?

FIG. 1-1 *(opposite)*
In what ways are the physical and human environments of this classroom like or unlike the environments in your classroom?

A main feature of geographers' work is identifying and explaining patterns on the earth's surface. By carrying out the activities that follow, you will think of more ideas about geography and develop more skills to help you identify and explain the earth's patterns.

Investigation 1.1

1. (a) Look at the following list of questions. Consider how these questions would be answered by people who have different kinds of training. Now sort the list into 2 columns based on what you think geographers do.

List A—**Problems That Geographers Could Play a Major Role in Solving**

List B—**Problems That Geographers Would Probably Not Play a Major Role in Solving**

   (i)   What is the fastest way to travel from your community to Stanley Park in Vancouver, British Columbia?
   (ii)   What causes the common cold?
   (iii) Should your community build a new arena?
   (iv)   If you were to run for mayor, what issues would you base your campaign on?
   (v)   Where, if any place, should high-rise apartments be built in your community?
   (vi)   Should the government increase family allowance and unemployment insurance benefits?
   (vii) Should a gas pipeline be built from the Canadian Arctic to the northeastern United States?
   (viii) Should Canada have the death penalty for convicted murderers?
   (ix)   Does Calgary need a subway?
   (x)   What is the quickest way to find survivors from an airplane crash near Ungava Bay, Québec?
   (xi)   In what neighbourhood should you buy a new house?
   (xii) How could you improve your chances of winning a car rally?

   (b) Write a paragraph that describes the kind of work that geographers do.

2. Draw the following chart (Fig. 1-2) in your notebook. Take those problems you said geographers could help solve, and divide them into the 3 groups shown in the chart. Each group should have at least one item. Add 3 more problems to each column. When you are finished, see if you can improve the statement you wrote in 1 (b). Discuss your statement with a classmate, and see if you have different ideas about what geographers do. Together write a statement about the geographer's role.

FIG. 1-2 PROBLEMS GEOGRAPHERS COULD PLAY A MAJOR ROLE IN SOLVING		
Where things are	Why they are there	Why these things are important

Resources in Your Classroom and School

Some problems can be solved using the tools and **resources** that geographers know best. Other problems are best dealt with using help from people who are trained in subjects other than geography. For example, suppose we want to look at the possible effects of drilling for oil and gas in the Arctic Ocean. Geographers would probably look for help from the following specialists:

- *geologists* to advise us on the places where oil and gas are likely to be found
- *marine biologists* to tell us how plants and animals in the Arctic Ocean are affected by oil and gas
- *chemists* and *physicists* to tell us how oil and gas behave in the Arctic
- *oceanographers* to give us information about water currents and ice movements

Can you suggest others?

People can't do all jobs by themselves. Some jobs need a wide range of skills and resources. The same is true on a smaller scale in your school. If you ask, there are many people who can help you solve problems. Here are some groups of people found in most schools:

- students
- teachers
- maintenance staff
- principals and vice-principals
- support staff
- community support workers
- coaches
- librarians

We often refer to people as **human resources** because of the usefulness of their knowledge and skills. Chapter 5 looks at Canada's human resources. In the meantime, let's consider the people in the above list as part of the human resources of your school.

Perhaps you don't realize that you, yourself, are also a resource. You have knowledge, skills, and attitudes that can help both you and others. Your knowledge ranges from simple facts about people, places, and things to ideas about how and why things happen the way they do. Here are some sources from which you may have gained geographic knowledge that is now stored in your memory:

- camping and holiday travels
- museums, exhibits, fairs
- newspapers, magazines, books
- radio, television, films
- computer simulations and other games
- parents, grandparents, other relatives
- neighbours, friends

Students in any classroom have a range of ages, skills, ethnic backgrounds, reading levels, and problem-solving abilities. Some classes will have more variety or differences within them than others. These classes may also have more variety in their ideas about the world. Most people agree that different ideas about the world will help us understand it better. In a subject such as geography, you and your classmates will find that the differences in your homes, ethnic backgrounds, and attitudes towards people and events will help you in understanding and solving problems.

To ensure that your knowledge is a useful resource rather than a reserve buried in your head, you must treat your ideas as miners treat rock. Miners don't enter a mine and look only for little pieces of gold. They bring all the rock that might have gold in it out of the mine, then sift and sort until they find the gold. In the same way, if you don't share your knowledge and ideas with your classroom community, the "gold" in the raw material of your mind will not be discovered. So don't be afraid to share your ideas. You have millions of pieces of remembered information that could be helpful in your geography class.

Your classroom has many other resources for finding out about the world, as well. You can also use **physical resources**. Here are some examples: computers, textbooks, atlases, maps, globes, stereoscopes, models, projectors, dictionaries, slides, films, and reference books. You are familiar with many of these resources already.

Other classrooms in your school will also have resources that will be useful to you when studying geography. For example, the science room might have balances, rocks and minerals, thermometers, compasses, altimeters, measuring devices, rain gauges, soil test kits, and beakers which you may need for some of your lessons. Stories about other lands may be found in the language room. The history classroom and the library will have resources you may need as well. For example, the library might have computers. They will be helpful when you draw graphs. Remember that you can find information useful to your study of geography all around the school.

To check your understanding of human and physical resources, study Figures 1-3 and 1-4.

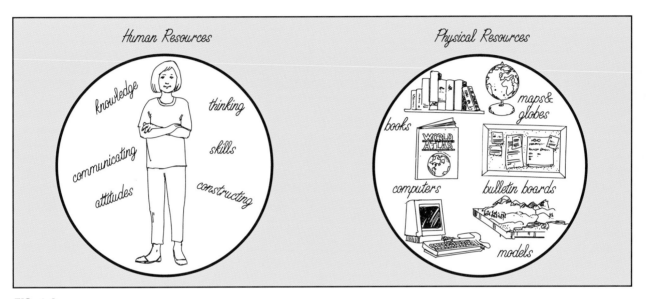

FIG. 1-3

FIG. 1-4

What geography and communication skills do these students need to use these physical resources?

Investigation 1.2

SKILL
BUILDERS
COMPARATIVE
THINKING

1. Here is a list of jobs you might do in a geography class. In your note-book, make 2 columns entitled ***Things I Can Do Well*** and ***Things I Need to Improve***. Divide all the jobs between the 2 columns.

- read maps
- make maps
- sketch neatly
- read easily
- draw posters
- make lists
- make models
- read graphs

- draw flow diagrams
- use a calculator
- research a topic
- make a presentation
- discuss ideas
- read statistics
- use atlases
- explain to others

- use a globe
- operate projectors
- listen to others
- use a computer
- interpret pictures
- ask questions
- draw graphs
- make measurements

2. Write a report on either topic (a) or (b) to show that your understanding of what geography is has improved since you began this chapter.

   (a) Write a short 3-paragraph report entitled ***"Why Geography Is Important."*** Include the things geographers do, the topics geography covers, and the skills geographers need.

   (b) Write a 3-paragraph biography of yourself showing that you have some geographical knowledge and skills. Note where your family originally came from, all the places you have lived, places you have visited, and geographic activities you enjoy. In your closing paragraph, tell how your background makes you a useful resource for the geography classroom.

3. Take a full page in your notebook and draw a chart like Figure 1-5. Title it ***Physical Resources for Studying Geography***. In the top half of the chart, list all your classroom's physical resources that would be useful to the study of geography. In the bottom half, list the physical resources in the rest of the school that would help you learn more about the subject. For each resource, indicate, in the appropriate column on the right, whether you need some training to use it. Try to think of at least 20 resources. Make sure each list has at least 5 resources.

FIG. 1-5 PHYSICAL RESOURCES FOR STUDYING GEOGRAPHY			
	Name of resource	**Training required?**	
		Yes	**No**
C L A S S R O O M	1 compass	√	
	2		
	3		
	4		
	5		
	6		
	7		
S C H O O L	1 soil test kit (science classroom)	√	
	2		
	3		
	4		
	5		
	6		
	7		

Note: Try to make your chart as easy to read as possible.

Your Classroom as a Community

Being part of a **community** is important because the members of a community help one another accomplish the jobs they decide are worth doing. Suppose your school decides to raise money to support a children's hospital. With many people helping, the fund raising wouldn't be nearly as difficult as it would if only a few individuals tried to do it.

Investigation 1.3

1. (a) Think about the following questions for a few minutes. What is a community? How can people sitting with you in your classroom be a community? Write down your ideas about what a community is.

WORKING
WITH GROUPS

(b) Find a dictionary definition of "community" and compare it to your ideas about what a community is.

(c) Now, discuss with a small group and then with your whole class whether or not your ideas fit the dictionary definition of "community."

2. (a) Copy the chart in Figure 1-6 into your notebook. In the left-hand column are 6 groups that may or may not be communities. The headings for the next 4 columns identify the most important characteristics of any community. Once you clearly understand what these headings mean, go through the chart and check off what characteristics each group has.

(b) Look at the checks for each group, and indicate in the far right column whether or not you think the group is a community.

(c) Add joining words between the ideas in the headings to form a definition of "community."

FIG. 1-6 COMMUNITIES

Characteristics of communities/groups	Two or more individuals	Definite area	Common purpose	Depend on each other	Is it a community?	
					Yes	No
Soccer team						
Library users						
Support staff at your school						
Shoppers at a grocery store						
Members of your class						
Members of Parliament						

Whether the group is the United Nations or the school basketball team, its members must work for the good of the whole to help achieve that community's aims. For example, if the members of your class don't agree that they have a common purpose, namely, for everyone to pass the course and do as well as they can, teaching and learning this year or semester will be difficult.

Sharing Resources

People in a classroom, as in all communities, use human and physical resources to help them achieve their goals. Some of you want to get good grades, some want credits, and others simply enjoy learning. Each one of you can use the available resources to achieve your goal and, at the same time, be a resource for the rest of the class.

There is a problem, however. Resources, like un-mined ore, are only **reserves** if they can be used. Having a school computer is of no use to your geography class if a math class books it first! If you can't use the computer on a certain day, then it isn't an active resource for that day. Similarly, you must share your knowledge and skills to be a valuable resource to your classmates.

Such participation suggests that talking and listening are important life skills. Beyond what we know and what we know how to do, there are skills that enable us to make our knowledge available to other people. We must share our knowledge — communicate — if we are to make some sense of the world.

Let's discuss **communication skills** further. These skills fit into four main categories — oral, written, numeric, and graphic. Each category has many sub-categories (Fig. 1-7, p. 10).

Schools have usually stressed numeric and written skills; but they are now putting more emphasis on oral and graphic ones. The growing use of calculators, computers, and video cassettes, as well as greater knowledge about the way the brain works, has brought about this change.

FIG. 1-7 COMMUNICATION CATEGORIES

Written		Graphic	
	printing on a map or graph		using overhead transparencies
	making lists		sketch mapping
	making charts		drawing accurate maps
	making point-form notes		field sketching
	expanding points into sentences		sketching from pictures or slides
	answering in sentence form		making flow diagrams
	explaining		drawing profiles or cross sections
	writing paragraphs		making graphs
	writing reports or stories		making labelled diagrams
	writing up experiments		
Numeric	calculation	**Oral**	explaining
	accounting and budgeting		questioning
	making tables		listening
	recording measurements		discussing in a group
	using formulas		acting a role in a game

Some activities involve a combination of these skills. Using a computer, making a videotape, making a model, doing an experiment, and preparing a report or presentation are examples of more complex forms of communication.

As a resource in the classroom, you will be better at some forms of communication than others. Think about which forms of communication you are best at and which ones you need to improve. When you do projects or assignments, be sure to consider your strengths carefully.

As a learner, you will find some learning methods easier for you than others. Refer to Figure 1-10 (p. 12) to consider how well you learn by various methods.

FIG. 1-8   *Your teacher is a valuable human resource.*

FIG. 1-9   *The communication skill of listening is important for gathering information about the world around you.*

FIG. 1-10 METHODS OF LEARNING

Individual workbook/exercises	Group activities
Notes taken from chalkboard	Field work
Slides and filmstrips	Library use for research
Lectures	Activity centres
Demonstrations	In-class projects
Film/video-based lessons	Homework
Computer-assisted learning	Textbook and questions
Experiments/labs	Discussions/debates

Investigation 1.4 will help you (and your teacher) identify your strengths as a resource in your classroom and the areas where you will need help and support.

Investigation 1.4

1. (a) Looking at Figure 1-7 (p. 10), determine in what communication categories your strength as a resource lies. Which types of communication do you need help with? Write a sentence about each of your assessments using the word "resource."
   (b) In your notebook, make a chart with 3 columns. Entitle the chart **How I Learn** and the columns **Best**, **OK**, and **With great difficulty**. Using Figure 1-10, sort the 16 items into the 3 columns in your chart.
2. Practise your communication skills by trying the following:
   (a) Find a map in this book, then describe it in words to a classmate.
   (b) Locate and study a table of numbers in the text. Write in words one thing you learned from the table.
   (c) Without speaking, study a photograph in the text with a friend, and write a description each. Now, share your written work. Write a new description together, using the best ideas from your earlier work.
   (d) In the text, locate and study a photograph. Make a simple sketch of it.

Summing Up

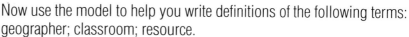

Investigation 1.5

1. Before we leave the study of your classroom, let's be sure we understand some ideas basic to this book. Working in groups of 3 or 4, discuss thoroughly what the following words mean: community; environment; human resources; physical resources; planning; learning methods; oral; written; graphic; numeric.
2. One way to be sure you understand an idea is to see whether you can define it clearly. Here is a model for definition writing that will be helpful to you throughout the book:

FIG. 1-11 MODEL FOR DEFINITION WRITING

A(n) *(idea to be defined)* *is a* *(general classification)* ***that (who)*** *(things that make it different from others in this classification).*

Using this model, your definition of a community might look like this:

A *community* ***is a*** *group of two or more people* ***who*** *occupy a definite area, share a common purpose, and depend on each other.*

Now use the model to help you write definitions of the following terms: geographer; classroom; resource.

3. Another way to check your understanding is to map, sketch, or make a diagram of something. Label your work so that it creates a mental map or picture in your mind. Don't think of your drawing as "art"—it's only a way of making an idea clear to you. Now, practise doing this in your notebook by making quick, labelled, pencil sketches of the following:

SKILL
BUILDERS
SKETCHING

- one wall of your classroom
- top or bird's-eye view of the floor plan of your classroom
- map showing streets from home to school with arrows showing your route
- one wall map hanging in the classroom
- a diagram to show your idea of human resources in the classroom

By now you will have formed a model in your mind of the things geographers do, the skills they need, and the resources they use. This mental model will be helpful to you in the rest of the book when you study your local area, your country, and the world.

CHAPTER TWO

Your Neighbourhood and Municipality

I N THIS CHAPTER YOU WILL investigate your local neighbourhood and municipality through maps. Maps are easiest to read and make the most sense when you can match them with real things or pictures. So, try to find as many different kinds of maps of your local area as you can.

The geographer's most important tool is the map. Throughout this book and indeed, throughout life, you will need to read and interpret many kinds of maps. You already learn from maps in atlases and textbooks, but you may not have thought about how often you use them on other occasions. When you watch the weather and news on TV, when you play a computer game, or when you are trying to find your way in a park or shopping mall, you also rely on these resources.

Maps have a language of their own, and to understand them you need to learn that language. This language includes numbers, words, colours, and symbols, so in some ways it's complex. Once you learn to read the language, however, you can use it to understand where you are, plan where you want to go, and make decisions about the present and future.

Building Images Through Maps

Sitting in a classroom, we can easily get information just by looking around. It's harder to get facts about the environment beyond the classroom. Fortunately, pictures and maps of an area will help you understand less familiar environments.

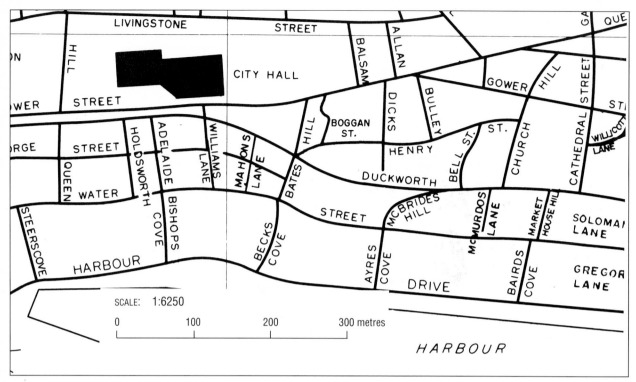

FIG. 2-1   *A street map of St. John's, Newfoundland*

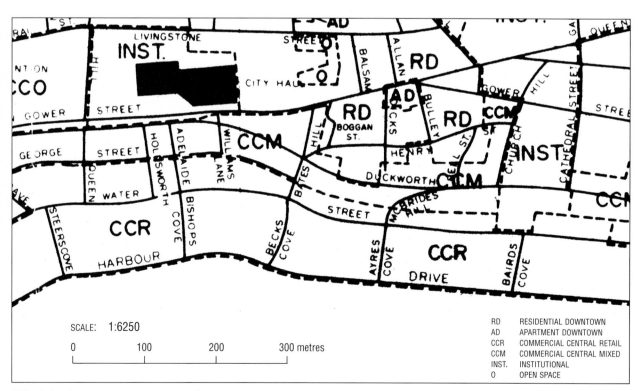

FIG. 2-2   *Part of a land-use map of St. John's, Newfoundland*

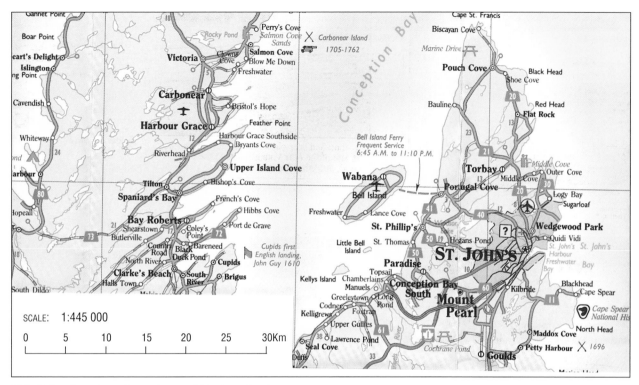

FIG. 2-3 *A portion of a road map of Newfoundland*

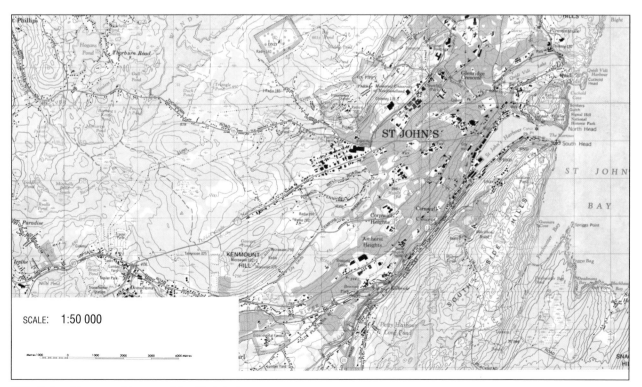

FIG. 2-4 *A topographic map of the St. John's area*

Figures 2-1 to 2-4 (pp. 16-17) show four different maps of St. John's, Newfoundland. Each map is at a different scale and gives a different kind of information about the area. A couple of the maps give a lot of detail. Others show only a little. By putting the ideas in all the maps together, you can build an image of Newfoundland's capital city.

Investigation 2.1

1. Copy the chart in Figure 2-5 into your notebook. Using the 4 maps in Figures 2-1 to 2-4, fill in the blanks.

FIG. 2-5 COMPARING MAPS

	Street map	Land-use map	Provincial road map	Topographic map
Scale				
Kinds of information shown				
Symbols used				
Uses of map				

2. Copy the chart in Figure 2-6 into your notebook. Now consider how you can use maps in many ways. Match up the activities, listed (a)-(j), with the 4 types of maps identified in Figure 2-6. Mark each activity's letter under the most appropriate type of map.

FIG. 2-6 MAP USES

Street map	Land-use map	Provincial road map	Topographic map

Activity
(a) finding your way around a city (town, village)
(b) deciding on a good place to build an apartment building
(c) determining the direction in which rain will run off during a storm
(d) figuring out the fastest surface route to a neighbouring city or town
(e) calculating the distance between your home and the nearest beach

(f) determining the highest land within 1 km of your home
(g) plotting the location of churches
(h) finding the best place to park near a football stadium
(i) determining the latitude and longitude of your home
(j) calculating the percentage of land in your community set aside for parks

SKILL

BUILDERS

WORKING
WITH GROUPS

After you have finished, discuss each choice with 2 or 3 classmates. Make sure you all agree on where you have put (a)-(j). Get help from your teacher if you can't decide.

3. Find a street map, a land-use map, a provincial road map, and a topographic map of your local area or the town or city nearest you. Draw the chart in Figure 2-5.
   (a) Fill in the chart for these 4 maps of your own local area.
   (b) List 3 ways in which the maps are different.
   (c) List 2 ways in which all the maps are the same.
   (d) Use the model for writing definitions on p. 13 to write a good definition of **map**.
   (e) In what ways do maps help you create an image of your local area?

Investigating Your Neighbourhood

You and your classmates live in a specific area. Each of you knows particular places in that area well. These places might be stores, churches, malls, or other buildings, or they might be public places such as parks or street corners. The places with which you're most familiar and where you often spend time make up your **neighbourhood**.

Although everyone in your class may not share the same neighbourhood, the areas will probably overlap. The total area can be called the class neighbourhood. Neighbourhood size varies quite a bit. Outside a city, the class neighbourhood may cover an area many kilometres in diameter; in a city, neighbourhoods may be measured in blocks rather than kilometres. The conditions within each area may also vary widely. Neighbourhoods make interesting studies.

FIG. 2-7 *Shopping malls and plazas are often meeting places for people. They are areas where neighbourhoods overlap. Can you think of any other areas where neighbourhoods overlap?*

Investigation 2.2

1. (a) Obtain a street map that includes your school area. Mark your home, school, and the route that you take to school on the map. Measure the distance in kilometres.
   (b) Decide on the limits or boundaries of your neighbourhood by marking on your map 10 places you usually visit several times during a week. Draw a line to enclose the 10 places.
   (c) When everyone in the class has finished, transfer everybody's lines to a class map. How might you identify a class neighbourhood?
   (d) Use the definition-writing model (p. 13) to write a general definition of "neighbourhood".
2. Neighbourhoods are made up of more than land and buildings. They also include people. A neighbourhood offers a combination of human and physical resources to the people who live in it. Let's find out what your neighbourhood has to offer.
   (a) Make a list of all the human and physical resources you think should be available within a neighbourhood. Use general headings for related resources, for example, **health services** (drugstores, hospitals, doctors, etc.), **emergency services** (ambulances, fire department, police department, etc.), and **institutional services** (libraries, schools, churches, etc.).

(b) Obtain or sketch a large scale map of your neighbourhood. (You may want to use a street map and enlarge the section you need by using a photocopier.) Locate all examples of one resource you listed in (a). Use telephone books and street maps to figure out the locations and names of this resource. If you have chosen a resource of which there are many examples, you can mark just 25 of them on your map.

(c) For the resource you chose in (b), describe what you think would be the best or ideal situation for your neighbourhood. For example, you might decide that for ideal emergency services, there should be a firehall every kilometre and a hospital every 2 km.

(d) Estimate how closely you think your neighbourhood meets the ideal you have described. Choose excellent, average, or poor as a rating. List 2 reasons for your rating.

(e) Examine the maps your classmates made of other resources.

(f) Write a report, **The Benefits of Living in Our Neighbourhood**. Use specific examples to support your comments.

Your neighbourhood is part of a larger community called a **municipality**. Each municipality has political boundaries that separate it from other municipalities.

Today eight of every ten Canadians live in **urban areas**. An urban area is an area of high population density, trade, transport and industry; in other words, a town or city. Each town or city has a local government or organization that is responsible for providing services for people who live within its boundaries. The services include snow plowing, waste disposal, and road building.

Governments at this local level are called municipal governments, and we speak of towns and cities as municipalities. **Rural areas**, or open areas with small or scattered populations, also have municipal governments. Usually called **townships**, these governments may contain several villages within their boundaries.

Investigation 2.3

1. (a) Find out some facts about your municipality. Here are some ideas you could begin with:
   (i)   When was the area settled?
   (ii) In what year did it become a municipality?
   (iii) What is its population?
   (iv) What is its total area in square kilometres?
   (v)   Who is the chief elected official?

(b) Make a sketch map of your municipality, showing its boundaries and the location of major transportation routes. Include your neighbourhood boundary and the location of your school on the map. (Remember, a sketch map is not "art." It is a way of showing information.)

The earth's surface is a physical resource, and in any municipality people use land in a variety of ways. The main land use categories are:

(a) **Commercial** Land occupied mainly by places where people go to shop for goods or services. It is usually found close to important roadways or in **Central Business Districts (CBDs)**.

(b) **Industrial** Land used mostly by factories, workshops, and warehouses. Since industries often need large amounts of land, new ones often locate near the edges of built-up areas.

(c) **Residential** Land used mainly for homes. Apartments, townhouses, semi-detached and single homes, and mobile homes are included.

(d) **Institutional** Land used for schools, hospitals, churches, government buildings, and libraries.

(e) **Transportation** Land used for such purposes as roads, train tracks, airports, bus stations, parking lots.

(f) **Recreational** Land used for parks, arenas, tennis courts, baseball diamonds, etc. Green spaces and buildings for recreation are included.

Each land use is determined by the characteristics of the area and the needs of the activity itself. For example, a service station needs a location convenient to many drivers. A service station that is located close to a heavy traffic area has a better chance of success than one that is built on a quiet side street. Similar forms of land use tend to be located close to each other. As a result, land uses in a municipality may form patterns that can be mapped.

FIG. 2-8   Examples of land uses in municipalities
a Commercial,   *b* Industrial,   *c* Residential,   *d* Institutional,   *e* Transportation,   *f* Recreational

Investigation 2.4

1. From your knowledge of your municipality, describe the likely location patterns of the following:
   (i)   variety or small grocery stores
   (ii) large department stores
   (iii) elementary schools
   (iv) fast food restaurants

What factors influence the patterns of land use in a municipality or neighbourhood? Here are some ideas to consider.

Physical features Features such as lakes or rivers may influence the location of activities in a municipality. For example, a municipality's commercial centre may be built only on one side of a river because shoppers want to be able to move freely throughout the whole commercial area. The shoppers might not want to be bothered crossing a river.

Transportation systems Some businesses are attracted by a municipality's major transportation routes. Examples include fast food restaurants, gas stations, and car rental agencies.

Space requirements Auto wreckers, lumberyards, and golf courses need much space. These land users usually try to move where land is least expensive. Bookstores and offices need far less room.

Zoning decisions The elected officials of a municipality decide where activities should and should not be located. For example, they determine where unsightly or smelly activities can establish and can try to keep heavy traffic out of residential areas. They create "zones," or areas of land for particular purposes. They would therefore permit a factory to locate in an industrial zone, but not in a residential one.

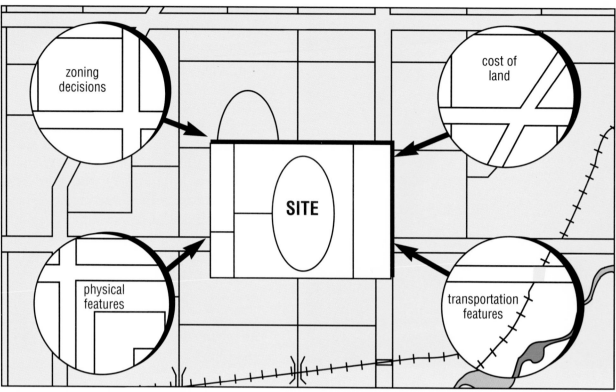

FIG. 2-9 *Where to locate in a city?*

Investigation 2.5

1. You will need a land-use map of your local area for this Investigation. Make 5 statements about patterns of land uses in your municipality. An example might be: "Most of the industrial land use is found in the northern part of the municipality between the highway and the farmland."
2. For each of the following activities, list 3 factors that the owner should consider before deciding where to locate within a community: slaughterhouse; chemical factory; daycare centre; parking lot; bus depot; football stadium; small grocery store.

Land-Use Planning

Today the population of a community may not remain the same for very long. Some people leave and others, perhaps with new ways of thinking, move into the area. People who stay in the same area may change their views as well. New ideas about the community, either brought in by new people or resulting from

changing ideas within the area, lead to changes in land uses in neighbourhoods and municipalities.

Change can be good for an area. Old, out-of-date land uses and activities may be replaced by more desirable ones. The new activities may create an excitement or new enthusiasm in an area. People often react to changes with new ideas of their own. Soon a whole area can be renewed and refreshed and be a more attractive place in which to live and work. What desirable changes are taking place in your neighbourhood or municipality? Why do you think the changes are desirable?

FIG. 2-10   *Change is always taking place in our communities. How can we ensure that the change is good?*

FIG. 2-11

Some people dislike the changes in their community. This photo shows residents' opposition to a new dump.

Change can also be harmful to a community. This is especially true if the change hasn't been carefully thought out.

- Have you ever watched attractive older houses being torn down so that developers can build apartment buildings, office buildings, or parking lots?
- What are your thoughts about cities expanding onto good farmland?

Some people think that such changes are harmful. What harmful or undesirable changes seem to be taking place in your community? Why do you think they are undesirable?

Most municipalities try to avoid change that is harmful by planning for change. Figure 2-12 shows the steps they take to plan for the future. They know change will occur, and they try to make sure it will be good for the area rather than harmful.

To plan well, municipalities and individuals must look carefully at their **assets**. Assets are the tools, people, events, activities, and resources that will help planners achieve their goals. Municipalities and individuals must also consider those things that could stand in the way of their goals, in other words, their **liabilities**. Understanding our assets and liabilities can help us plan more effectively.

FIG. 2-12 THE PLANNING PROCESS

Decide what you want to accomplish and why.
Find out what your resources are.
Figure out different ways of accomplishing what you want, using your resources.
Consider the effects your plans will have on others.
Select the best plan from your options.
Do it.
Check to see if you achieved what you wanted.

Investigation 2.6

SKILL
BUILDERS
DECISION
MAKING

1. Imagine you want to go on a 20-km bike ride this weekend.
   (a) Make a chart in your notebook similar to Figure 2-13. Put each item in the following list in the appropriate chart column: sunny, warm weather; bicycle is broken; money in the bank; have a cold; lots of homework to do; work at a variety store; new video game.

FIG. 2-13 ASSETS AND LIABILITIES

Assets (resources)	Liabilities (obstacles)

   (b) What decision does your chart suggest?
   (c) Now decide what you would really like to do this coming weekend. Do an **Assets and Liabilities** chart in which you consider how 10 factors will affect your plans.

You may find that some items are difficult to place on an **Assets and Liabilities** chart. For example, depending on the circumstances, a visit from an aunt or an uncle may or may not help you have a good time on the weekend. People use what is available to them in the best way they can to meet their goals.

If your assets outnumber your liabilities, you should be able to reach your goals. If, however, your liabilities outweigh your assets, you have a problem. You must consider your options, including the following:

- Do nothing.
- Try to change the conditions so that some of your liabilities become assets. (For example, if the weekend is snowy, switch from cycling to skiing.)
- Think of some assets that you forgot the first time. (Perhaps you can switch shifts at the variety store.)
- Try to remove some liabilities. (Getting your homework done before the weekend might help.)

You can already see that planning for your weekend can take time and isn't always simple. Imagine how hard it is then, in cities like Toronto, Montréal, or Vancouver, to make planning decisions that seem good to all groups and individuals.

Planning for Change

Changes are constantly occurring in our communities. Some changes occur quickly and often without careful planning. However, almost all Canadian municipalities now have planning departments. These departments help elected officials make better informed decisions about land-use changes.

Investigation 2.7

1. This list shows changes that might occur around your municipality:

   - large increase in number of people moving into the area
   - departure of many people from the area
   - change in climate
   - erosion of coastline
   - large numbers of young people leaving
   - fish plant shut-down
   - natural tourist attractions wiped out by acid rain
   - building of new highway
   - earthquake
   - building of new government offices
   - joining town with larger city
   - closing of railway station
   - tornado
   - trees destroyed by spruce budworm

   (a) Draw Figure 2-14 in your notebook and sort the list of possible changes to your municipality into the 2 categories.

(b) Which kind of change causes the most serious problems for people at the time it happens? Explain.

(c) Which kind of change causes the most serious long-term problems? Explain.

(d) Which kind of change is most likely to occur around your municipality?

FIG. 2-14 CATEGORIES OF CHANGES		
Force	**Happens quickly**	**Happens slowly**
Natural		
Human		

Summing Up

A planning department examines trends in a given municipality and tries to determine the best possible uses of human and physical resources. It does not work independently, however. The decisions to put plans into effect are made by elected officials who must react to many different pressures. Sometimes the pressure is from citizens' groups, sometimes from outside the community, and sometimes by other levels of government. The next chapter deals with the responsibilities of provincial governments.

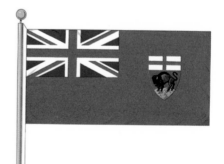

Your Province or Territory in Canada

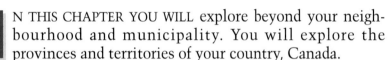

I N THIS CHAPTER YOU WILL explore beyond your neighbourhood and municipality. You will explore the provinces and territories of your country, Canada.

The first part of this chapter will help you sort out the responsibilities of various levels of government (not an easy task). You will then have an opportunity to create your own map of Canada and to make and name a whole new set of provinces and territories. As you do this, you will learn the names of major mountain ranges, rivers, resource areas, and other details about Canada.

Chapter 3 closes with a personal exercise called **Connections** which ties Chapters 1, 2, and 3 together and helps you look forward to the rest of the book.

Boundaries

As you know, your municipality is part of a larger community — your province or territory. Your province or territory is part of an even larger community — Canada. This community is made up of ten provinces and two territories, each having political boundaries that separate it from the other provinces and territories.

Each province has an elected government that governs or makes rules for the people within its boundaries. After it makes decisions, a provincial government enforces these decisions through laws and regulations. It also provides its municipalities with most of the money to pay for their operations. Unlike the

31

provinces, each territory is governed by a locally elected territorial council and by the federal government. On the map in Figure 3-1, you can see the boundaries of the provinces and territories.

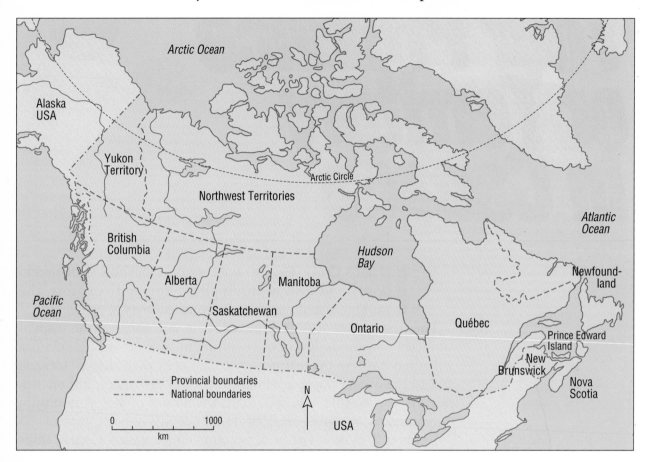

FIG. 3-1 The provinces and territories of Canada

Canadians also have a government that ties the municipalities, provinces, and territories together. This is the federal government. The federal government's political boundaries are Canada's international boundaries. This government, located in Ottawa, is responsible for those decisions that affect the whole nation. Its role is much like that of a juggler. The federal government must keep all the parts of Canada moving together. This is sometimes difficult, because the provinces and territories have different concerns. The federal government's role will be examined in Chapter 13.

Each government — municipal, provincial, and federal — must carry out all the responsibilities given to it by law. Some of these responsibilities are listed in Figure 3-2.

FIG. 3-2 GOVERNMENT RESPONSIBILITIES

Federal	Provincial	Municipal
post office	education	fire protection
defence	prisons	water supply
navigation and shipping	roads	hockey arenas
citizenship	courts	public libraries
currency and coins	marriage	parks

Having three levels of government sometimes leads to conflict or confusion about which government is responsible for a particular situation. For example, suppose a pulp and paper company allowed its **pollutants** to enter a stream that supplies the water for a town. Who would be in charge of the situation? The provincial government, which looks after natural resources? The federal government, which is in charge of maintaining waterways? Or the town, which must supply its residents with clean water? The answer isn't always easy to determine. With different responsibilities, all levels of government must co-operate with each other if the nation is to run smoothly.

Provincial Boundaries

One question geographers, planners, and other people sometimes ask is "Are the provincial boundaries in the best possible places?" You will examine this question in Investigation 3.1. In the meantime, look at Figures 3-3, 3-4, 3-5, and 3-6 (pp. 34-35) which show some of the natural or physical boundaries in Canada. As you can see, some of the provincial boundaries match the physical ones. Some don't. Would it be better if all provincial and physical boundaries matched?

Human and physical resources are distributed unevenly among the provinces. When the boundaries were created in the 1800s and early 1900s, many resources were unknown or undiscovered. Oil and natural gas were not important then. Fresh water seemed to be in never-ending supply. Waterfalls were a liability, not an asset for the production of electricity as they are today. Now that we know where most resources are, do you think the provincial boundaries should be redrawn?

The following Investigation will give you a chance to explore the boundaries of Canada's provinces and learn some more about Canadian resources. You will need to refer to an atlas of Canada. You may also find other useful maps and pictures by using the index of this text.

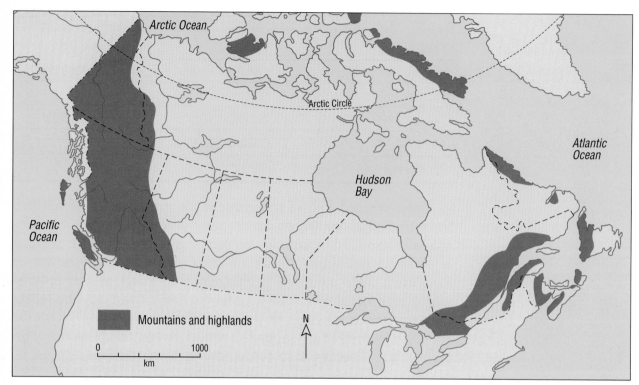

FIG. 3-3   Mountains and highlands of Canada

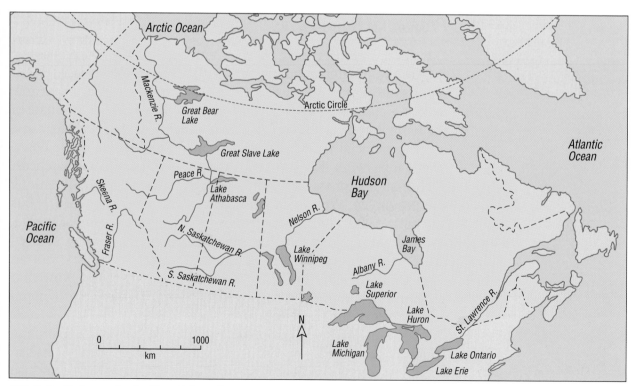

FIG. 3-4   Major water bodies of Canada

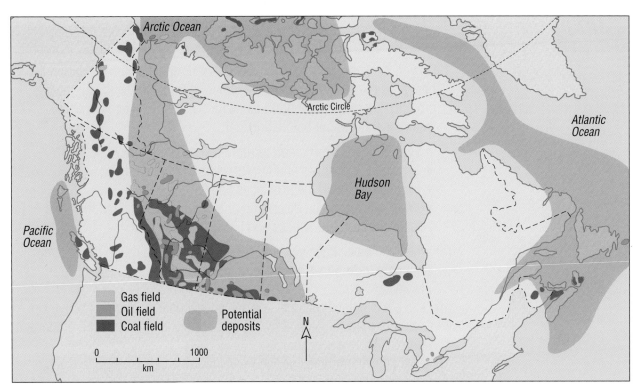

FIG. 3-5   Oil, gas, and coal reserves

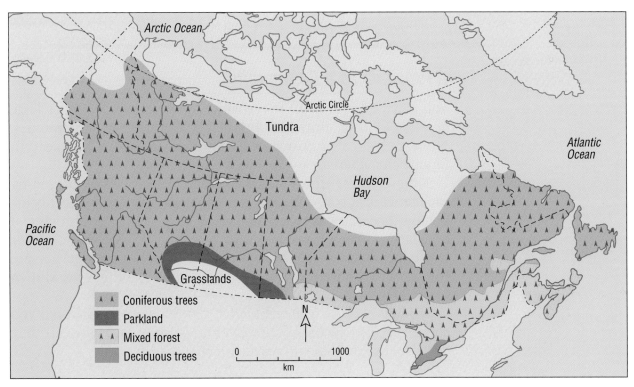

FIG. 3-6   Forest areas of Canada

Investigation 3.1

1. Do you think the provincial and territorial boundaries are located in the best possible places? Sketch the outline of Canada. Decide on the best provincial and territorial boundaries for the country. Here are some factors to think about before you start:

   • How many provinces and territories should there be?
   • Should all provinces and territories be the same size?
   • How large should the provinces and territories be?
   • What factors should determine or influence the size, number, and locations of the provinces and territories?

(a) When you have made your decisions, sketch out a rough draft of your boundary locations. Check it with your teacher. Name each of your provinces.

(b) On a blank outline map of Canada, draw and label your new provinces.

(c) Give your map a legend showing the title, scale, and any other important information.

(d) Make point-form notes providing at least one good reason for each of your boundary lines. Prepare an outline for a speech defending your boundaries.

(e) If you wish to give your speech to your class, transfer your map to a transparency so you can show it on an overhead projector.

A Province as a Community

You may find it difficult to recognize a province, especially a large one like Québec, British Columbia, or Ontario, as a community. Nonetheless, a province is a community which has certain unique characteristics.

Some of these unique characteristics are the laws passed by each provincial government. Laws about schools, exams, seat belts, income tax, sales tax, and pollution are made at the provincial legislature. They are applied throughout the province. Other special characteristics that help hold a province together are the symbols chosen by the province. Some examples are shown on page 30.

Symbols such as flags, emblems, and flowers can often tell you about the history and resources of a community. However, they can also lose their meanings due to changes over time.

Investigation 3.2

SKILL
BUILDERS
RESOURCE
CENTRE

1. Pick 2 provinces or territories (not your own), and use an encyclopedia and other reference books to figure out the meaning of all the symbols in their flags and crests.
2. For these 2 provinces or territories, make a list of other symbols, resources, or parts of their culture that help make the people into a community.
3. Make a poster with a paragraph, sketches, maps, and pictures about one of your choices. Give your poster a title.

Investigation 3.3

Connections

So far you have looked at your neighbourhood, your municipality, and your province. All of these places can be thought of as communities that you belong to. In the rest of this book, you will be taking a close look at an even larger community that you belong to — Canada.

You can easily see yourself as a member of your neighbourhood community, because that is where you spend much of your time and where you meet most of the people you know. Seeing yourself as part of the larger communities you belong to may not be quite as easy. This is because your connections with these communities are probably not as obvious. However, if you look closely, you can discover many different ways in which you are connected to places outside your neighbourhood. In the following Investigation, you will look at how many connections you have with the rest of Canada. You will also see the different ways in which you are connected with people and places there. You will use geographical methods to show the pattern of your connections with the rest of the country.

STEP 1 Trace and colour 4 maps, one for each of the following communities:
(a) *Your class neighbourhood:* Show only the borders, your home, and school.
(b) *Your municipality:* Show only the borders, important bodies of water, and the boundaries of your neighbourhood. Mark the neighbourhood in the same colour as you used for your large neighbourhood map in (a).
(c) *Your province or territory:* Show only the borders and the important bodies of water. Mark the location of your municipality with a coloured dot (the same colour that you used for the map of your municipality).

(d) *Canada:* Show only the borders, the Arctic islands, and the Great Lakes. Draw in the boundaries of your province, using the same colour as you used for the map of your province.

Give each map a title, scale, north arrow, and frame.

Glue the 4 maps onto a larger sheet of paper or Bristol board, as follows.

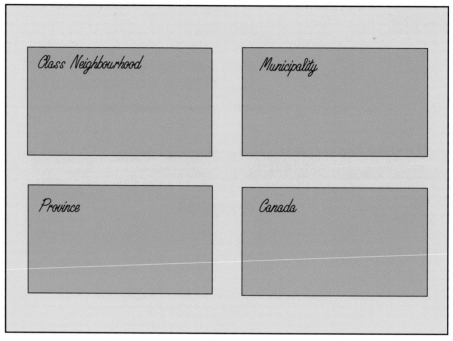

FIG. 3-7 *Organize your 4 maps like this. Make sure each map has a title.*

STEP 2 Think of as many links between you and places outside your neighbourhood as you can. To help you do this and to organize your information, look at Figure 3-8 and read the following descriptions of the various types of connections.

FIG. 3-8 MY CONNECTIONS CHART				
Type of connection	**Direct**	**Map**	**Indirect**	**Map**
Family / Friends	– my brother in Edmonton	Canada	– mother's brother in Halifax	Canada
			– Dad's sister in Flin Flon	Prov.
Travel / Vacations				

DIRECT This word describes any personal connection you have with a place. For example, you have a direct connection with any place where you have lived.

INDIRECT This word describes any connection you have with a place through a member of your household. For example, you would have an indirect connection with a place where your mother went to school. (You will probably have to ask other family members for some of this information.)

Family/Friends This category refers to relatives and friends with whom you are in contact with but who live outside your neighbourhood. For example, you might have a connection with Moose Jaw through a cousin who lives there.

Travel/Vacations Places that you have gone to for summer holidays, school trips, and family vacations count as direct connections. Places that other members of your household have visited should be included as indirect connections.

Recreation This type of connection refers to any away-from-home places where you or members of your household have played sports such as swimming, hockey, baseball, and volleyball.

Culture Wherever you have visited as a member of a group such as Scouts or Guides or as a member of a club for hobbies such as dancing, singing, antique collecting, and model-building should be listed. Remember to ask members of your family where they have gone to enjoy similar activities, as well.

Entertainment This category covers any event that you or your family attended as a spectator, for example, concerts, football or hockey games, drama festivals, and fairs.

Government Think of how you and your family are connected to your provincial or territorial capital and to the national capital. Who issues drivers' licenses? How is medical care paid for? What taxes do you or members of your household pay? Where do family allowance payments come from?

Occupation Note whether you or members of your household work outside of your neighbourhood and where.

List, in rough, all of your connections with places in Canada outside your neighbourhood. When you have done so, draw a full-page chart like the one started in Figure 3-8 and fill it in.

STEP 3 Plot each of your connection locations on one of the 3 maps of the areas outside your neighbourhood. Each location should be marked on one map only. Municipal locations should go only on the map of your municipality. Places outside your municipality but inside your province should go only on the provincial map. Places outside your province should go only on the national map. Using one colour for direct connections and another for indirect ones, draw a line from your house or school (on your neighbourhood map) to each of the locations on the other maps.

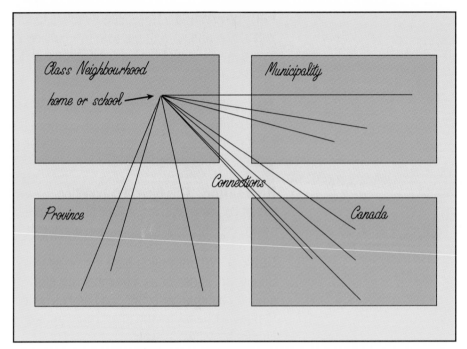

FIG. 3-9 *Your finished poster should look like this.*

STEP 4 In one paragraph, describe where most of your connections are and explain why they form this pattern.

Now write a second paragraph describing what you think the pattern of your connections might be 20 years from now.

In a third paragraph describe the possible nature of the pattern 50 years from now.

STEP 5 Compare your connections with those of others in the class, and write a class paragraph with your teacher. Be sure to note and explain the major similarities and differences in the class's connection patterns.

Summing Up

The ***Connections*** investigation concludes Chapter 3 and the first part of this book. In ***Connections*** you have seen the relationships between you and your family and all parts of Canada. ***Connections*** provides a review of the first three chapters and begins to introduce Canada as a whole country.

As you work through the rest of the book, you will often find it helpful to return to parts of Chapters 1, 2, and 3. Here, in the study of familiar local areas, you have an introduction to the basic knowledge and skills you need as a geography student.

CHAPTER FOUR

Images of Canada

AN IMAGE IS A PICTURE. When you look into a mirror or at a photograph of yourself, you see a self image. The image, of course, is not really you. It just shows or represents you.

A word, on the other hand, brings to mind a picture of someone or something. For example, when you hear the word "large," you get an idea of size. The statement "That is a large building" is likely to suggest to you a tall structure of many stories or one that covers a whole city block. Through the word "large," you can create your own mental picture of the building.

How do you form such an image? There are many possible ways. Your senses help you to do so by letting you see, hear, touch, smell, and taste. You also draw upon what you have read, learned by talking to people, seen on TV and at the movies, and noticed while travelling. All of your abilities and experiences help you form images or impressions of things.

You form images of countries as well as of people and things. In this chapter you will examine four images of Canada, images that a great many people have whether they have ever been here or not. These images may well be ones that you, yourself, have. The words suggesting these images are:

VAST	referring to Canada's size and shape
NORTHERN	referring to Canada's location
UNCROWDED	referring to where we live and how much space we have
RICH	referring to our standard of living and our many resources

You will examine these images to test their accuracy and to gain some useful impressions of Canada in general.

Impressions That You Already Have

Before you begin to examine the four images, think about the impressions that you already have of Canada. To do this you will have to depend on what you know. Look at the photographs, maps, and other illustrations throughout this book and in other available books to refresh your memory.

Investigation 4.1

1. The purpose of this Investigation is to discover your impressions of Canada.
   (a) Look at the 5-choice line in Figure 4-1. Now rate how Canada compares to most other countries in the world for each of the 20 items that follow. Each rating will reflect a personal "impression."
   (b) Title a page in your notebook **My Impressions of Canada**.
   (c) For each of the 20 impressions, write a sentence based on the 5-choice line. For example, if you thought a description at the right-hand end of the line was true of Canada, you might write in your notebook, "I believe that compared to most countries Canada has a great deal of wealth."
   (d) After you have finished (c), pick 5 descriptions that you feel very sure about. Explain to a partner why you have these impressions and try to figure out where you got them. Are your impressions based on
      (i) facts that you read or heard about from information sources such as books or newspapers?
      (ii) general observations obtained from films and TV programs?
      (iii) comments and opinions not backed up by facts?
   (e) State where you think you could find the facts to test your impressions.

FIG. 4-1 COMPARING CANADA TO OTHER COUNTRIES

I believe that compared to most other countries in the world Canada

1.	(has) little wealth	below average	average	above average	(has) a great deal of wealth
	LOW				HIGH
2.	has very few minerals				has many minerals
3.	is a young country				is an old country
4.	covers a small area				covers a big area
5.	has a small population				has a large population
6.	has few ethnic groups				has many ethnic groups
7.	has few provinces				has many provinces
8.	has few official languages				has many official languages
9.	has few traditions				has many traditions
10.	produces little food				produces a great deal of food
11.	has few lakes				has many lakes
12.	has a short seacoast				has a long seacoast
13.	has almost no unemployment				has high unemployment
14.	has few poor people				has many poor people
15.	allows little freedom of speech				allows full freedom of speech
16.	supports public education poorly				supports public education
17.	has few forests				has many forests
18.	has few parks				has many parks
19.	has few rivers				has many rivers
20.	is very cold				is very hot

2. Let's see if you can back up some of your impressions now. Work with 3 classmates.
   (a) Take a large piece of newsprint or poster paper and fold it into 4.
   (b) Entitle each of the 4 sections, or quadrants, as shown in Figure 4-2 (p. 46).

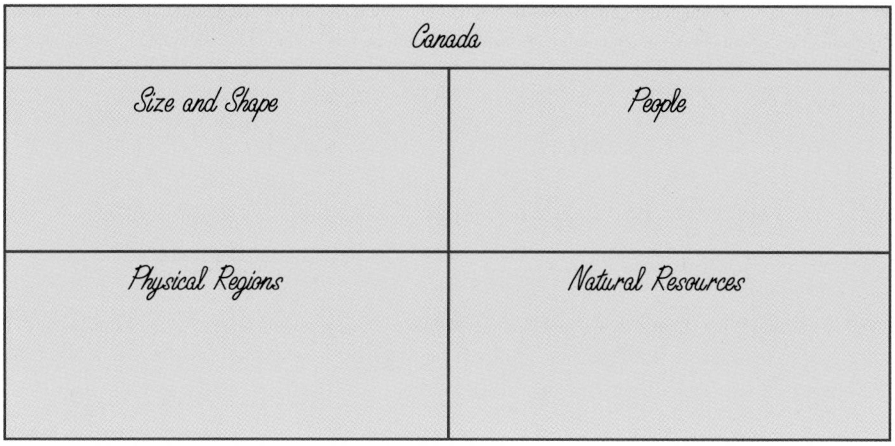

Canada	
Size and Shape	*People*
Physical Regions	*Natural Resources*

FIG. 4-2 *Your 4 quadrants should look like this.*

(c) In the top left quadrant, draw from memory a sketch map of Canada. Don't worry about details or your drawing ability. When you have finished, label the provinces, major lakes, and oceans.

(d) Trace or paste an outline map of Canada in each of the other 3 quadrants. Such a map might be found in an atlas or this book.

(e) Fill the top right quadrant with as much information about the people of Canada as you can. Use dots, words, sketches, or any other method you can think of. Rely on your own ideas rather than those of this book or an atlas.

(f) Turn to the landforms map (Fig. 4-8, pp. 52-53). Reproduce the map as accurately as possible in the bottom left quadrant. Make a legend that uses proper symbols for each region.

(g) Use an appropriate map in an atlas to find 10 natural resources in Canada. Mark the location of these resources on the map in the bottom right quadrant. Make a legend that uses proper symbols.

3. One way people try to create images through words is by writing poetry. Each of the following verses says something about Canada.

The Unnamed Lake
It sleeps among the thousand hills
Where no man ever trod,
And only nature's music fills
The silences of God.
Great mountains tower above its shore,
Green rushes fringe its brim,
And o'er its breast forevermore
The wanton breezes skim.

FREDERICK GEORGE SCOTT

Winter Uplands

The frost that stings like fire upon my cheek,
The loneliness of this forsaken ground,
The long white drift upon whose powdered peak
I sit in the great silence as one bound:
The rippled sheet of snow where the wind blew
Across the open fields for miles ahead;
The far-off city towered and roofed in blue
A tender line upon the western red;
The stars that singly, then in flocks appear,
Like jets of silver from the violet dome,
So wonderful, so many and so near,
And then the golden moon to light me home;
The crunching snowshoes and the stinging air,
The silence, frost and beauty everywhere.

ARCHIBALD LAMPMAN

Prairie Graveyard

Wind mutters thinly on the sagging wire
binding the graveyard from the gouged dirt road,
bends thick-bristled Russian thistle,
sifts listless dust
into cracks in hard gray ground.
Empty prairie slides away
on all sides, rushes toward a wide
expressionless horizon, joined
to a vast blank sky.

ANNE MARRIOTT

(a) Write down the words in each verse that describe the landscapes.
(b) Study the paintings by two members of the Group of Seven in Figures 4-3 and 4-4 (p. 48). Describe the landscapes by making a list of words.

FIG. 4-3
*Eclipse Sound and Bylot Island,
1930, Lawren Harris*

FIG. 4-4
*Cathedral Lake Peak, Lake
O'Hara, 1927, J.E.H. MacDonald*

In the previous Investigation, you saw that Canada can be described in many ways. Some words, however, describe the country *as a whole* better than others do. These four words — *vast, northern, uncrowded,* and *rich* — refer to the four images of Canada that you are going to examine. Before you do so, however, consider what these images mean to you now. It will be interesting to compare these thoughts with those you will have by the end of the chapter.

Vast

Vast means huge or great in size. When a country is vast, it covers a great area. Let's try to appreciate Canada's vastness. The first way is by comparing it to some other countries.

Investigation 4.2

To complete this Investigation you will need to refer to an atlas. You will also need some clear tracing paper or acetate sheets. If you use acetate sheets, you will need some acetate marking pens.

1. Find a world map in your atlas. Make a base map by tracing the outline of Canada on one sheet of tracing paper or acetate. (You don't need to add any details such as provinces, lakes, or cities.) From the same map, trace the outlines of Cuba, Japan, France, Italy, and China onto another piece of paper. Fit them all on the same sheet, and be sure to label each country so that you can keep track of them all.
2. Place the sheet on which you have traced the 5 countries on top of the sheet showing the outline of Canada. (If you do this using an overhead projector, the outlines will show up very clearly!) Keep shifting the top sheet around so that you place, one after another, the outline of each of the other 5 countries within the outline of Canada. It doesn't matter where you place each outline within Canada. Move each one around to get an idea of how many parts of Canada it will fit into. How many of these 5 countries could fit into Canada at the same time?
3. Write a short statement to say what you have discovered about Canada.

Canada's Shape and Major Landforms

The shapes of most countries of the world can be shown simply as rectangles, squares, triangles, circles, or ovals. When showing the shapes this way, however, important details are sometimes left out. So, sometimes exceptions must be made.

Investigation 4.3

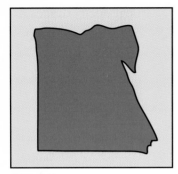

FIG. 4-5
An outline of Egypt

1. Figure 4-5 is an outline of Egypt, for example. Which form is Egypt most like? Look up Egypt in an atlas and identify the body of water on its east side that makes an exception to this form. Find countries that are similar in shape to the other forms.
2. Look at a map of Canada. If you ignore the Arctic islands, the country's shape could be described as a rectangle.

FIG. 4-6
The basic shape of Canada

Six main exceptions to this shape exist. Numbers 1 and 2 (Fig. 4-7) refer to the bodies of water, and letters A, B, C, and D refer to the sections of land. The 2 bodies of water take bites out of the rectangle and 4 sections of land add to it. What are their names?

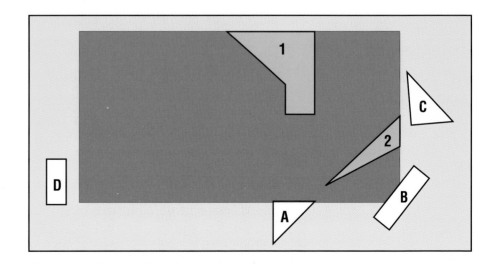

FIG. 4-7
The main exceptions to Canada's basic shape

A landform is really just what it says, a formation of land. Plains, plateaus, mountains, hills, and valleys are all landforms.

Canada's main landform regions are shown in Figure 4-8 (pp. 52-53). A landform region is a large area dominated by one or two kinds of landforms. The western mountain system, for example, has mainly mountains and valleys, but it also has some plateaus, hills, and small plains.

Figure 4-8 a to g shows what each of Canada's seven landform regions looks like.

Investigation 4.4

1. In your opinion, which region(s)
   (i) would be the most difficult to build railways and highways across?
   (ii) would be the easiest to build railways and highways across?
   (iii) would be the easiest to build towns and cities on?
   (iv) would be the easiest to develop large farms on?
   (v) would provide useful natural resources for Canadians?
   (vi) would you most like to live in?
   With a partner, discuss why you answered each of these questions the way you did.
2. Across these vast landform regions flow some of the largest **drainage systems** in the world. A drainage system is a series of rivers and lakes. All the water in these rivers and lakes eventually flows into an ocean.
   Here is a description of one of Canada's most important drainage systems:

   > It is located in the south and is made up of several huge lakes that flow into one main river. The system also contains several other important rivers that flow into these lakes and the main river.

   (a) Match the image you just got from the description with a picture of a drainage system shown on an atlas map of Canada. Name the lakes and the main river.
   (b) The rivers that flow into the lakes and the main river are called **tributaries**. Name 3 tributaries.
   (c) How might this system have helped in the exploration of North America centuries ago?
   (d) Name 5 large cities that are located on this system. For what reasons might they have been located on it?
   (e) Identify the rivers and, where necessary, the lakes of 2 other large drainage systems in Canada. How do these systems make the image of Canada's vastness even clearer?

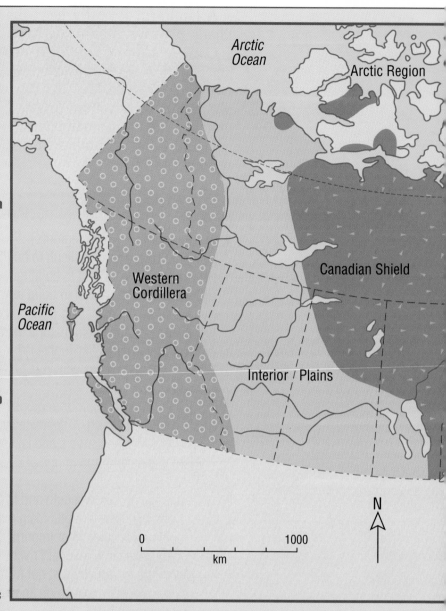

FIG. 4-8
Major landforms of Canada

a   *Glaciation exposed the ancient rocks of the Canadian Shield and left the region with countless lakes.*

b   *The good, deep soils of the Great Lakes-St. Lawrence Lowlands are excellent for growing crops.*

c   *The old mountains of the Appalachian Region have been worn smooth by erosion.*

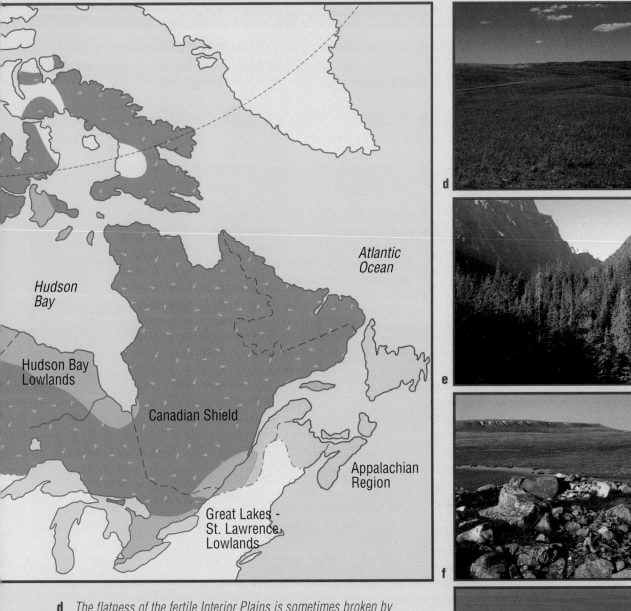

Atlantic
Ocean

Hudson
Bay

Hudson Bay
Lowlands

Canadian Shield

Appalachian
Region

Great Lakes -
St. Lawrence
Lowlands

d *The flatness of the fertile Interior Plains is sometimes broken by rolling hills and wide river valleys.*

e *High, sharp-peaked mountains and plateaus make up the Western Cordillera.*

f *The Arctic Region is made up of mountains and lowlands. It is covered by ice and snow for much of the year.*

g *Flatness is the most important characteristic of the Hudson Bay Lowlands.*

Investigation 4.5

It's time to consider another way of showing Canada's vastness. Look at Figure 4-9, a map of Canadian time zones. Note that a time zone is an area in which everyone sets his or her clocks to the same time.

1. How many time zones does Canada have? What does this suggest to you about the size of Canada?

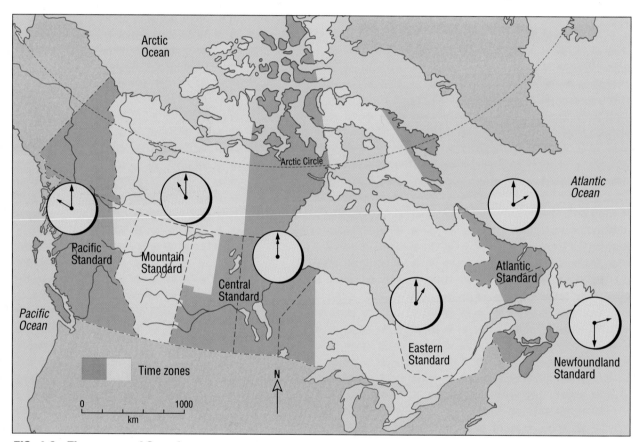

FIG. 4-9   Time zones of Canada

2. What is the most common time difference between side-by-side time zones? Where and what are the exceptions? What happens to time as you move across Canada from west to east?
3. What is your time zone? In which time zones are each of the following cities: Calgary, Winnipeg, Montréal, and Halifax?
4. When it is 9:00 a.m. in Toronto, what time is it in Calgary? When the time in Toronto is 9:20 a.m., what time would it be in Calgary? If the time in St. John's, Newfoundland, is 11:00 a.m., what is it in Vancouver?

Northern

North is both a direction and a way of looking at our country and its history. When we say we are a *northern* people, we don't just mean that we live "up north." We also mean that the north is important in our thinking. Much of our economy depends on the natural resources of our northern regions. Our way of life, as well, is influenced by the northern climate.

FIG. 4-10   *The northern environment shapes the lives and behaviours of Canadians. How is your lifestyle different from that of someone who lives in a warmer climate such as Florida?*

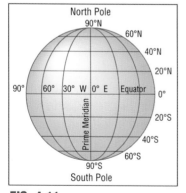

FIG. 4-11

Latitude and longitude lines form a grid on a globe or a map. They help you determine locations.

North as a Direction and a Location

Directions are used to help us identify **locations**. The term "location" refers to where a place is. There are two ways of defining any place's location. One is by **relative location** and the other is by **absolute location**.

Relative location describes the location of a place relative to or compared to some other place. For example, Canada lies north of the United States. Absolute location, used mainly by geographers, describes the location of a place in terms of two intersecting lines. One intersecting line runs east-west. The other runs north-south.

For maps of large areas and of the world as a whole, latitude and longitude are used to determine absolute locations. The east-west lines are called **parallels of latitude**. The north-south lines are called **meridians of longitude**. Every twentieth parallel and meridian appear on Figure 4-11 (p. 55). This particular sketch also shows where the equator and the prime meridian are. As you may guess, the **equator** is the starting or zero line for measuring distances north and south on the globe. The **prime meridian** is the starting or zero line for measuring distances east and west on the globe. The parallels of latitude show how far north or south of the equator a place is, and the meridians show how far east or west of the prime meridian a place is.

Investigation 4.6

SKILL
BUILDERS
MAPPING

The absolute location of Toronto is 43° north latitude by 79° west longitude. That is, Toronto's absolute location is 43° north of the equator and 79° west of the prime meridian.

1. Using an atlas, give the absolute locations of Halifax, Nova Scotia, and of St. John's, Newfoundland?
2. Write 2 sentences about the relative locations of Halifax and St. John's.
3. Using an atlas, give the absolute and relative locations of your community.

Canada's Location in North America and the World

Let's look at Canada's location compared to other parts of the world. This way you can begin to examine your image of Canada as a northern country and see if that image is true.

Investigation 4.7

1. (a) Using an atlas, find out the latitude of our capital city, Ottawa.
   (b) Make a 3-column chart like Figure 4-12 in your notebook. In the first column, write the names of the 18 cities listed in Figure 4-13. In the second column, state the latitude of each city, and in the third column, write either "north of Ottawa" or "south of Ottawa," depending on the latitude of the city compared to that of Ottawa. Figure 4-12 shows an example using the first city, London.
   (c) How many of these cities are located north of Ottawa? What does this suggest about Canada's northerness?
2. You have already seen why you can easily think of Canada as northern. Where a country's people live within that country, however, is also important to consider. Look at Figure 5-12 (p. 84) in the next chapter.

FIG. 4-12 LOCATIONS OF CAPITAL CITIES

City	Latitude	North or south of Ottawa
London, England	51° N	north of Ottawa

FIG. 4-13 CAPITAL CITIES

London, England	Athens, Greece
Paris, France	Budapest, Hungary
Lisbon, Portugal	Bern, Switzerland
Rome, Italy	Warsaw, Poland
Copenhagen, Denmark	Berlin, East Germany
Oslo, Norway	New York, USA
Vienna, Austria	Los Angeles, USA
Moscow, USSR	Tokyo, Japan
Helsinki, Finland	Beijing, China

This map shows generally where people live in Canada, what parts of the country they have settled over the years, and what parts still remain empty or almost empty.

(a) How would you describe Canada's settlement pattern shown in Figure 5-12?

(b) Does this pattern suggest that most Canadians probably think of themselves as northerners? Give reasons for your answer.

(c) Would people in the United States regard Canadians as northerners? Would people in Norway think of Canadians as northerners? in Italy? in Cuba?

Canada's Climate

Another way of looking at Canada's northerness is through its climate. An area's climate is the average over a long period of time of its weather conditions, as measured by temperature, rainfall, snowfall, pressure, and wind direction and speed. Our climate is affected by the movement of great sections of the atmosphere called **air masses**. Figure 4-14 (p. 58) focusses on the main air masses that affect Canada and shows what each is like. Remember that storms usually occur when unlike air masses meet.

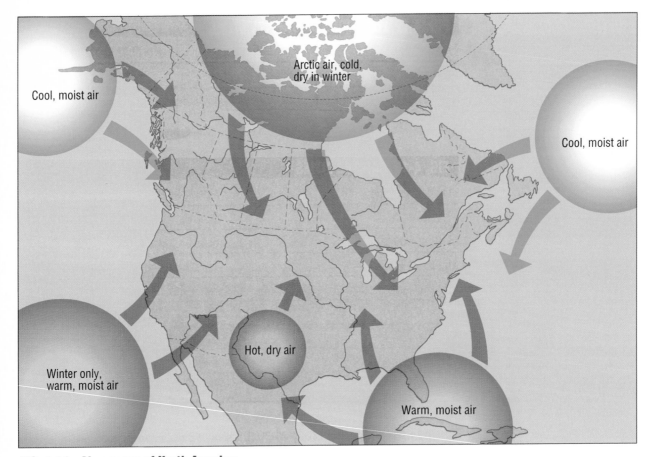

FIG. 4-14 Air masses of North America

Investigation 4.8

1. The table in Figure 4-15 shows temperature conditions for 8 cities, 4 of them Canadian. The temperatures are given in degrees Celsius and are monthly averages.
   (a) Mark the cities in Figure 4-15 on an outline map of the world supplied by your teacher.
   (b) Copy Figure 4-16 into your notebook. With help from your teacher and classmates, create a range of temperatures (high to low) for each of the chart's 5 weather descriptions. Choose a colour for each description as well. For example, you might decide "hot" is 25°C and over, and bright red is a suitable colour for it.

FIG. 4-15   TEMPERATURES OF SELECTED CITIES (°C)

Place	J	F	M	A	M	J	J	A	S	O	N	D
Alert, Northwest Territories	-32.1	-33.3	-33.0	-24.7	-11.2	-0.6	3.9	0.9	-10.1	-19.7	-26.1	-29.8
Churchill, Manitoba	-27.6	-26.7	-20.3	-11.0	-2.3	6.1	12.0	11.5	5.7	-1.0	-11.9	-21.8
Thunder Bay, Ontario	-14.8	-13.0	-6.2	2.4	8.3	13.8	17.5	16.5	11.3	6.1	-2.5	-10.8
Windsor, Ontario	-4.4	-4.4	0.5	7.8	13.9	20.0	22.2	21.1	17.2	10.6	3.3	-2.8
Moscow, USSR	-10.3	-9.7	-4.6	3.8	11.8	16.1	18.3	16.3	10.7	4.3	-2.2	-7.9
Tokyo, Japan	3.3	3.9	7.2	12.2	16.7	20.6	24.4	26.1	22.2	16.7	10.6	5.6
Los Angeles, California	13.2	13.9	15.2	16.5	18.2	20.0	22.8	22.8	22.2	19.7	17.0	14.5
Cairo, Egypt	13.3	14.7	17.5	21.1	25.0	27.5	28.3	28.3	26.1	24.2	20.0	15.0

FIG. 4-16   TEMPERATURE DESCRIPTIONS

Weather description	Temperature range	Colour
Hot		
Warm		
Cool		
Cold		
Frigid		

(c) Using the colours you selected in (b), make a coloured bar to show temperatures through the year for each city listed in Figure 4-15. Figure 4-17 (p. 60) shows an example using Cairo. Notice that only 3 terms have been used to apply to Cairo, because temperatures usually don't drop very low there.

(d) Draw each of these graphs on your map of the world. Label your map **World Temperatures**.

(e) Calculate the average yearly temperature for each city. Do this by adding up all the monthly average temperatures, getting a total, then dividing the total by 12. Cairo's average yearly temperature, for example, is 21.75°C.

(f) On a page in your notebook, rank (list in order) the cities from the coldest to the hottest.

(g) What seems to happen to temperatures the farther a city is from the equator?

(h) How many cities are colder than Windsor? Which ones? Why?

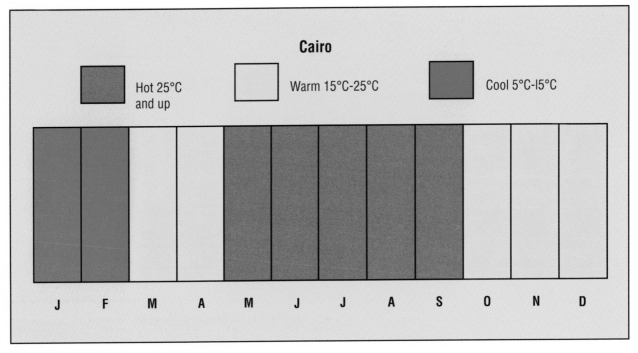

Cairo

Hot 25°C and up | Warm 15°C-25°C | Cool 5°C-I5°C

J F M A M J J A S O N D

FIG. 4-17

2. Write a short paragraph to describe Canada's temperatures in relation to those in other parts of the world.

3. Think about the ways in which our lives would be different if we did not have temperatures that go below freezing. Organize these differences under the following headings: ***Transportation; Clothing; House Construction;*** and ***Sports.*** Add any other headings you can think of.

Uncrowded

Not everyone has the same image of "crowded." Some people would consider two persons in a two-bedroom apartment crowded. Others might think that if four people were sharing that apartment, they would not be crowded.

A useful term when thinking about crowded or uncrowded conditions is **density**. Density means the number of people or things in a particular area. As an example, let's take a square kilometre in the centre of a city. If there were 1000 people living in that square kilometre, the area would have a high (or great) density of population. If the square kilometre were in a farming region, far fewer people would be living in it. If there were ten people, for example, the square kilometre would have a low population density.

Nearly everyone has an image of Canada as a place of low population density — a land of wide, open spaces. In Investigation 4.9, you will explore the accuracy of the uncrowded image of Canada. You will consider the ideas of density and **distribution**, the way people or things form location patterns within a density area, as you do so.

Investigation 4.9

1. Look at the squares in Figure 4-18. In each square there are 10 dots representing 10 people. The density for each square is 10.

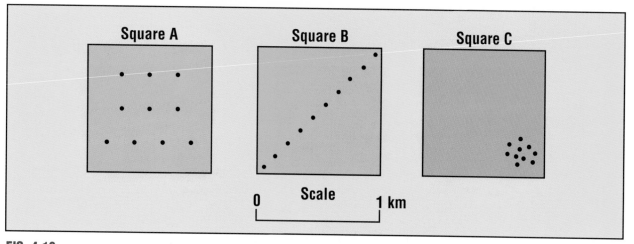

FIG. 4-18

(a) In which square do the dots (or people) seem the least crowded?
(b) In which square are the people most crowded?
(c) Which distribution square seems to show that the people all live along the same street?

From this Investigation, you can see that saying "the density is 10 people per square" doesn't necessarily give a true picture of whether the square is crowded or uncrowded.

2. To calculate the population density in any area, you divide the number of people by the size of the area in which they live. For example, take an area of 10 km². In it live 50 000 people. To find the density, the calculation would be

$$50\,000 \div 10 = 5000 \text{ people/km}^2$$

Canada has a population of approximately 25 000 000. The total area of Canada is about 9 976 000 km². What is the density of Canada's population?

Canada's population density seems to be extremely low, doesn't it? The country appears to be *uncrowded*. But, as in the case with the dots and squares, that figure alone doesn't tell the true story.

FIG. 4-19 *These photographs show a variety of different living conditions in Canada.*

3. To end this section, work with a partner and refer to Figure 4-19 and Figure 5-12 (p. 84).
   (a) Which areas in Canada seem to have fairly high population densities?
   (b) Look carefully at each photo. State whether you think the scene in each is crowded, fairly densely populated, or uncrowded. Where might each picture have been taken?
   (c) What are some positive and negative effects of high densities? In which area shown in the photos would you prefer to live? Why?

(d) You can see that it isn't always easy to tell if a place is crowded or uncrowded. Form a small group with some classmates and discuss this problem. Try to reach a **consensus**.

Is Canada a crowded or uncrowded country? Were you able to reach a consensus? If you were, explain your answer. If you were not, explain why your group found the question so difficult to answer.

(e) Identify 3 problems that could be created by Canada's population distribution.

Rich

When most of us hear the word "rich," we think of money. A rich person has much money. But that's not the only meaning "rich" has. A person can be rich in many ways, because *rich* really means having things in great amounts or abundance. Money can be one thing, certainly, but persons, things, and countries can have an abundance of anything.

To appreciate whether you are rich or not, you must think of all the riches you have. Think of your **standard of living** as geographers like to say. Factors in determining your standard of living, or how well off you are, include not only money, but also education, health care, and life expectancy.

Standard of Living

Figures 4-20 to 4-23 (pp. 64-67) provide information about standards of living in three important ways. They show
• the amount of income received by families in different parts of Canada and the world
• the value of goods and services that different countries produce
• life expectancy

Income

Income is the amount of money that a person or family receives in a certain period of time. The most common kind of income is in the form of a wage for work done. How much income families across Canada received in 1986 is shown in Figure 4-20 (p. 64).

Investigation 4.10

SKILL
BUILDERS
GRAPHING

1. Look carefully at Figure 4-20.
   (a) Divide the provinces into 2 categories: those with family incomes above the national average and those with incomes below. Write the 2 lists in your notebook.
   (b) Suggest 3 influences on how much a family earns.
   (c) What are some reasons that might explain why some provinces' family incomes are lower than others?
   (d) Draw a bar graph to show the information in Figure 4-20. Put the bars into 3 groups: western Canada, central Canada, and eastern Canada. (If possible, use your school or home computer to draw the bar graph.)
   (e) Write a paragraph describing patterns in family incomes across Canada.

FIG. 4-20 AVERAGE FAMILY INCOME (1986)	
Canada	$39 589
Newfoundland	$27 687
Prince Edward Island	$31 097
Nova Scotia	$33 480
New Brunswick	$31 811
Québec	$36 759
Ontario	$44 098
Manitoba	$35 990
Saskatchewan	$35 779
Alberta	$41 794
British Columbia	$39 085
Yukon/NWT	No data available

Source: Statistics Canada

2. Figure 4-21 gives us a comparison of average incomes in 10 cities around the world. The amount of income is not given in actual dollars. It is given as a figure that is either higher or lower than the figure for Zurich, Switzerland. This table, therefore, *compares* the cities. Zurich has been set at 100 because 100 is a good starting point from which to compare other figures. Zurich is used rather than some other city, because the information comes from the Union Bank of Switzerland, located in Zurich.

Knowing how to read comparative tables like this one will be useful to you, because you often find them in newspapers and magazines.

| FIG. 4-21 A COMPARISON OF INCOMES AMONG 10 MAJOR CITIES (1985) ||
Cities (alphabetical order)	Income compared to Zurich (Zurich = 100)
Bombay, India	8
Hong Kong	42
Istanbul, Turkey	13
Los Angeles, USA	128
Milan, Italy	52
Montréal, Canada	99
New York, USA	126
Rio de Janeiro, Brazil	20
Toronto, Canada	102
Vienna, Austria	56

Source: Union Bank of Switzerland

(a) Rank the cities by income level ("best" to "worst").
(b) Which cities seem to be the richest and which, the poorest in income?
(c) Use a world map to find the locations of these cities. How do the 2 Canadian cities compare to those in the United States, Europe, Asia, and South America?

The Value of Goods and Services

One way of estimating a country's wealth is to add up the value of everything it produces. The things a country produces fall into two groups. One is **goods**, such as food, cars, watches, clothes, and records. The other is **services**, such as those provided by doctors, bank clerks, entertainers, and teachers. In general, a poor country will produce a fairly small amount of goods and services. A wealthy country will produce a large amount of goods and services.

The total value of the goods and services produced by a country yearly is called the country's **Gross National Product** or **GNP**. This value is difficult to determine, so much so, that only highly trained people can do it properly. The GNP is, however, a useful figure for comparing the wealth of various countries.

Investigation 4.11

Figure 4-22 is a map that compares the GNPs of nearly all the countries of the world for the year 1984-1985.

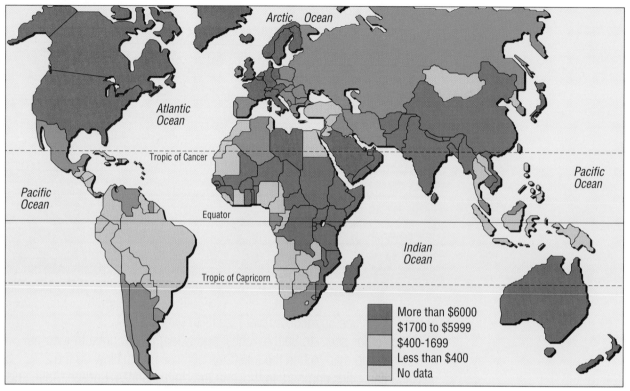

FIG. 4-22   Gross National Products per capita (US $), 1984-1985

1. The world can be divided into the Northern, Southern, Eastern, and Western Hemispheres. Other large parts are the continents. What hemispheres and continents have the highest GNPs? Which ones have the lowest?
2. What have you learned about the richness of Canada from this map?

Life Expectancy

People in rich countries generally have a better chance of living long lives than do people in poor countries. There are, of course, exceptions to this "rule," but in rich countries, most people live in better houses, eat better, and suffer less from disease. **Life expectancy**, or the length of time one can expect to live, helps determine richness. Figure 4-23 shows that life expectancy varies greatly from one continent to another. (Your school may have a data base that contains more up-to-date statistics on life expectancy.)

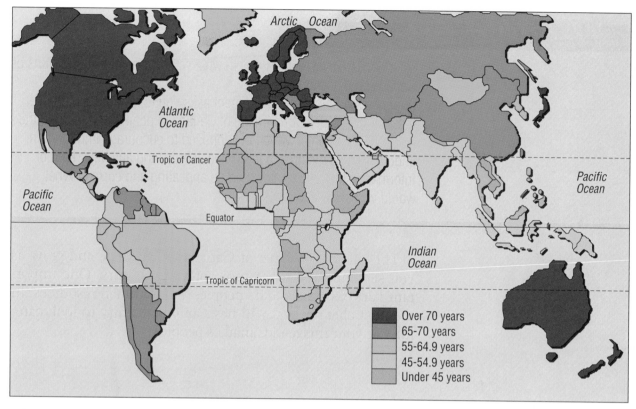

FIG. 4-23 Life expectancies in the world

Investigation 4.12

1. Which continents enjoy the highest life expectancy rates?
2. Which continent's inhabitants clearly have the lowest life expectancy? Why might living conditions be particularly difficult in some parts of this continent?
3. How does Canada's life expectancy rate compare to that of other countries?

Summing Up

At the beginning of this chapter, you were told you would be looking at four images of Canada, those images being: vast, northern, uncrowded, rich.

You were also asked to think about your own impressions of Canada, and to compare the thoughts you had by the end of the chapter with those you had first.

Investigation 4.13

1. (a) Refer back to Investigation 4.1. In what ways have your impressions of Canada changed since then?

   (b) Suppose the Canadian government asks you to produce a pamphlet that will give a clear, true image of Canada to people from around the world. The pamphlet, which is supposed to encourage immigration, should include pictures, a few maps, words, and any other kind of information that you think would be appealing and correct. What would you show and say?

The image you have of Canada will change and grow as you see and experience more of your country. One important part of Canada is its peoples — its human resources. In the next chapter, you will have an opportunity to look carefully at your image of Canada's people.

CHAPTER FIVE

Population: Our Human Resources

WE ARE NOW GOING TO LOOK AT the population of Canada. Through this study, you will see how Canada's people are more than just dots on a map or figures in a table. As you probably recall from Chapter 1, we introduced the idea of people as resources. You were asked to think about resources in your classroom then. Now it's time to consider Canada's people as a kind of wealth or source of richness enjoyed by the country as a whole.

What do you need to know about Canada's people to get a better understanding of this country and your place in it? There are three major questions that must be answered, and they make up the main sections of this chapter. The questions are:

Where did we come from?
How many of us are there?
Where do we live?

As you might guess, these questions aren't completely separate from each other. They overlap a little, so as you go from one section to the next, you will find that you're learning more and more about all of the questions.

Investigation 5.1

1. (a) Using an outline map of Canada, show the following things: the directions north, south, east, and west, the Pacific, Atlantic, and Arctic oceans, Hudson Bay, and the US.

    (b) Now, without looking at any maps, indicate where you think Canadians live. Don't forget these facts:

     • There are only 25 million Canadians, not many compared to the size of the country.

     • Our vast northland is home to few people.

     • "Pockets" or clusters of population exist across the country. There are only a few large cities.

    (c) Now check the population map of Canada in Figure 5-12 (p. 84). How close did you come to representing the actual population patterns of Canada? Adjust your map so that it shows Canada's population patterns correctly. What did you learn about Canada from doing this Investigation?

      Keep these patterns of where people live in mind as you go through the rest of this chapter.

Where Did We Come From?

Canada's first inhabitants, the Native peoples, migrated here thousands of years ago. Today, more than 700 000 Native people live in Canada. The rest of our population is made up of people whose families arrived in Canada in the last few hundred years.

Population Growth

A country's population grows in two ways. One is through births among the people already living in the country. The other is through the arrival of people from other countries. This is called **immigration**. However, when dealing with population growth, you must remember to subtract the number of people who move away each year. This movement is called **emigration**. When you subtract the number of people who leave from those who enter, you get a figure called the **net migration**.

The number of births and deaths also affects a country's population. When you subtract the number of deaths in any time period, say a year, from the number of births, you get a figure called the **natural increase**. Look at Figure 5-1. Try to determine what the pictograms (simple drawings) and letters mean by referring to the terms just explained.

What would you get if you were to add the natural increase to the net migration?

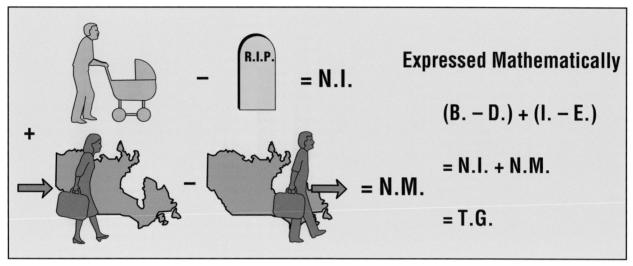

FIG. 5-1 *You can find the total growth in population by using the information in this pictogram.*

Investigation 5.2

Figure 5-2a shows the births and deaths in Canada's population by decade for the period of 1851 to 1981. Figure 5-2b (p. 74) shows net migration for the same period. Figure 5-2c (p. 74) reflects the effects of natural increase and net migration by showing Canada's overall population growth.

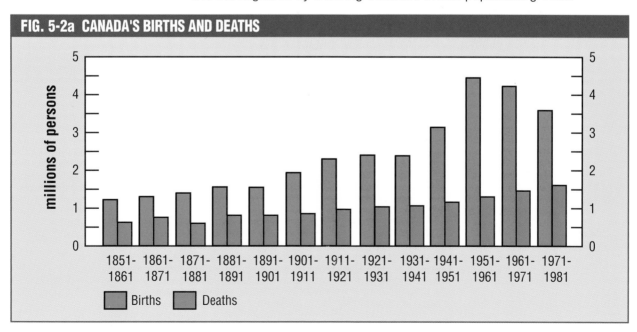

FIG. 5-2a CANADA'S BIRTHS AND DEATHS

FIG. 5-2b NET MIGRATION

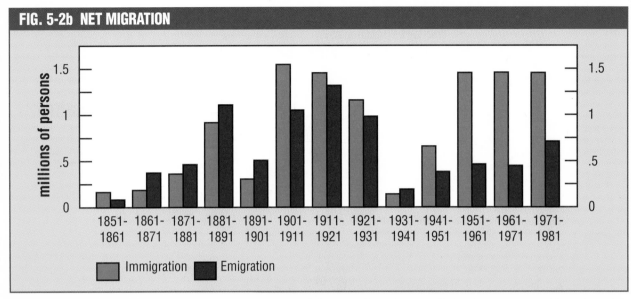

Immigration   Emigration

FIG. 5-2c POPULATION GROWTH

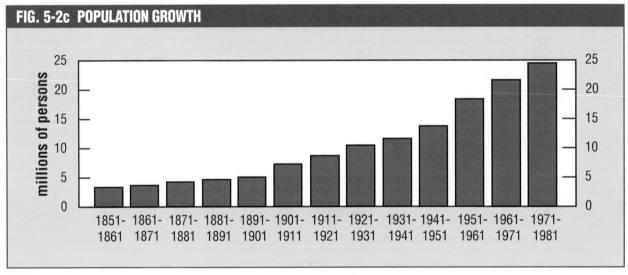

1. Using the 3 bar graphs just given, make up a chart as follows. Complete the chart for the decades listed in the left column.

SKILL

BUILDERS

COMPARATIVE
THINKING

FIG. 5-2d CANADA'S POPULATION GROWTH

Decade	Natural increase	Net migration	Total population
1871-81			
1901-11			
1931-41			
1961-71			
1971-81			

2. Write a paragraph describing what has happened to Canada's population growth since 1851. You will soon learn more about the reasons for the changes in population growth.

Immigration

Immigration usually results from two factors. The first is the **push factor**, something that makes life so difficult or uncomfortable in a country that people are "pushed" out to look for better lives. Here are some examples:

- High unemployment rates pushed Robbie and his family out of Scotland. Robbie's parents thought they would have a better chance of finding jobs in Canada.
- Kristina and her family moved from South Africa because they feared that the conflict between blacks and whites would erupt into civil war.
- Lin was afraid that she wouldn't get into university in Hong Kong because of the intense competition for spaces.

Such push factors encourage people to think about leaving their home country. Nonetheless, making the decision to leave is difficult. Think of how hard you would find it. You have so many ties to your country. It is your home. You would have to leave behind friends with whom you share interests in music, sports, and school. Also, you probably wouldn't know much about the lifestyle or people in your new country.

Once people decide to leave their home country, they must decide where they want to go. Their decision wouldn't be easy to make. So many conditions in the new country have to be considered. The good conditions that attract people to a new country are called **pull factors**. Here are some examples:

- Greater freedom to practise the Moslem religion made Ahsan choose Canada.
- Canada's large size and uncrowded lands appealed to Manuel, tired of living in a crowded city in Portugal.
- More schools and a greater variety of courses attracted Shabina's parents to Canada.

Canada offers many advantages to people from other countries. Most of these immigrants see Canada as a land where they can succeed through hard work and the use of their skills. High quality health care, schools, and recreational facilities, as well as less

FIG. 5-3 PUSH AND PULL FACTORS

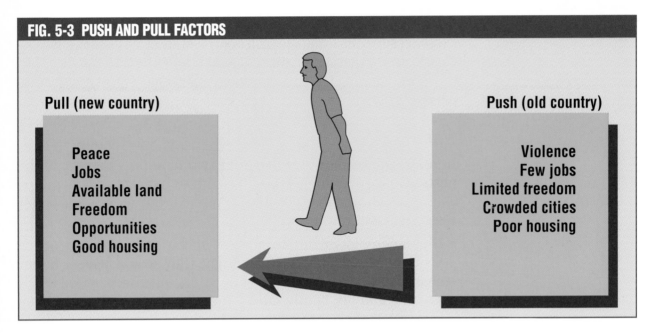

Pull (new country)

Peace
Jobs
Available land
Freedom
Opportunities
Good housing

Push (old country)

Violence
Few jobs
Limited freedom
Crowded cities
Poor housing

These are some of the many reasons why people leave their homelands for new countries.

expensive household goods and high wages, give Canada a high standard of living. But sometimes, Canada's size and open spaces are so new to people from crowded European and Asian countries that they need time to get used to them.

Investigation 5.3

1. List 5 push factors that might cause *you* to think about leaving Canada. Put check marks beside the 2 most important ones.
2. Like most of the students mentioned earlier, you probably wouldn't have much say about where you and your family were going to move. If you did, what country would you choose? Name 5 pull factors that would attract you.
3. Your school may have students who have recently moved to Canada. Make up a questionnaire to ask a few of them about immigration. Here are some topics you might ask about:
   - reasons for leaving their home countries
   - reasons for choosing Canada
   - changes in food, sports, clothes, and schooling that they had to adjust to
   - things they like about Canada
   - problems they have faced since arriving in Canada

What are some other topics you might explore?
When you interview the students, don't forget their right to privacy. Respect it by not recording their names. Remember to summarize your information before sharing it. Write a short report about your findings.

SKILL
BUILDERS
SURVEYS

Because of our country's advantages, thousands of people apply to come here each year. Only a certain number, however, are permitted to settle. Who and how many people can stay depends greatly on Canadian employment conditions. For example, our immigration officers recently gave special consideration to people trained and experienced as tool-and-die makers. Such workers were needed by our engineering industries.

Canada also gives special consideration to people who are living under very difficult conditions. In 1980, for example, more than 25 000 Vietnamese, many of them "boat people," came to Canada. Seeking freedom, these people had escaped from Vietnam in small boats, and had become refugees in the camps of Southeast Asia.

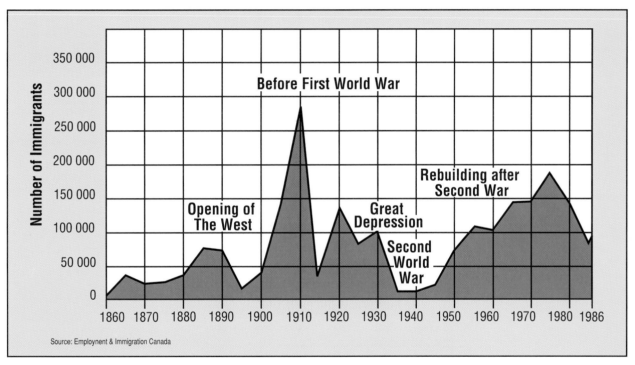

Source: Employnent & Immigration Canada

FIG. 5-4

The number of people immigrating to Canada is affected by events here and in other parts of the world.

As you can see from Figure 5-4, the number of people coming to Canada has gone up and down several times since Confederation. Great events caused these push and pull changes. Early in this century, thousands of people, especially Europeans, came to settle the Canadian West in response to the government's offer of free land. In the early 1930s, though, people did not want to come to Canada due to a terrible depression that wiped out job opportunities and created great poverty throughout the world. Push and pull factors changed again when the Second World War ended in 1945. Conditions in Europe's war-ravaged cities were so bad that many people came to Canada to start new lives.

Canada's Immigration Policy

The federal government determines our immigration policy, or the rules and guidelines for deciding who may enter Canada. **Immigration policy** has not always been the same. Until the end of the Second World War, Canada had a policy that kept out people from some countries. At the same time, other people, especially those from Britain and France, were welcomed.

After the Second World War, Canada adopted a more open immigration policy. People from many more countries were allowed to enter. Selection became based more on Canada's job opportunities and the immigrant's possible contributions than on the applicant's race, home country, or religion.

Today Canada's immigration policy is based on a point system, which is designed to attract the best qualified people. As you can see from Figure 5-6, the point system is based on 10 factors. Applicants must obtain a total of 50 points out of a possible 100 before they will be considered for admission to Canada.

Investigation 5.4

1. (a) Why would an educated person with a job skill be a more attractive immigrant to Canada than one who does not have a job skill?
   (b) Why would Canada particularly want people between the ages of 18 and 35?
   (c) Why would the immigrant's home country not want to lose young, educated people?
   (d) Why does our government try to encourage new immigrants to move to less populated parts of Canada?

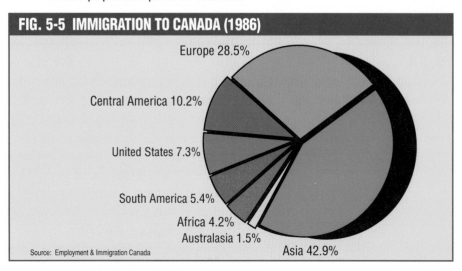

FIG. 5-5 IMMIGRATION TO CANADA (1986)

Europe 28.5%

Central America 10.2%

United States 7.3%

South America 5.4%

Africa 4.2%

Australasia 1.5%

Asia 42.9%

Source: Employment & Immigration Canada

FIG. 5-6 CANADA'S IMMIGRATION POINT SYSTEM

Factors	Considerations	Maximum points
1. Education	One point for each year of primary and secondary education successfully completed.	12
2. Job training	To be measured by the amount of formal professional, vocational, apprenticeship, in-plant or on-the-job training in the occupation under which the applicant is considered in Factor 4.	15
3. Experience	Points awarded for experience in the occupation under which the applicant is considered in Factor 4.	8
4. Occupational demand	Points awarded on the basis of employment opportunities available in Canada in the occupation that the applicant is qualified for and is prepared to follow in Canada.	15
5. Arranged employment	Ten points awarded if the person has arranged employment in Canada provided that employment would not interfere with the job opportunities of Canadian citizens or permanent residents.	10
6. Location	Five points awarded to a person who intends to go to an area having a general need for people. Five points subtracted from a person who intends to proceed to an area designated as not having such a need.	5
7. Age	Ten points awarded to a person between the ages of 18 and 35. For those over 35 one point shall be subtracted from the maximum of ten for every year over 35.	10
8. Knowledge of English and French	Ten points awarded to a person who reads, writes, and speaks both English and French fluently. Five points awarded to a person who reads, writes, and speaks English or French fluently. Fewer points awarded to persons with less language knowledge and ability in English and French.	10
9. Personal suitability	Points awarded on the basis of an interview held to determine the suitability of the person and his/her dependents to become successfully established in Canada. The person's adaptability, motivation, initiative, resourcefulness, and other similar qualities are all considered.	10
10. Relative	If a relative in Canada has undertaken to assist an applicant, the person shall be awarded five points.	5

2. Look at Figure 5-5 (p. 78). Which part of the world contributed the greatest number of people to Canada? What percentage of people came from Asia? from Europe?

3. People are often not clear about what is required for admission to Canada. As a result, they may be unhappy about how the immigration system treats some groups of people. For example, sometimes the government ignores the point system (Figure 5-6) and admits refugees or special groups for reasons that the immigration minister thinks are important. On the other hand, some people enter Canada and stay illegally. In the late 1980s, the Canadian government decided that some people were taking advantage of our immigration system. It introduced a tougher immigration policy.

There is no question that many people would choose to come to Canada if there were no rules or restrictions. You might conclude this section with a class debate on the following statement.

Compared to much of the world, Canada is rich. We should therefore let anyone who wishes to live here do so.

4. Research and present a report on Canada's refugee policies. You might want to explore these questions: Who does Canada accept as refugees? How many people have been accepted as refugees in recent years? What happens when someone applies to become a refugee?

SKILL
BUILDERS
COMMUNICATION
SKILLS

Emigration

So far we have talked only about people moving to Canada. There have been a number of years in Canada's history when more people moved out of the country than moved in.

Investigation 5.5

1. (a) Look at Figure 5-2b (p. 74). During what decades did more people move out of Canada than moved in?
   (b) Discuss with a history teacher what was happening in Canada in those decades.
   (c) How do those historical events help to explain why so many people wanted to leave Canada?

2. Even today there are thousands of people moving out of Canada. Work with 2 or 3 classmates to answer these questions:
   (a) What countries do you think most Canadian emigrants would move to?
   (b) Make a list of 10 reasons why people might move away from Canada. Divide your list into push and pull factors.

Natural Increase

Immigration has added millions of people to Canada's population. But, as we mentioned at the beginning of this section, the population has also grown due to natural increase.

Each country has a **birth rate** and a **death rate**. Each rate is expressed as a certain number of people per 1000 people in the country. In 1986 Canada's birth rate was 14.7. This means that there were 14.7 births for every 1000 people living in Canada. The death rate was 7.3 (the number of people who died out of every 1000 in the total population). The natural increase is the birth rate minus the death rate (14.7 − 7.3 = 7.4). Therefore, for every 1000 Canadians in 1986, the population increased by 7.4 people through natural increase.

Let's compare Canada's rate of natural increase to those of other countries for the year 1986. In Figure 5-7, all figures have been rounded off.

FIG. 5-7 A COMPARISON OF NATURAL INCREASES (per 1000 people)			
Country	Birth rate	Death rate	Natural increase
Canada	15	7	8
China	16	8	8
India	33	12	21
Nigeria	46	18	28
USSR	19	11	8
West Germany	10	12	-2
United States	15	9	6

Source: Statistics Canada

You will notice that Canada has a low death rate. That goes hand in hand with a young population and good medical care.

Investigation 5.6

1. (a) Figure 5-8 (p. 82) shows Canada's birth and death rates. Calculate the natural increase for each year shown in the table.
   (b) Suggest 2 reasons why the death rate has fallen.
   (c) What reasons might cause the birth rate of a country to fall?
   (d) Predict what Canada's birth, death, and natural increase rates will be in the year 2001.

FIG. 5-8 CANADA'S BIRTH AND DEATH RATES

Year	Birth rate	Death rate
1921	29	12
1941	22	10
1961	26	7
1981	15	7

Source: Statistics Canada

How Many of Us Are There?

There are several ways in which to consider this question. We are going to look at:
• how many of us there are in Canada compared to the whole world
• how many of us are male and how many are female
• how many of us are young, middle aged, and old
• how many of us there may be in the future
(Canada's population in 1986 was 25 354 000.)

Investigation 5.7

1. Refer back to Figure 5-2c (p. 74). How much has Canada's population increased in the last century? since the end of the Second World War? in the last 15 years?
2. In July 1987, the world's population reached 5 billion. It's hard to imagine how many people that actually is, but Figure 5-9 shows how Canada's population size compares to it.

FIGS. 5-9 (left) and 5-10 (right)

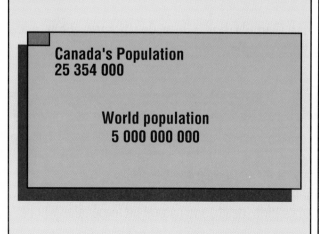

Canada's Population
25 354 000

World population
5 000 000 000

Canada's area 9 970 000 km^2

World's total land area
148 429 000 km^2

(a) Complete the following calculation. You will then know what percentage of the world's population lives in Canada.

$$\frac{25\ 000\ 000}{5\ 000\ 000\ 000} \times 100 = ?$$

(b) Look at Figure 5-10 which shows the area of Canada compared to the total land area of the world. Complete the following calculation. You will be able to figure out what percentage of the world's land area Canada has.

$$\frac{9\ 970\ 000}{148\ 429\ 000} \times 100 = ?$$

(c) Compare the answer you reached in (a) to the answer you reached in (b). What is the difference?

(d) What does this Investigation tell you about Canada and its population?

3. Knowledge of past rates of growth, natural increase rates, net migration rates, and world events that affect our growth can help us to predict our future population size. Such predictions help us plan properly to meet our future needs.

Figure 5-11 shows changes in Canada's population and makes a prediction about its future. It is based upon Canada's rate of growth since 1951. The part of the graph that goes beyond 1989 is called a **projection**, or forecast, because it is based on estimates.

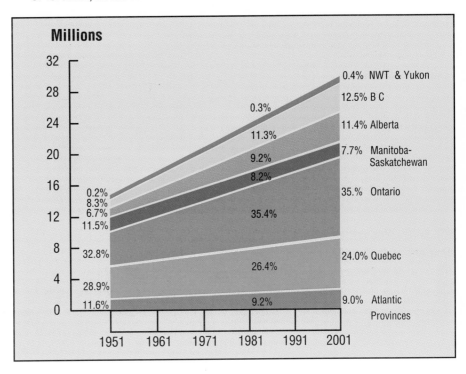

FIG. 5-11

(a) What do the forecasters estimate Canada's population to be in the year 2001?
(b) Which parts of the country do they think will grow the fastest? Try to think of some reasons for this.
(c) State 5 ways in which planners could use information about Canada's future population.

Where Do We Live?

If you were in a satellite travelling 80 km above the earth, you could see at a glance where Canadians live. The view would be clearest of all on a cloudless night. The lights of all the farms, towns, and cities would show our population patterns very well.

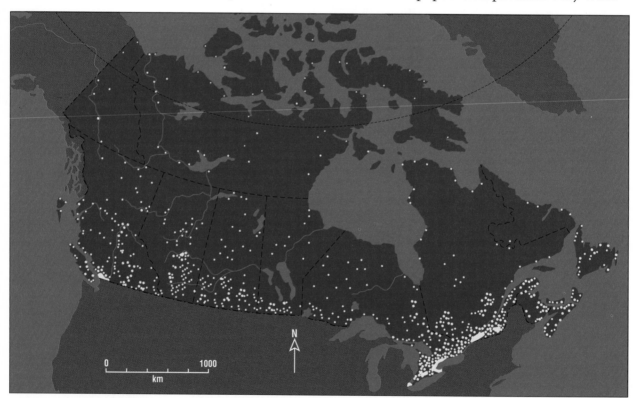

FIG. 5-12   Population distribution in Canada

This map shows what areas Canadians live in today. The dots represent concentrated settlements of varying sizes.

One Canadian geographer has called the overall pattern made by the distribution of Canada's population "the Canadian Archipelago." An **archipelago** is a group of islands such as those that form our Arctic Archipelago in the far north. If you look carefully at Figure 5-12 you can make out four major population "islands" in Canada. They are, from east to west, the Maritimes Island, the Great Lakes-St. Lawrence Island, the Prairie Island,

and the Southwestern BC Island. More than 90% of all Canadians live in these four "islands." As you can see, the remaining 10% are spread across the country in smaller clusters. What are the reasons for this distribution of the population?

We can get a slightly different picture of Canada's population distribution if we look at the location of cities. Figure 5-13 shows the locations of all the cities in Canada with more than 50 000 people.

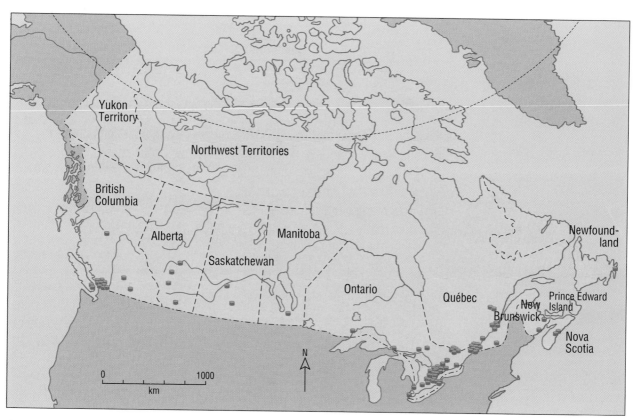

FIG. 5-13 Canadian cities with more than 50 000 people

Investigation 5.8

SKILL BUILDERS

BRAINSTORMING

1. (a) Use Figures 5-12 and 5-13 to write 3 statements that describe Canada's population distribution.
   (b) With 2 or 3 other students, brainstorm a list of factors that might have helped create the population distribution pattern. (It might be easier to first consider the factors that would have encouraged people to settle in some areas and then consider the reasons people might not have settled in other areas.)

(c) What helped to create the population pattern in each of these parts of the country?
- British Columbia's interior
- the western end of Lake Ontario
- northeastern Québec, east of Hudson Bay
- Prince Edward Island

Record your answer in a chart similar to Figure 5-14.

FIG. 5-14 POPULATION PATTERNS		
Part of Canada	Description of population pattern	Reasons for population pattern

2. Use the line scale on Figure 5-13 to answer these questions about the locations of Canadian cities. You will also need your atlas.
   (a) How many cities with more than 50 000 people are farther than 300 km from the Canada-US border?
   (b) How many cities are more than 300 km from an ocean or Great Lake?
   (c) How many cities over 50 000 are north of 50°N?
   (d) How many cities are south of 45°N?

In 1867, Canada had only one city with more than 100 000 people — Montréal. By 1921, six cities boasted populations greater than 100 000. Twenty cities had reached that number in 1961. In 1986, twenty-seven places had passed the 100 000 mark and others were fast approaching it.

The rapid increase in the number of large cities was caused by two factors. The total population of the country has increased and so there are more people to cause the cities to grow. However, equally important has been a major change in Canadian society — the shift from a rural society to an urban one.

Urban and Rural Populations

Urban people live in towns and cities. **Rural** people live outside of towns and cities. Today, far more Canadians are classed as urban than rural, but this was not always the case. In 1867, at the time of Confederation, about 80% of the country's population lived in rural areas. By the 1980s less than 25% did. Almost 80% of Canadians today live in towns and cities. Many of the reasons for this change relate to changes in the way people work and in the kind of work they do.

In early years, industries were small and most jobs were done by hand. Blacksmiths, for example, did much of a town's metal work. But in the late 1800s and early 1900s large industries began to develop. More and more factories were built in towns and cities where there was a good supply of workers for operating newly developed machinery.

During these same years, farming became easier and more efficient. The invention of machines such as tractors made it so. Farmers found that they had to buy machinery to be competitive or they had to leave farming. Many farmers and their employees, decided to leave rural areas to take advantage of the growing number of jobs in towns and cities.

Most Canadians now live in large urban centres rather than on farms and in villages.

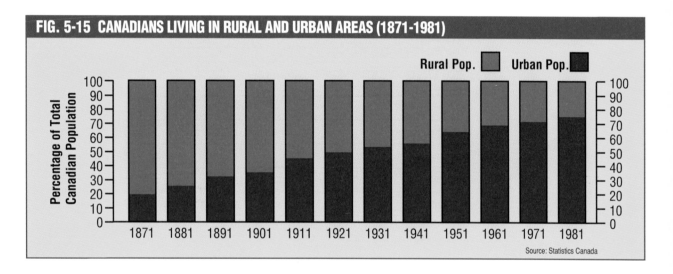

FIG. 5-15 CANADIANS LIVING IN RURAL AND URBAN AREAS (1871-1981)

Rural Pop. ☐   Urban Pop. ■

Percentage of Total Canadian Population

1871 1881 1891 1901 1911 1921 1931 1941 1951 1961 1971 1981

Source: Statistics Canada

Investigation 5.9

1. (a) Look at Figure 5-15. What percentage of Canadians lived in urban areas in 1981?
   (b) What was the change in the percentage of people living in urban areas from 1901 to 1981?
   (c) Figure 5-15 illustrates the process of **urbanization**. In your own words write a definition of this term.
2. Urbanization stopped during some periods in our history — the 1930s, for example. Why do you think this might have happened?
3. (a) Estimate the percentage of Canada's population that will live in urban areas by the year 2001. How did you make this estimate?

(b) Suggest reasons why this percentage will not likely reach 100.
4. Most recent immigrants to Canada have settled in the cities. Suggest 3 reasons why they chose cities over rural areas.
5. Figure 5-16 shows the populations of the 24 largest urban areas in Canada (in alphabetical order). These urban areas are called **Census Metropolitan Areas** (**CMAs**). Each one includes the city's population and that of the built-up area around it.

FIG. 5-16 POPULATION OF CENSUS METROPOLITAN AREAS (1986)

Census Metropolitan Areas	15 025 900
Calgary	671 300
Chicoutimi-Jonquière	158 500
Edmonton	785 500
Halifax	296 000
Hamilton	557 000
Kitchener-Waterloo	311 200
London	342 300
Montréal	2 921 400
Oshawa	203 500
Ottawa-Hull	819 300
Québec City	603 300
Regina	186 500
St.Catharines-Niagara	343 300
St. John's	161 900
Saint John	121 300
Saskatoon	200 700
Sudbury	148 900
Thunder Bay	122 200
Toronto	3 427 200
Trois-Rivières	128 900
Vancouver	1 380 800
Victoria	255 600
Windsor	254 000
Winnipeg	625 300

Source: Census of Canada

(a) Using the population figures in Figure 5-16, list, in order, the 10 largest Canadian urban areas and their populations.

(b) Add up the populations to find the total number of people living in these 10 urban areas.

(c) What percentage of Canadians lived in the 10 most populated urban areas in 1986? The total population of Canada in that year was 25 354 000. Make your calculation this way:

$$\frac{\text{total population of 10 urban areas}}{\text{population of Canada}} \times 100 = ?$$

(d) In 1951, 35% of Canadians lived in the 10 largest urban areas. Did the percentage go up or down between 1951 and 1986? by how much?

6. Refer to Figure 5-16 again.

(a) Divide the cities into 3 classifications as follows:
- those with populations of 1 000 000 and over
- those with populations between 500 000 and 1 000 000
- those with populations under 500 000

Create symbols to represent the cities in each classification.

(b) Use your symbols, your list, an outline map of Canada, and an atlas to create a map called ***The 24 Largest Urban Areas in Canada***.

(c) Which province has most of these 24 cities? Are they in any particular part of the province? If so, where? In which province are there no large cities? Which provinces have only one large urban area?

(d) Give 5 reasons why these cities are clustered where they are.

Activities in Cities

There are many reasons why cities grow, and each major city developed for a different reason. But usually a city grows because it's near a transportation route — either rail or water. The transportation route attracts businesses and manufacturers. These, in turn, draw people seeking work. The jobs are tied to the economic functions or activities that exist in the community.

Central-place functions are services provided by businesses and governments for the people who live in the town or city and its surrounding area. A large department store in a mall is a central-place function. Figure 5-17 lists other central-place functions.

Most of the towns and cities in the more populated parts of Canada have a variety of functions. Many of the communities' early functions served the local farmers. From that beginning, the urban areas developed other functions, and often, manufacturing activities.

FIG. 5-17 ACTIVITIES IN URBAN PLACES

Central-place functions	Examples
Retail sales	Grocery, department and specialty stores
Financial services	Banks and finance companies, insurance offices, accountants
Recreation and entertainment	Theatres, arenas, concert halls, sports attractions
Education	Universities, colleges, specialized training centres
Health care	Hospitals, clinics, doctors, dentists, specialized labs
Wholesale trade	Warehousing, wholesale distribution
Transportation	Airports, train stations
Government services	Federal and provincial government offices

Some towns developed because of a local resource and depend on this resource for their survival. These towns are called **single-industry towns**. Most single-industry towns are located outside of the population "islands." Thompson, Manitoba, is one such town.

Thompson is located 740 km north of Winnipeg. Its economy is based on nickel which was discovered in the area in 1956. INCO, a major nickel producer, and the Manitoba government built the town of Thompson. Unlike many northern resource towns, Thompson is involved in all areas of nickel production. Nickel is mined, smelted, concentrated, and refined there.

FIG. 5-18

Lynn Lake, Manitoba, is another single-industry town. What economic problems might it have?

The economies of many single-industry towns are not stable. If the world demand for a town's resource drops, people lose their jobs and are forced to move away. This happened in Schefferville, Québec, when the Iron Ore Company of Canada closed its mines in 1983.

Levels of Services

Each size of community offers a range of services. Usually larger places have a greater variety and more sophisticated services. Villages have basic services, such as variety stores and gasoline stations: these are **low-order services**. Towns have **middle-order services**, such as grocery stores and banks. In cities, we find **high-order services,** like hospitals, universities, and art galleries. High-order services usually require a large population to support them. So, they are found mainly in larger places.

FIG. 5-19

Country stores are examples of low-order services.

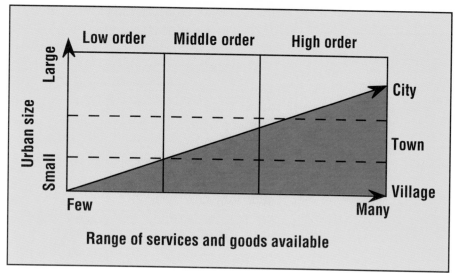

FIG. 5-20

What is the relationship between urban size and range of services?

Investigation 5.10

1. (a) Refer to Figure 5-17. For each function listed in the left-hand column, name one business or agency in your area that provides that function.
   (b) In your notebook, create a chart with the headings **Low-order services**, **Middle-order services**, **High-order services**. List up to 10 services in your community for each category.
2. Locate Thompson, Manitoba, in an atlas. In a few sentences, explain why Thompson has remained a single-industry town.

Problems of Urban Growth

The movement of many people into urban areas has caused a number of problems. Let's look at three problems that have been caused by rapid urban growth: urban sprawl, transportation problems, and providing services.

Urban Sprawl

As cities increase in population, land at the edge of the city is taken over for urban uses. This process may go on over a long time, slowly changing a rural area into an urban one.

The first sign of urban expansion in the countryside is the appearance of activities that need a great deal of land. Golf courses, automobile scrap yards, and tree nurseries buy land on city outskirts because land costs less than in a city. Other uses soon follow, such as factories, trailer parks, and lumber yards. These businesses are seeking cheaper land, but must be located near their urban customers. Finally, housing subdivisions and shopping centres appear, completing the change to urban uses.

Since many cities originally started in areas with good agriculture, farming is the major land use around most cities. As a city grows, farmers benefit because the value of their land rises. City developers offer the farmers high prices for their land. However, farmers who don't want to sell face some difficult problems. The new urban uses demand improved services — paved roads, better fire protection, larger school systems, and the like. These services are paid for by all the residents' taxes, so the farmers' taxes rise. In addition, new residents often object to the sights and smells that are part of agriculture. The conflict between old, rural uses and new, urban uses takes place in many ways on the edge of cities, sometimes causing hard feelings among the people involved.

Transportation Problems

Jobs aren't spread evenly throughout cities. They are concentrated in areas with commercial and industrial activities. Every morning people leave their homes in residential parts of the cities to travel to their jobs in businesses and factories. These peak travel periods, or **rush periods**, cause the transportation facilities of cities to become overcrowded. Streets and highways often become clogged with commuters in the morning, and again in the evening as workers return home. Public transit facilities — buses, subways, and rapid transit lines — in many larger centres simply can't handle the huge number of passengers. Growth of the cities puts even more pressure on the transportation systems.

FIG. 5-21 *What causes crowding on city roads? What could be done to improve conditions?*

So why don't the cities expand their transportation services? The main reason is often lack of money. It costs millions of dollars to build new highways or public transit facilities. It's difficult and expensive to build a highway in a developed area because it will most likely disrupt neighbourhoods and homes will have to be torn down. Plans have to be made years in advance so that land can be set aside and the necessary money made available. Cities often expand faster than planners had anticipated, and so proper preparation isn't done.

Another problem is deciding on what transportation facilities are needed. In large urban areas, governments have to choose between building highways, enlarging road networks, expanding bus and train services, or developing subways. Individuals or groups pressure the government for services that they feel will benefit them and their communities the most. Decision makers must be aware of the costs to taxpayers and make wise decisions. Sometimes, reaching a decision takes a long time. In the meantime, transportation facilities become overloaded, and commuters suffer.

Providing Services

Municipal, provincial, and federal governments have a responsibility to provide services to everyone. If they don't provide services quickly enough in growing urban areas many people are affected. Rapid growth means that residents are forced to deal with overcrowded schools and inadequate postal service. Social services like day care and assistance for the disadvantaged are often unavailable. These services haven't yet expanded to serve the larger population. Such services are often not provided until there is such a demand that officials can't ignore it any longer.

Providing services for growth areas is expensive. For example, schools have to be built quickly. The local taxpayers have to pay a large part of the construction costs for new schools. Later on, when the population growth has slowed, the expenses won't be so great. In a rapidly growing community, residents have high costs for services, not just for schools but also for recreation, protection, transportation, and sanitation. These are the costs of urban growth.

Investigation 5.11

SKILL
BUILDERS
DECISION
MAKING

1. (a) Write a definition for the term **urban sprawl**.
   (b) Put the following activities into 3 lists with these headings: ***Could Be Located in Rural Area, Should Be Located in Urban Area, Could Be Located in Either***.

   - golf course
   - hotel
   - youth hostel
   - variety store
   - building supplies store
   - shoe store
   - sports stadium
   - farm implement dealer
   - bank
   - government employment centre

   (c) Suggest 2 things that could be done to limit the harmful effects of urban sprawl. Write a short paragraph explaining your ideas.
2. Research the rate of population growth in your community. Express your answer as a percentage rate of growth. If the population of your community has been going down, you'll need to show that there has been a negative rate of growth.

Three CMAs: Toronto, Montréal, and Vancouver

Canada's three largest cities were founded at different times and in different parts of the country. All three places have been influenced by a unique set of growth conditions and so have developed in individual ways into the largest CMAs in Canada. Examine the maps, photos, and tables in this section and come up with ways the CMAs are different. Also, try to determine in what ways they are similar.

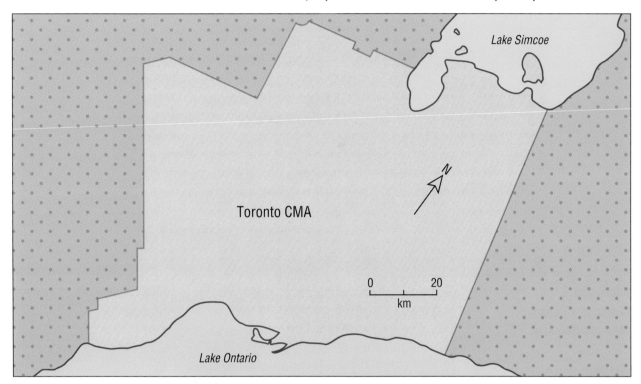

FIG. 5-22a
Toronto's Census Metropolitan Area

FIG. 5-22b
The centre of Toronto as seen from the CN Tower.

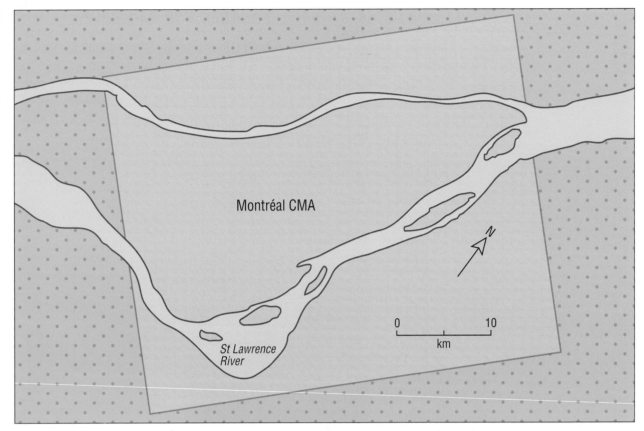

FIG. 5-23a
Montréal's Census
Metropolitan Area

FIG. 5-23b
Montréal's CBD

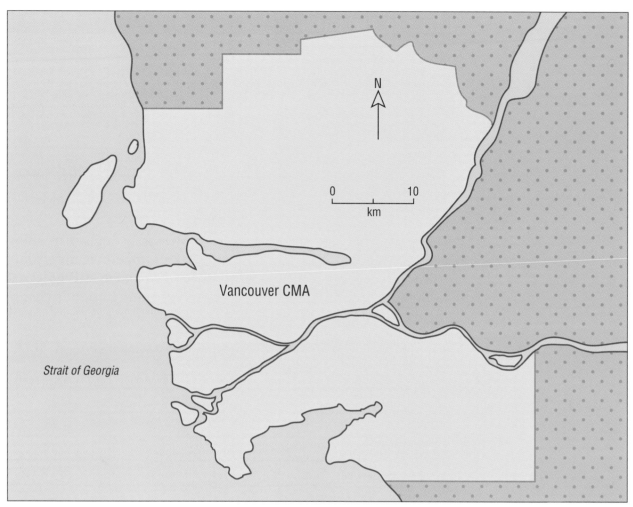

FIG. 5-24a
Vancouver's Census
Metropolitan Area

Vancouver CMA

Strait of Georgia

0   10
km

N

FIG. 5-24b
Port facilities are a prominent
part of Vancouver's CBD.

FIG. 5-25   POPULATION

Characteristics (1986)	Toronto CMA	Montréal CMA	Vancouver CMA
Area	5614 km²	3509 km²	2786 km²
Population	3 427 168	2 921 357	1 380 729
Population change (1981-1986)	9.5%	2.1%	8.9%
Population density	610.5/km²	832.6/km²	495.5/km²

Source: Statistics Canada, 1986 Census

Toronto and Vancouver were settled by mostly English-speaking people. Montréal, on the other hand, was an important fur-trading town in New France. The origins of these cities are still reflected in the CMAs populations. However, recent immigration is changing the population characteristics in important ways.

FIG. 5-26   FIRST LANGUAGE

Characteristics (1986)	Toronto CMA	Montréal CMA	Vancouver CMA
First language: English	73.6%	15.7%	78.8%
French	1.3%	71.7%	1.3%
Other	25.1%	12.6%	19.9%
Immigrant population	36%	15.7%	28.4%

Source: Statistics Canada, 1986 Census

A CMA's economic activities help to create the place's wealth. Many factors encourage or discourage strong economic activities, including availability of resources, transportation facilities (such as expressways, public transit, and airports), and access to markets. Figure 5-27 contains two simple statistics comparing the economic situations of Canada's largest CMAs.

FIG. 5-27   INCOME

Characteristics (1986)	Toronto CMA	Montréal CMA	Vancouver CMA
Average family income	$46 573	$37 865	$41 351
Families with income under $5000/year	3.2%	4.2%	3.6%

Source: Statistics Canada, 1986 Census

Government policies play an important role in shaping a CMA's housing characteristics. Government agencies can hold or release land for housing, make policy decisions that promote one type of housing over another, influence the costs of renting through rent-control laws, and develop subsidized housing units. The number of available housing units and the demand for housing because of growth determines the cost of housing in large urban areas.

FIG. 5-28 HOUSING

Characteristics (1986)	Toronto CMA	Montréal CMA	Vancouver CMA
Average value of dwellings	$142 282	$87 180	$127 311
Average monthly rent	$532	$450	$559

Source: Statistics Canada, 1986 Census

Investigation 5.12

1. Use Figures 5-25, 5-26, 5-27, and 5-28 to answer the following questions.
   (a) According to the statistics, which Canadian CMA has the highest population?
   (b) What CMA has the largest land area?
   (c) Based on the average population change, which CMA will likely be the largest in 2025?
   (d) Which CMA has the highest proportion of people whose first language is not one of Canada's official languages?
   (e) Name the CMA with the lowest proportion of families with incomes under $5000 per year.
   (f) How much more does a house cost in Toronto than in Montréal?
2. Suggest 2 reasons to explain each of the following observations from the statistical information.
   (a) The percentage of the immigrant population is considerably less in Montréal than in Toronto or Vancouver.
   (b) The costs of homes in Toronto is higher than in other cities.
3. Compare the first languages spoken in the 3 CMAs, using a graph. You might use circles, bars, or divided bars (the length of the bar equals 100%; it is divided into segments to represent the parts of the whole). Before you begin, think about which would be your best choice and write 3 reasons for your selection. When you are finished, decide whether your choice really was the best.

SKILL
BUILDERS
GRAPHING

Population Migration from Province to Province

All through this section you have been looking at where people live. But Canada's people also move from one province to another.

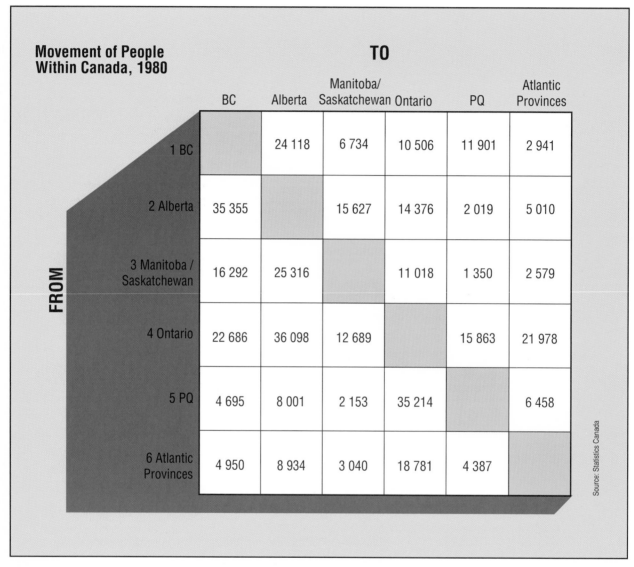

Movement of People Within Canada, 1980

FROM	TO					
	BC	Alberta	Manitoba/ Saskatchewan	Ontario	PQ	Atlantic Provinces
1 BC		24 118	6 734	10 506	11 901	2 941
2 Alberta	35 355		15 627	14 376	2 019	5 010
3 Manitoba / Saskatchewan	16 292	25 316		11 018	1 350	2 579
4 Ontario	22 686	36 098	12 689		15 863	21 978
5 PQ	4 695	8 001	2 153	35 214		6 458
6 Atlantic Provinces	4 950	8 934	3 040	18 781	4 387	

Source: Statistics Canada

FIG. 5-29

Where are the people from your province moving to?

Figure 5-29 is a ***From/To*** chart. It shows how many people moved from one province to another in 1980. You can see that the Yukon and NWT have been left out. No information was available for these areas and the numbers of people moving in and out would be small. The chart can tell you a lot about Canada and Canadians.

Investigation 5.13

1. Here are a few questions designed to help you read Figure 5-29. First, an example. In 1980, 24 118 people moved from British Columbia to Alberta. Nobody moved from British Columbia to British Columbia, of course, so that's why the first square is left blank.
   (a) How many people left BC to move to Manitoba and Saskatchewan?
   (b) How many people left Québec to move to Ontario?
   (c) How many people migrated to Alberta from the Atlantic provinces?
   (d) What is the largest number on the chart? Can you suggest what movement this represents? What is the smallest number on the chart? What movement does it represent?

2. Now let's see what is important in this information. To do so, it would be best to work in groups of 4. Decide who in your group is good at making maps, who is good at math, who is good at working with symbols such as arrows, and who is good at organizing and supervising. You are going to make a map from the chart. Here is what to do.
   (a) Firstly, your map maker will design an "exploding" map of Canada on a large sheet of poster paper. The map should look something like this.

FIG. 5-30

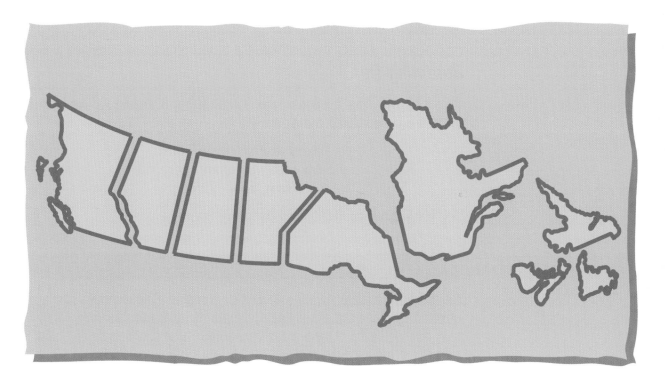

Secondly, your math person will group all the numbers in Figure 5-29 (p. 100) into 4 classifications: 0-5000 people, 5000-10 000 people, 10 000-20 000 people, and more than 20 000 people.

Thirdly, your symbol person will make arrows of varying lengths to show people's movements. These arrows can be made efficiently. Cut long strips of paper and colour them, using 4 colours to represent the 4 classifications. Then get ready to cut the strips into arrows of different lengths. You will be sticking them on the poster map to show how many people moved from one province to another. For example, you could use a short brown arrow from British Columbia to Alberta to show that 24 118 people (see Figure 5-29) moved in that direction. Stick the arrows on with masking tape so that you can easily change their positions. You will probably need to do this to ensure that all arrows are positioned properly.

(b) Now get together as a group again. Pool your ideas to answer this question: Why is an exploding map better than an ordinary map in showing this kind of information?

(c) Make a list of all the push and pull factors that might explain such migrations. Take into account living conditions, employment, natural resources, culture, scenic beauty, climate, cities, national and world events, etc.

Summing Up

This chapter has been about Canada's population. At its beginning, we listed three major questions:

Where did we come from?
How many of us are there?
Where do we live?

You have investigated them in many ways.

Investigation 5.14

You are going to design your own chapter summary. The summary can be in picture or story form. The choice is yours. But whatever the form, you must deal with each of the 3 major questions. These suggestions will help you with your summary.

- Make an overall plan.
- Collect data on each of the 3 major questions (from your notes, the Investigations, and the information in this chapter).

- Organize the data.
- Make a rough copy of your summary.
- Make the final copy.
- Review your work.

CHAPTER SIX

Employment

IT IS IMPORTANT TO UNDERSTAND a country's economic activities. That is because the strength of a country's economy determines whether people can maintain or improve their standard of living. In this chapter, you will look at the jobs Canadians do. You will begin by grouping jobs into three categories so that you will be able to understand the Canadian economy more easily. You will then have case studies on various types of jobs. This study of employment concludes by giving you some tips about finding or creating your own job.

Investigation 6.1

1. (a) Make a list of 30 different businesses. The word "business" means any activity that provides people with work. Under that definition you can class governments as businesses. If you're having trouble finding enough businesses for your list, ask your classmates where their friends and relatives work or look through the yellow pages of your telephone book.
   (b) Now, think about ways of combining these businesses into categories. Do some of them have things in common? Perhaps you could group them according to the kind of equipment they use. With a few of your classmates, try to find 3 or 4 other ways of grouping the businesses on your list.
   (c) Pick your best method and use it to group the businesses you've thought of.

As you can see, there are many ways of putting businesses into categories. The method you should choose is the one that best serves your purpose. If you want to investigate the use of tools in businesses, then you would use categories based on the equipment workers use. Geographers find it useful to group businesses according to the end products they produce. These final products are either **goods**, such as food, cars, and records, or **services**, such as haircuts and television repairs. As you may recall, we talked about goods and services and how their total value helps determine a country's wealth in Chapter 4. For now let's group industries by product type.

Primary, Secondary, and Tertiary Industries

FIG. 6-1 TYPES OF INDUSTRIES

Primary industries **first step**	Industries that obtain natural resources and change them into partially finished products
Secondary industries **second step**	Industries in which partially finished products are obtained and changed into finished goods
Tertiary industries **third step**	Industries that sell finished goods to consumers or provide services

You will notice all categories refer to industries. Although we often think of an industry as a business that manufactures something, any kind of economic activity can be called an industry. Therefore, we can talk about the entertainment industry or the farming industry in the same way that we talk about the steel industry.

Canada has all three kinds of industry. That is because few of our natural resources can be used without being changed in some manner into finished goods. These finished goods must then reach the consumer.

Primary ← → **Secondary** ← → **Tertiary** ←→

FIG. 6-2 *The natural resource iron ore is mined and turned into steel, a partially finished product. The steel is then used to make such finished goods as stainless steel pots. The pots are sold to consumers by a store, which is a service.*

Primary industries refine or improve the quality of the natural resources being used. For example, after an ore is mined, it is sent to a refinery. There the waste, or worthless rock, is removed from the valuable mineral. Partially finished products are almost always smaller in volume or bulk than the original natural resources used. For this reason, primary industries are often located close to the natural resources rather than where the partially finished products are needed. Transporting heavy and bulky raw materials (made up of both waste and valuable resources) is much more expensive than shipping the lighter, less bulky, partially finished products over the same distance.

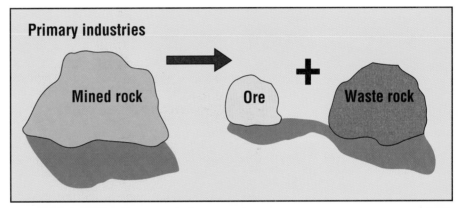

FIG. 6-3

The volume of output from primary industries is normally less than the volume of raw materials.

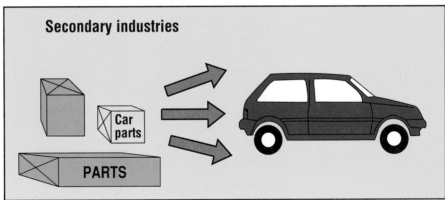

FIG. 6-4

The total volume of car parts is less than the total volume of a car. Therefore, it's cheaper to move parts long distances.

Secondary industries find it better to locate near the places where their finished products will be sold. Usually manufactured goods have a larger volume or bulk than the partially finished products they are made from. For example, the size of a finished automobile is larger than the size of its parts. Therefore shipping finished goods for great distances is usually more expensive than shipping partially finished materials over the same distances. To keep costs down, secondary industries try to be close to the people who will buy their finished products.

Tertiary industries don't make products. They provide services that we can't or won't do for ourselves. For instance, most of us don't repair our own televisions or stereos when they break down. We go to repair services.

FIG. 6-5

The sale of a product to a consumer is the last stage of a process that began with obtaining and processing natural resources. Sales is one form of tertiary industry.

Tertiary industries are located near the people they serve. Some such activities have many locations, with each serving a relatively small number of people. How far is it, for example, from your home to the nearest place to buy milk, see a doctor, go to a show, or shop at a hardware store? Other services in your community may have only a few locations and serve many people. Hospitals, concert halls, and hockey arenas are examples of this service type.

There are some problems in classifying work into primary, secondary, and tertiary. Sometimes it's difficult to decide which category a business fits into. Many companies take raw materials and process them into consumer products. They cross all three stages. Others clearly cover at least two categories. Kodak, for example, produces photographic film, a secondary activity. But the company also processes the film taken by consumers, a tertiary activity. Despite such problems, this method of classifying work remains useful to our investigations in the classroom.

Let's check your understanding of the ideas presented so far in this section.

Investigation 6.2

1. (a) Draw the following chart in your notebook. For each of the partially finished goods, list the natural resources that were used to make it and at least one finished good that is made from it.

FIG. 6-6 NATURAL RESOURCES AND GOODS		
Natural resources used	**Partially finished goods**	**Finished goods**
	flour	
	lumber	
	fox fur	
	gold bricks	

(b) Divide the following products into 2 lists, one entitled ***Output from Primary Industry*** and the other ***Output from Secondary Industry***.

- blue jeans and jackets
- cattle
- fresh fish
- shoes
- video games
- bread and baked goods
- aluminum pots and pans
- raw sugar
- steel building beams
- cross-country skis

2. Ten jobs that are considered to be tertiary occupations are hidden in the word search puzzle. Without putting marks on your textbook, find and list these 10 occupations in your notebook. The answers are on page 363.

```
C  T  M  O  F  T  F  W  M
L  S  I  N  G  E  R  T  D
E  I  L  J  N  A  E  X  R
R  T  B  U  K  C  T  L  I
K  N  K  R  R  H  S  G  V
L  E  O  R  A  E  I  Q  E
Z  D  O  T  S  R  N  V  R
M  E  C  H  A  N  I  C  I
Y  W  N  J  O  C  M  A  B
P  U  S  L  E  S  R  U  N
```

FIG. 6-7 CANADIAN EMPLOYMENT BY CATEGORY (percentages)	1951	1961	1971	1981
Primary	22.8	14.2	9.1	6.2
Secondary	33.3	30.2	28.3	28.8
Tertiary	43.9	55.6	62.6	65.0
Total	100.0	100.0	100.0	100.0
Total employed in Canada (in millions)	5097	6055	8078	11 006

SKILL

BUILDERS

GRAPHING

3. (a) Look at the table in Figure 6-7. Now turn that data on the percentages of Canadians employed in different categories into a set of 3 line graphs. (You could use a computer to do this.) These graphs will show the percentages of the Canadian work force employed in primary, secondary, and tertiary industries between 1951 and 1981. Use a different colour for each line and plot all 3 lines on the same piece of graph paper.

   (b) Write a paragraph that describes the trends in your graphs.

   (c) What do you think would explain these patterns?

Regional Differences in Employment

As you have seen, certain factors attract businesses to certain areas or locations. Primary activities are pulled to the locations of the natural resources, often far from the populated parts of the country. On the other hand, secondary and tertiary activities do better by being close to their markets. This means that many such businesses locate in the more populated parts of Canada. An uneven spread of job opportunities across the country results from these various influences. Figures 6-8 and 6-9 give some information about regional differences.

Many conditions influence the employment opportunities in an area. Here are some conditions that should be considered.

Available natural resources   Since Canada is rich in natural resources, many Canadians work in primary industries. But our resources aren't spread evenly across the country and they may vary from one area to the next. These differences in resources influence the kinds of jobs available. For example, if you live in Alberta, you may find a job in the oil industry, in farming, or in ranching, but if you want to work in the fishing industry, you would have to go to one of the coasts.

You can see the differences in the kinds of jobs workers are able to find in different parts of Canada.

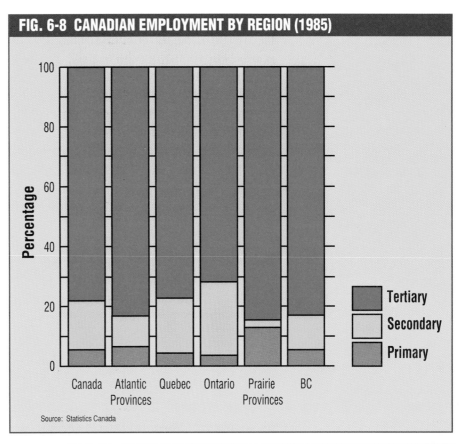

FIG. 6-8 CANADIAN EMPLOYMENT BY REGION (1985)

Percentage (y-axis: 0 to 100)

Regions: Canada, Atlantic Provinces, Quebec, Ontario, Prairie Provinces, BC

Legend: Tertiary, Secondary, Primary

Source: Statistics Canada

FIG. 6-9 PROVINCIAL EARNINGS AND UNEMPLOYMENT (1986)

Province	Average weekly earnings ($)	Unemployment rates (%)	Average family income ($)
Newfoundland	466.55	20.0	27 687
Prince Edward Island	387.53	13.0	31 097
Nova Scotia	424.57	13.4	33 480
New Brunswick	435.84	14.4	31 811
Québec	464.42	11.0	36 759
Ontario	493.26	7.0	44 098
Manitoba	434.68	7.7	35 990
Saskatchewan	418.87	7.7	35 779
Alberta	469.31	9.8	41 794
British Columbia	477.91	12.6	39 083
Canada	474.39	9.6	39 589

Source: Statistics Canada

Changes in the demand for materials   A region's prosperity may be influenced by the changing needs for certain materials or goods. For example, during the 1970s and early 1980s, Canadians became concerned about a shortage of petroleum. Oil prices rose. Much money was spent trying to develop the petroleum reserves found in Canada. Areas that contained large amounts of petroleum prospered. Governments and businesses spent much money to expand the petroleum industry. Workers migrated to the newly prosperous areas seeking jobs. But what goes up can also come down. When oil prices fell in the mid-1980s, workers in the petroleum industry were laid off and forced to look elsewhere for jobs.

Past rate of growth   You must work harder to get a bicycle moving from a standstill than to keep it going at a steady speed. Regions of the country are affected in the same way. Those that are already growing and developing find it much easier to continue to grow and prosper than the areas of little or no growth. The slow-growth areas must work much harder to reach the same levels of prosperity. For much of Canada's history, the **Industrial Heartland** from Windsor to Québec City has grown more rapidly than other parts of the country. It has done so largely because of its access to US markets and good transportation.

Transportation   Industries depend on cheap, reliable transportation. Reliable transportation means that finished goods can be produced from raw materials, brought into the plant, and shipped out to markets on time. Cheap transportation means that transportation doesn't add much to the price of finished products. Those parts of the country that have well-developed highway, rail, water, and air transportation systems are more attractive to industries than places where these facilities are poor.

Labour   Goods are produced using equipment and workers' labour. Some jobs can be done with no particular training or skill, and unskilled workers to fill them can usually be found easily. Industries that rely on highly trained workers may have more trouble. These industries need to make sure that the places in which they locate have people with the appropriate skills. As a result, they often locate in areas where similar industries are already employing such people. That is why manufacturing industries are often attracted to Canada's Industrial Heartland in Ontario and Québec.

These conditions show that the number of jobs found in any area is a result of many factors. Not all areas of the country have the same opportunities, and some regions are much less prosperous than others. As you may see in newspaper and TV reports, this difference or unequal distribution of opportunities is called **regional disparity**.

Investigation 6.3

1. Examine the information in Figure 6-9 (p. 111). Which parts of Canada seem to be suffering from a shortage of opportunities? Give reasons to support your answer, referring to the factors you've just read about.
2. Write a paragraph comparing the opportunities for a young person in a poor region with those of a young person in a prosperous region. Consider these ideas in your paragraph: part-time jobs; career choices; organized sports; concerts and shows; consumer goods.
3. Suppose you had to choose a career for yourself today. What type of job would you select? Write a paragraph identifying some job-hunting problems you might have. Think about such aspects as training needed, job location, necessary equipment, job availability, etc.

Employment Case Studies

Now that you have looked at the three categories of industry in Canada, let's look at some specific case studies. Activities from the primary, secondary, and tertiary categories have been selected to show you a variety of jobs. But, as was mentioned before, putting activities into categories is quite difficult. Sometimes the industries fit into several categories. They have been grouped here according to the largest part of their activities.

Here are the case studies listed by category:

Primary	Dairy Farming
	The Mining Industry
Secondary	The Automobile Industry
	Bombardier Inc.
Tertiary	Canadian Tire Corporation
	The Recording Industry

CASE STUDY

Dairy Farming

Agriculture is an important primary activity in Canada. It not only provides much of our food, but also employs both full- and part-time workers throughout the year. Dairy farming is just one small part of the whole agricultural industry. But it's an interesting part. It shows clearly some of the important trends in employment, particularly the impact of technology on jobs.

While the total number of jobs in dairy farming is small, many other jobs are linked to this activity. Veterinarians, feed suppliers, equipment distributors, and the like provide services to dairy farmers. Other workers are hired to process the milk into consumer products: cream, yogurt, ice cream, butter, and cheese.

Although dairy farms are scattered throughout most of the southern part of Canada, they are quite concentrated in certain locations. As you can see from Figure 6-10, these locations are in Nova Scotia and New Brunswick, southern Québec and Ontario, and southern British Columbia. Important characteristics these places have in common are fertile soils and a relatively warm climate. Another important factor is a large market nearby.

Because milk and fresh dairy products are perishable, they have to get to customers quickly. They can't sit on a railway siding for several days or on a loading dock over a weekend. They should be hauled only short distances, preferably by refrigerated trucks, which are faster than trains. Therefore, most farms are near large population centres. Compare the map of dairy farming areas to the map of population densities in Figure 5-12.

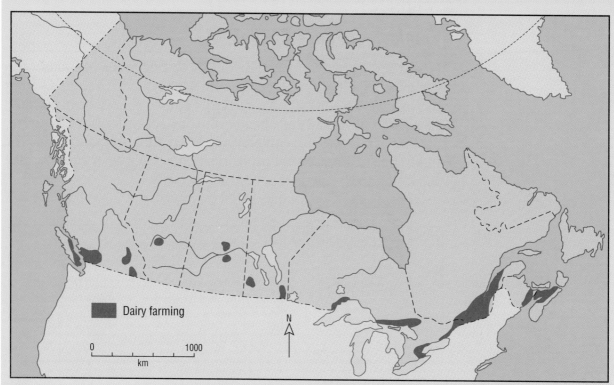

Dairy farming

0　1000

km

N

FIG. 6-10　Dairy farming areas in Canada

In the early years of this century, agriculture employed a far greater percentage of the population than it does today. Many people worked on family farms, producing food for their own use and selling any surplus. The farms were usually small and worked mainly with human and animal labour. Times have changed, however. Figure 6-11 shows the number of people employed in agriculture over the past few decades.

FIG. 6-11 EMPLOYMENT IN AGRICULTURE (1960-1987)

	1960	1965	1970	1975	1980	1985	1987
Number of workers	683 000	594 000	491 000	483 000	479 000	488 000	475 000
% of Canada's labour force	11.5	8.7	6.3	5.2	4.5	4.3	4.0

Source: Statistics Canada

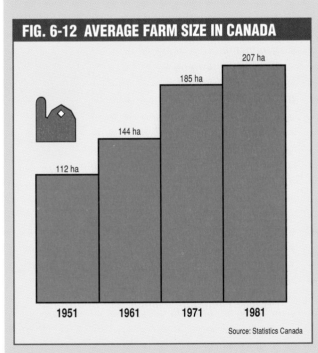

FIG. 6-12 AVERAGE FARM SIZE IN CANADA

207 ha
185 ha
144 ha
112 ha

1951 1961 1971 1981

Source: Statistics Canada

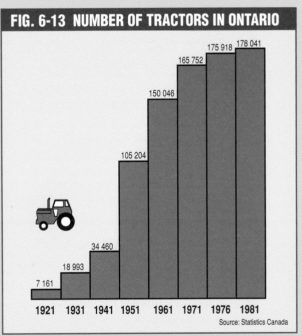

FIG. 6-13 NUMBER OF TRACTORS IN ONTARIO

178 041
175 918
165 752
150 046
105 204
34 460
18 993
7 161

1921 1931 1941 1951 1961 1971 1976 1981

Source: Statistics Canada

FIG. 6-14 DAIRY STATISTICS

	1950	1960	1970	1980	1986
Milk cows (000 head)	3119	2965	2389	1773	1456
Milk (000 t)	6762	8049	8176	7692	7283

Source: Statistics Canada

Investigation 6.4

1. (a) For each of the Figures 6-11, 6-12, 6-13, and 6-14 (p. 115), tell what has happened over the time period shown.
   (b) Suggest 1 or 2 reasons for each of the changes you identified in (a).
2. **Mechanization** has brought about changes in agriculture. Consult a good dictionary or reference book to find a suitable definition of the term. Write the definition in your notebook.

Farmers have mechanized their businesses through the use of high-tech electronics. Many of them now use microcomputers to cut costs and increase production. The following newspaper report looks at the use of computers in the milking barn.

Farmers Install Hi-tech Equipment

Karen and Joe Archer say their new high-moisture silo and computerized feeding system seem to have improved milk output.

But even with an increase in production from their 60 milking cows, Joe Archer has reservations about the high-technology equipment. "It's just so expensive to buy," he says. "The computerized feeders were about $25 000 and the silo alone more than double that amount. You have to sell a lot of milk to see a profit on those kinds of expenses."

The high-moisture silo will save money in the long run. It allows the Archers to mix their cattle feed, using grain and hay they produce on their farm. Before they bought the silo, prepared feed had to be purchased.

The computerized feed system was bought both to increase production and reduce labour costs. "This machine is great," says Karen Archer. "The cattle receive just the right amount of high-nutrition feed."

Each cow wears a device around its neck called a transponder. When she enters a feeding station the transponder sends a signal to the computer. The computer identifies the cow and dispenses just enough feed to meet that cow's needs. Once the computer determines that a cow has had enough feed for the day, it stops dispensing food.

"At the cost of labour these days, this system will pay for itself in a few years," said Karen Archer.

In spite of the success of the new technology, Joe Archer remains cautious. "Too many bad crops, or major breakdowns in equipment, will really hurt our profits. We have to be cautious, but we also have to take advantage of any new advance in technology that comes along. It's a risky business, no question about it."

FIG. 6-15
Today farmers use machines to milk their cattle.

FIG. 6-16 CANADIAN INTEREST RATES* (1977-1988)			
1977	8.5%	1983	11.17%
1978	9.69%	1984	12.06%
1979	12.90%	1985	10.58%
1980	14.25%	1986	11.00%
1981	19.29%	1987	9.52%
1982	15.81%	1988	10.83%

* The rates charged to secure major customers

Source: Canadian Economic Observer, Statistics Canada

Investigation 6.5

1. One reason given for the new dairy equipment was to reduce labour costs on the farm. Why are farmers concerned about this?
2. Put the following skills into 3 lists: those needed by farmers in times past, those needed by present-day farmers, and those needed by farmers both past and present.
   - repair machinery
   - give injections to cows
   - judge the quality of cows
   - operate machinery
   - predict future milk prices
   - decide best crops to plant
   - treat sick animals
   - milk cows
   - shoe horses
   - clean barns
   - do accounting
   - plough fields
   - operate computers
3. Suppose the Archers had to borrow $75 000 to purchase a silo and feeders.
   (a) Use Figure 6-16 to calculate how much the annual interest was on $75 000 in 1977. How much was the amount of interest in 1988?
   (b) Explain why farmers are concerned about interest rates.

CASE STUDY
The Mining Industry

Mining is an important primary activity in Canada. In 1988, there were 106 375 people directly employed in this sector of the economy.

FIG. 6-17   Mining areas in Canada   *What areas contain Canada's most important minerals?*

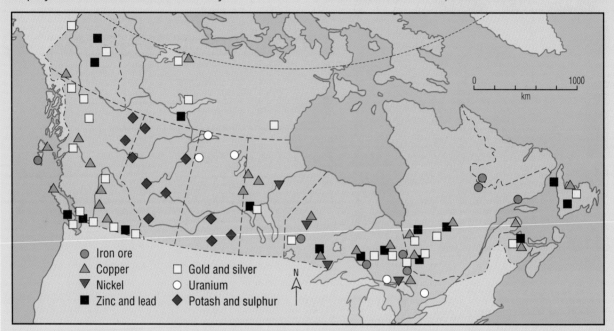

Legend:
- ● Iron ore
- ▲ Copper
- ▼ Nickel
- ■ Zinc and lead
- □ Gold and silver
- ○ Uranium
- ◆ Potash and sulphur

0 ——————— 1000 km

Investigation 6.6

1. Using Figure 6-17, list the various minerals mined in Canada.
2. Compare this map to the population distribution map of Canada in Figure 5-12. In several sentences, compare the patterns shown for both the distribution of mining and the distribution of the population.
3. Suggest 2 problems that could result from the difference in distribution.

In recent years, mining companies operating in Canada have been faced with a difficult situation. They find themselves competing more and more with mining companies in other parts of the world. Their customers, many in other countries such as the US, Japan, and the United Kingdom, buy the products they need at the lowest prices they can find. Increasingly these customers are turning to Chile for copper, the USSR for nickel, and Australia for iron ore.

A major advantage that Canada's mining competitors have is a lower cost of labour. The far lower wage rates in many of these places mean that the total costs to mine and refine the ores are less than in Canada. The lower wage rates also mean that these countries can get business at the expense of

Canada, because they can sell their products at lower prices. When demand for their ores drops, Canadian mining companies lay off workers and shut down mines. This problem of lost markets is what happened at Schefferville, on the Québec-Labrador border. The Iron Ore Company of Canada operated mines in this area from 1954 until 1983. When it discontinued operations, hundreds of workers were thrown out of work or forced to take jobs in other communities. The population of the town fell from about 3500 people to under 300. Much ore still remains in the ground, but there is no demand for it.

To become more competitive, mining companies try to reduce their costs. They have introduced high-volume, efficient machines to dig out the rock and refine the ore. Mechanization usually means fewer workers are required to produce the same amount of ore. However, mining still employs a large number of people at high salaries and keeps many communities alive in Canada.

In Canada's early history, mines were quite dangerous work places. Cave-ins, deadly gases, and the like took many lives. Nowadays, health and safety are major concerns of workers, mining companies, provincial governments, and the public as a whole. A new commitment to safety practices is helping to reduce mine hazards. Read the article on mine safety (opposite) and Figure 6-19 (p. 120). Then complete Investigation 6.7.

Safety First

As mining increases in complexity, today's miner must keep pace. Improved training programs and techniques are offered to those who are new to the industry. They are also provided, on a continuing basis, throughout the miner's working life. For those with no experience, initial training may consist of a one-week course in drilling, and perhaps a two-week session on the work of a production stope [where the drilling and blasting takes place]. With this training, most potential miners would then be ready to begin underground work under direct supervision.

In addition to vocational training, two aspects of the miner's work life receive special emphasis: safety training and mine rescue. We don't live in a perfect world, and miners, like all other industrial workers, must be prepared for accidents and emergencies. The highest possible standard of accident prevention is sought through constant caution, preparation, and co-operation. The co-operation of those operating the mines and those working in them is supported by a government inspection service that ensures that safety regulations are followed.

The seriousness with which miners approach safety can be measured, in part, by their interest and involvement in the mine rescue teams at each operation. These teams are specially trained and equipped to deal with emergency situations. To ensure a high standard of training, yearly safety competitions are held among mines, leading to the selection of a provincial champion. Fortunately, the occasions when the safety teams have been required to use their skills have been rare, but the expertise is available should it ever be needed.

Before starting a shift, the miners head for the "dry room" where they dress for the underground environment. The clothing and personal protective equipment of underground miners is designed for a specialized job in a very different surrounding. The miners don overall suits that are lightweight but strong, steel-toed rubber boots, and gloves. A heavy leather belt is worn around the waist to hold the battery pack for the head lamp. While underground they wear safety glasses, a protective helmet which holds the important two-element battery-operated lamp, and, where necessary, ear plugs or covers for noise protection.

Source: The Modern Miner, The Mining Association of Canada.

FIG. 6-18

The mining industry has many different jobs. Some people (left) work in the mines excavating the minerals. Others, such as mining engineers and technicians, work in laboratories

FIG. 6-19 DEATHS IN CANADIAN INDUSTRIES (1984)

Industry	# of Deaths	Deaths/1000 Workers
Agriculture	19	0.12
Forestry	56	0.98
Fishing	27	1.93
Mining	93	0.62
Manufacturing	118	0.07
Construction	142	0.41
Transportation	107	0.13
Trade	40	0.03
Finance	8	0.01
Services	56	0.02
Public administration	51	0.08

Source: Labour Canada

Investigation 6.7

1. (a) Examine Figure 6-19. Determine where the mining industry ranks in total number of deaths. Where does it rank in number of deaths per 1000 workers?
   (b) Which of the 3 industrial groups, primary, secondary, or tertiary, has the highest rate of industrial deaths? Suggest some reasons for this.
   (c) List the safety measures taken by mining companies in training their workers.
   (d) Using this section's photographs of miners and the description of the equipment miners must use, draw and label a picture of a miner ready for work.
2. Find out how various groups have sought to improve safety conditions in mining. Have several members of your class get in touch with such groups to obtain information on training programs, inspection procedures, emergency measures, etc. Here are some leads: your provincial Department or Ministry of Labour; Industrial Accident Prevention Association; United Steelworkers of America; Workers' Compensation Board.

CASE STUDY

The Automobile Industry

The auto industry has long been an important source of jobs for Canadians. It employs workers to supply raw materials to make cars, to assemble cars, and to supply all the services needed by car owners. Many people earn their livelihoods because of the automobile.

FIG. 6-20 ACTIVITIES IN THE AUTO INDUSTRY

Primary	• mining and processing of minerals such as iron, nickel, and chromium • extracting petroleum for use in manufacturing chemicals, lubricants, and plastics • harvesting rubber
Secondary	• designing the autos and the machines to produce them • manufacturing the parts that make up the automobiles • assembling the parts into finished vehicles • manufacturing chemicals used for paints, lubricants, solvents, etc.; manufacturing rubber products for tires and door seals; manufacturing plastics for interior and exterior parts
Tertiary	• selling the autos to customers • servicing vehicles • insuring vehicles • providing replacement parts and accessories

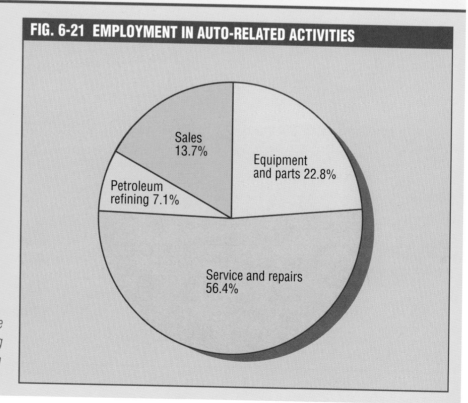

FIG. 6-21 EMPLOYMENT IN AUTO-RELATED ACTIVITIES

Sales 13.7%

Equipment and parts 22.8%

Petroleum refining 7.1%

Service and repairs 56.4%

Did you know that there are more jobs involved in looking after a car than there are in making one?

Although many people are employed because of the automobile, the industry's labour requirements are changing. Most new automobile plants are designed to use robots for much of the work. These computerized machines can complete complex tasks, over and over again. They have replaced many workers on assembly lines and will take over more jobs in the building and servicing of cars in the future. But, while the number of assembly-line jobs is dropping due to computers, more people are finding jobs in areas that require them to have computer knowledge. The automobile industry is in a state of transition.

In recent years, the auto industry in North America has had to adapt to other developments as well. Rising costs of raw materials and labour have forced up the prices of new cars. Many imported cars are less expensive and have been competing against North American-made cars quite successfully. Many of these imported cars also have lower repair costs than North-American built vehicles, making them even more popular with consumers. In order to compete, North American companies have had to respond with new styles, improved designs, and better service.

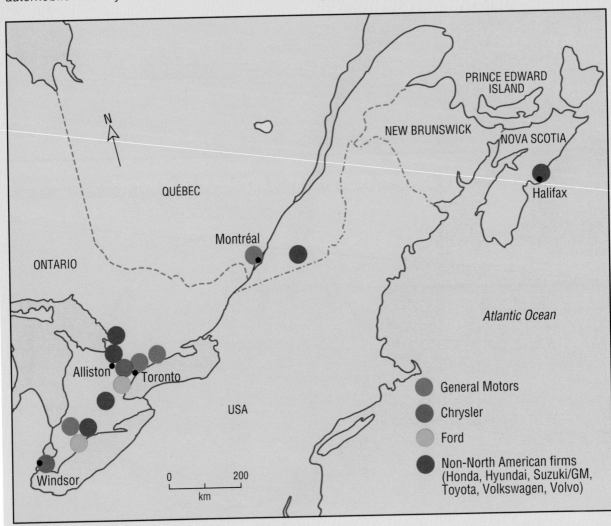

Figure 6-22 Locations of automobile assembly plants

The auto trade between Canada and the US interests Canadians greatly. This was reflected in the creation of the Autopact, signed by both countries in 1965. The goal of the Autopact has been to keep a **balance of trade** in autos and parts between the two countries.

Under the Autopact, autos and parts move across the Canada-US border, free of any **tariffs** or **duties**, taxes that would have raised the selling prices of the cars. Cars built in Canada are sold in the US at about the same cost as in Canada, and vice versa. Auto manufacturers take advantage of lower labour and distribution costs. Consumers benefit. Although the Autopact still exists, some guidelines have been changed because of the Canada-US free trade deal.

FIG. 6-23
The increasing use of robots means fewer workers are needed to make cars.

Investigation 6.8

SKILL
BUILDERS
DECISION
MAKING

1. List 6 examples of foreign cars you have seen on Canadian roads, and identify the countries of origin. How do sales of imported cars affect the number of jobs in Canada?
2. Honda of Canada chose Alliston, Ontario, as the location for a new factory to assemble autos. Find Alliston on Figure 6-22. After studying the map, list 5 reasons why Honda would consider the community attractive.
3. Imagine you have been put in charge of locating an auto assembly plant in western Canada. Where would you build it? Why would you build it there?

CASE STUDY

Bombardier Inc.

The auto industry is the most important transportation industry in Canada because it employs the largest number of workers. However, there are other major Canadian companies that make aircraft, railway cars, and recreational vehicles. Bombardier Inc., which produces a variety of vehicles for land, air, and water uses, is one such Canadian business.

Bombardier's headquarters are located at Montréal, Québec. The company also has plants in Canada, Belgium, the United Kingdom, Finland, Sweden, the US, and Austria.

Bombardier began as a company that manufactured vehicles that could travel over snow. Its founder, Armand Bombardier, was only 15 when he began building his first snow machine, finished in 1923. But it wasn't until 1937 that Bombardier patented one of his machines, a vehicle that could carry seven passengers. Bombardier Inc. became well known across Canada when it began production of the Ski-Doo in 1959. The company, the first to make one-person snowmobiles, produced over one-third of all snowmobiles sold in Canada in 1986.

FIG. 6-24 *Bombardier is well known in Canada for its recreational vehicles, as well as for its other products.*

FIG. 6-25 *From this humble beginning, Armand Bombardier founded a company that is now known around the world for the quality of its vehicles.*

FIG. 6-26 SNOWMOBILE SALES IN NORTH AMERICA (1978-1989)		
Year	Bombardier (units sold)	Bombardier and other North American retailers (units sold)
1978-79	70 498	260 154
1979-80	48 752	190 366
1980-81	52 627	166 199
1981-82	54 531	141 344
1982-83	23 333	78 648
1983-84	28 084	92 763
1984-85	31 439	84 778
1985-86	34 343	95 229
1986-87	38 180	102 616
1987-88	36 796	110 725
1988-89	40 219	129 031

Source: Bombardier Inc.

Investigation 6.9

1. (a) Draw a divided bar graph for each of the years from 1978 to 1989 to show Bombardier's share of total snowmobile sales.
   (b) Write a short paragraph to describe the information shown in your graph.
   (c) Suggest 3 reasons why the number of snowmobiles sold might change from one winter to the next.

2. As you can see, snowmobile sales do not remain constant. Bombardier Inc., fearing it was becoming too dependent on one product — the snowmobile — decided to make other products as well. This strategy is known as **diversifying**. By diversifying, the whole company doesn't suffer if one product sells poorly. Until 1986, Bombardier divided its products into 3 divisions: transportation equipment (e.g. subway cars, light-rapid transit trains) motorized consumer products (Ski-Doos), and defence. In 1986, Bombardier added a fourth division, aerospace products, which makes airplanes and airplane parts. Figure 6-27 shows the sales for each division.
   (a) Which Bombardier division had the greatest overall growth for the time period shown on the graph?
   (b) What 3 conditions might influence each division's sales?
   (c) How good was Bombardier's decision to diversify? Explain your answer by using evidence found in the graph.
   (d) Would this graph be useful in predicting sales for the year 1995? Explain your answer.

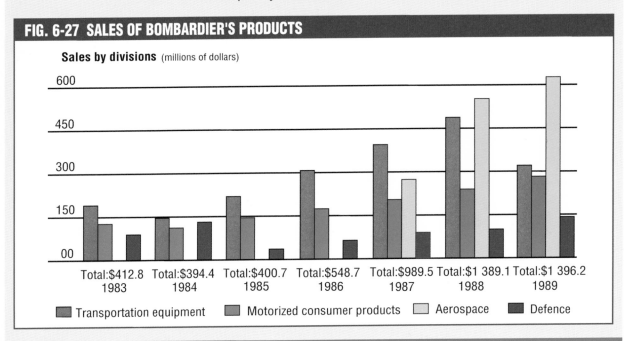

FIG. 6-27 SALES OF BOMBARDIER'S PRODUCTS

Sales by divisions (millions of dollars)

Total:$412.8	Total:$394.4	Total:$400.7	Total:$548.7	Total:$989.5	Total:$1 389.1	Total:$1 396.2
1983	1984	1985	1986	1987	1988	1989

■ Transportation equipment   ■ Motorized consumer products   □ Aerospace   ■ Defence

CASE STUDY

Canadian Tire Corporation

Many tertiary sector businesses, such as stores and fast-food restaurants, use part-time help. They often rely on students for such help, especially during late afternoons, evenings, and weekends.

Many stores are operated as **franchises** which means a person pays a fee to purchase the name and products of a parent company. The franchisee then owns the store and its contents. One particular tertiary sector business, the Canadian Tire Corporation, operates its stores a bit differently. They offer "authorized dealerships" which are part of the larger company. This means that Canadian Tire Corporation owns the store, but the dealer owns the products in the store. Unlike franchises, there are no fees involved. The Canadian Tire dealer-owners contract to buy goods from the parent company. In return, the parent company promotes overall sales through large-scale advertising.

The Canadian Tire Corporation, originally called the Hamilton Tire and Rubber Limited, was started in Toronto in 1922 by John W. and Alfred J. Billes. The brothers, who began by opening a garage and auto parts depot, took advantage of the new market for auto replacement parts. By 1923, they had retail-type facilities and within a few years, branch stores. By 1930, a great sales volume enabled the company to advertise batteries at attractively low prices. Canadian Tire was the first Canadian company to offer an unconditional guarantee on a tire, the "Super-Lastic."

FIG. 6-28

Canadian Tire stores sell more than automotive and household goods.

Retail stores supply goods not only for cars but for houses. Over the years, Canadian Tire has developed a wide range of goods and services for the auto and home improvement and repair markets. Its formula for success continues to work today.

Canadian Tire encourages consumer purchases by delivering detailed store catalogues to many homes. High-profile newspaper and television ads for special promotions are also part of its selling strategy. The goods for the corporation and each store are controlled and ordered through a large computer operation.

Canadian Tire encourages buying with cash. In some parts of Canada, customers paying by cash are given coupons worth 4-5% of their purchases. Customers can use these coupons to help buy merchandise at a later time.

In Canada there are more than 400 Canadian Tire stores, each owned by an associate dealer. Canadian Tire dealerships are highly sought after. For example, in 1981, 1000 people applied for only 16 new dealerships. That was the year the corporation spread nation-wide, opening 8 stores in British Columbia, the last province to get them. The corporation is now trying to fill in the gaps. It wants to have a store in every community with a large enough population to support it.

Despite being mainly self-service, the stores offer many job opportunities. Work ranges from stocking shelves to repairing cars, handling the cash to managing the store. Across the country, Canadian Tire employs more than 20 000 full- and part-time workers. Many young people are able to find part-time work in Canadian Tire stores.

Investigation 6.10

SKILL
BUILDERS
GRAPHING

1. (a) Use the following statistics to calculate the percentage of Canadian Tire stores found in each province. Show the information on a bar graph.

FIG. 6-29 DISTRIBUTION OF CANADIAN TIRE STORES

Province	Number of stores	Province	Number of stores
British Columbia	37	Quebec	89
Alberta	23	New Brunswick	15
Saskatchewan	11	Nova Scotia	19
Manitoba	13	Prince Edward Island	3
Ontario	187	Newfoundland	11
		TOTAL	408

(b) Why are far more than half the stores located in Ontario and Québec?

(c) Which provinces will probably see the greatest increase in the number of stores in the next few years? (Hint: Check provincial populations.)

2. Working in groups of 4, propose a type of dealership or franchise that might be successful in your community. Consider these factors: type of product; market size and location; staff needed; best location for the store; competition.

SKILL
BUILDERS
WORKING
WITH GROUPS

The Recording Industry

The recording industry in Canada is small compared to that in the US, but it does an important job in promoting Canadian musicians and song writers.

The industry has three parts. First, the music is written and recorded by the individuals or musical groups. Next, their music is recorded onto albums, tapes, or compact discs and distributed to retail stores. Finally, promotion activities encourage people to buy the songs.

The music is initially recorded on tape using 24 different tracks. Each track records a different component of the music (drums, bass, guitar, vocals, etc.). These 24 tracks are eventually "mixed down" to two tracks. It may take as many as 200 hours to record enough music for an album or tape. When finished, the tape from the recording studio is sent to a record company. Here the tape is transferred to either a vinyl master record or to digital form for the making of records, tapes, or compact discs, completing the first stage.

After a record, tape, or compact disc is produced, both the record company and the musicians must promote sales. The record company usually tries to persuade stores to display the new recordings, and radio stations to play the new songs. Its efforts to promote a well-known group are much more likely to be successful than for a new group that has never had a hit record. For their part, the musicians try to encourage sales by making public appearances and going on concert tours.

Investigation 6.11

SKILL
BUILDERS
SURVEYS

1. Set up an interview with a record store manager. Find out how the store promotes sales of new records. Where does the promotional material come from?
2. Do a survey of the music played on local radio stations between 7:00 and 10:00 p.m. one evening. Divide the work among all class members. Listen to a radio station, recording song titles on a chart similar to the following one.

FIG. 6-30 RADIO SURVEY FORM

Station: _____

Record title	Name of group or artist	Nationality Canada/Other

The next day analyze the chart to see how many Canadian artists are represented. What can you conclude?

3. Why is it so important for a record company to get its records played on the radio?

4. All Canadian recording companies face competition from outside the country. How well these companies do is affected by the actions of the federal government. The government can either allow free trade with other countries or use taxes and tariffs to keep the goods of other countries out of Canada.

Study Figure 6-31 which shows how Canadian and foreign-owned recording companies split the recording market in Canada.

FIG. 6-31 NET SALES OF RECORDS AND TAPES (1986-87)

Musical category	Origin of financial control		
	Canadian (percent)	Foreign (percent)	Total net sales (percent)
Top 40/rock/disco	22	67	62
Adult-oriented popular music	14	12	13
Country and folk	6	8	8
Classical	10	8	8
Children's	17	1	3
Jazz	1	2	2
Other/unspecified	30	1	4
($000s)	$29 039	$248 833	$277 872
Number of companies reporting	78	13	91

Note: Columns do not add up to 100% due to rounding.

Source: Statistics Canada

(a) Write 2 general statements about the facts shown in Figure 6-31.

(b) What 2 questions about the recording industry could you discuss with your member of Parliament? Take the viewpoint of a record company owner seeking government help.

5. (a) Study Figure 6-32 to see how the recording industry packages music for customers. What changes have taken place? Which method has shown the greatest gain?

(b) What new technologies have been competing with records and tapes since 1984?

(c) If you were president of a record company, how would you try to prepare for the effects of new technologies?

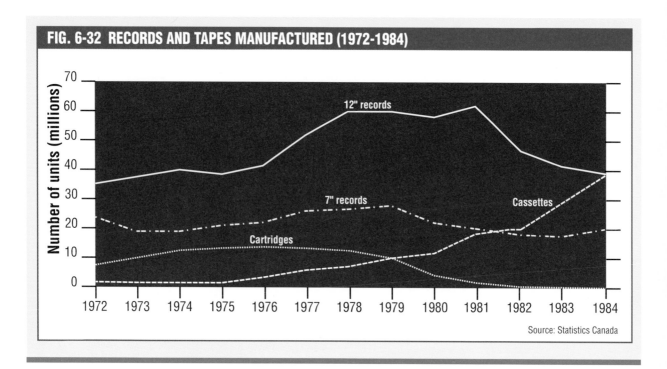

FIG. 6-32 RECORDS AND TAPES MANUFACTURED (1972-1984)

Source: Statistics Canada

Finding a Job

Finding a job that meets your needs isn't always easy. If you want to win just the right job you will have to think about it carefully and conduct a thorough job search.

Investigation 6.12

1. What are your needs? Make a list of the products you buy and services you use regularly. Beside each item in your list, write an estimate of the amount of money you spend in a month. Total your expenses. How much money do you need to earn each month?
2. Suppose you were able to get a job that pays twice as much money as you now need. Do you think your spending patterns would change? What else might you buy?

When you begin to look for work, be sure you analyze the job opportunities in your area. Otherwise, you could waste a great deal of time just walking from one business to another or by not doing anything because you don't know where to start. Figure 6-33 (p. 132) identifies some places to begin your search.

FIG. 6-33   LOOKING FOR A JOB

Source of information	Comments
Canada Employment Centres	• operated by the federal government • often have student job centres • jobs are usually posted on a display board • your name is kept on file
Newspapers	• have jobs listed in the classified ads section • announce the opening of new businesses • have articles about employment conditions
School guidance offices	• sometimes get information from employers • have information about job-hunting skills • have information about government summer job programs
Bulletin boards	• employers may post notices • you can advertise to find a job
Friends and relatives	• may know which employers hire young people • may have "inside" information about job opportunities • may have information about businesses in your area

By the time you have explored all the sources of information in your area, you should have a good idea of which businesses hire young people. Concentrate your job-hunting efforts on those places. But remember to keep watching and listening for any other opportunities.

Investigation 6.13

1. (a) Create a chart in your notebook with these headings: **Businesses**, **Types of Jobs**, and **Comments**. List places in your area that you know hire young people. Try to get the names of 10 businesses. In the second column, record the kinds of jobs students are hired to do. Write any additional details you might get, such as "hires people over 16 years old" or "students needed during the summer," in the third column. Ask your classmates for help if you have difficulty.
2. Examine the businesses you included in your chart. How many are in the primary sector? the secondary sector? the tertiary sector?

Normally, you would ask about a job opening by calling on a business in person. Be sure to dress neatly and stand erect. Be confident!

When you apply for a job, you should have a résumé with you. A **résumé** is a brief statement that gives employers some background information about yourself. Check the résumé outline in Figure 6-34 to see what kinds of information an employer usually looks for.

FIG. 6-34 RESUME OUTLINE

NAME: _____

ADDRESS: _____

_____

TELEPHONE: _____ BIRTH DATE: _____

SOCIAL INSURANCE NUMBER (SIN): _____

SCHOOL: _____ LAST GRADE COMPLETED: ____

JOB EXPERIENCE *(List most recent first):*

Company name and address	Job title	Dates
1.		
2.		
3.		

SKILLS AND SPECIAL TRAINING *(List areas of special knowledge or talent)*

1. _____

2. _____

3. _____

POSITIVE QUALITIES *(Example: loyal, reliable)*

1. _____

2. _____

3. _____

REFERENCES *(Make sure you get permission to use their names.)*

Name and address	Telephone
1.	
2.	
3.	

Write your résumé based on the outline. Keep in mind that thoroughness and accuracy are important and that your statements should be brief and to the point. In the job experience section, include work you have done before. Babysitting, paper routes, odd jobs, or volunteer work are examples. If necessary, ask your teacher or classmates for help. Once you have finished drafting your résumé, get a classmate's reaction to it. Now revise what you've written.

If an employer is impressed with your résumé, you may be asked for an interview. Here are some ways to continue making a good impression.

Make sure that you follow up on job opportunities. If you have given a company a résumé, check back in a week or so. If you have had an interview, visit or call in one or two days, asking for the person who interviewed you. Another excellent idea is to write that person a thank you letter in which you can say again how much you want to work for that business.

For practice, conduct an interview with a classmate who has a job interest similar to yours. This will give you confidence in a real job interview. Remember your guidance department will be able to give you more tips to help in your search for a job.

FIG. 6-35 JOB-HUNTING TIPS

Be prepared

- Know what the job involves.
- Know why you are qualified for the job.
- Know why you want the job.
- Know the name of the person who will be interviewing you.
- Take a résumé.

Complete the business's application form

- Take your time.
- Write as neatly as possible.
- Don't leave out anything important.

Think about the impression you are making

- Go alone (this shows maturity and independence).
- Be on time.
- Dress neatly.
- Listen carefully.
- Speak clearly.
- Look the interviewer in the eye.

Making Your Own Job

Many people in Canada decide they want to work for themselves, to be self-employed, rather than work for someone else. While there are many risks for people who start their own businesses, there are also rewards: independence, a sense of accomplishment, and the possibility of making good profits. Let's look at this way of making a living more closely.

People start their own businesses because they see unfilled needs in their communities. Perhaps they have heard people say they can't find some good or service, or perhaps they have been dissatisfied with the facilities that are offered. In any case, seeing certain needs has led them to start small businesses. Simple businesses include mowing lawns for neighbours and selling flowers on a downtown street. Businesses run by young people can also be more complicated. Running a snack bar and painting houses are examples.

People who start their own small businesses cannot depend on someone else to help them in times of trouble. They must rely on their own abilities and skills. Starting small, they do everything, learning all aspects of their businesses. If their businesses are successful, then they can possibly hire other people to help them. But even then they must make all the decisions.

Successful self-employed people start with business plans, or written summaries of what they intend to do. The plans outline how they will earn money and predict how much they will make. They also show how much their expenses will be. Self-employed people need to know this so they can determine their profit, or the money left over after all the bills are paid. The profits are their pay.

Business plans force people to think through what they want to do and help them identify problems that have to be overcome. Often an important problem is money. If you set up a business selling a product, you will need money to buy a supply of that product to sell, and you may need money to get a place to set up your business. If the business involves providing a service, such as landscaping or cleaning, you will need money to buy equipment. In both cases, you will need money to attract customers through advertising.

Banks provide most loans to small businesses, but there are other places to borrow money. You may be able to talk a relative into financing your business, perhaps at a lower rate of interest than a bank would charge. You might also try finance companies, trust companies, and credit unions. Also, don't overlook government programs that loan money to young people. Whatever your source, you will need to borrow enough money to cover your expenses and to give you something to live on.

What kinds of self-employment might you choose while still in school? Here are some examples:

FIG. 6-36 SELF-EMPLOYMENT IDEAS	
Retail sales	**Services**
Cosmetics	Landscaping
Clothing	Senior/child care
Cards	Cleaning
Jewellery	Car care
Arts & crafts	House painting & decorating
Baked goods	Catering
	Entertaining

The possibilities for self-employment are many. Planning, imagination, and hard work are necessary to make a business grow, but the rewards can be worth the effort.

Investigation 6.14

1. Suppose you decide to set up a small business. Prepare a business plan for one of these activities:
   - lawn and garden maintenance
   - souvenir sales at an amusement park
   - child care services
   - the manufacture of small games and toys

   Your plan should outline the following:
   - a suitable location for your business
   - potential customers
   - the amount of money you will need to start and run the business
   - the source of your money
   - the profit you expect to make
2. What could you do if your business does not make a profit right away? List your options.
3. Consider the self-employment opportunities in your area. Look at the list of possibilities in Figure 6-36. Which ones interest you? For each activity that you might find enjoyable, ask friends and relatives these questions:
   - Do you know of anyone now offering these products or services?
   - Would you be interested in these products or services?

• What chances of success do you think a person would have in running a business dealing with these products or services?

Complete a business plan for any business that looks promising.

Summing Up

This chapter has shown you how jobs can be grouped under categories, something that makes it easier for you to see patterns. Primary activities are those that take raw materials and change them into semi-finished products. Secondary industries convert semi-finished products into consumer goods. Service activities help people use goods to meet their needs. These industries all provide jobs for Canadians. The case studies in this chapter described some of the ways Canadians earn their livings.

Finding a job takes careful preparation and a thorough search of opportunities in your community. Some people, however, prefer to make their own jobs rather than work for other people. Careful planning and dedication are the keys to success in business.

CHAPTER SEVEN

Leisure and Recreation in Canada

FIG. 7-1 (opposite)

Many Canadians spend their leisure time involved in fitness activities, such as hiking.

Y OU HAVE ALREADY SEEN that Canadians have needs that must be filled if we are to lead happy lives. We need food and water, social and family life, and safe places to live. Chapter 6 has much information about ways people earn their livings. The money we earn helps meet many of our needs.

However, Canadians do more than work. We take leisure time. This is important because it provides opportunities for us to explore our interests. Maybe we are attracted to sports, enjoy music or drama, or just want to relax and watch television. Without leisure time, we could not take part in these activities.

Over the past decades, the amount of leisure time has increased greatly. Around 1901, the average work week was 60 hours. By 1951, it was down to 40 hours. It's expected to be only 28 hours by 2001. This trend means that people are spending less time earning their livings and have more time for leisure. Providing facilities and services for leisure time is one of the fastest growing industries in North America.

This chapter will provide you with some information about the ways we use our leisure time and the facilities we need. As you explore the ideas, think about your own use of leisure time. What do you do? What leisure activities are available in your area?

Now let's look at how you spend your time.

Investigation 7.1

1. Draw 7 circles, the same diameter, on a page. Label one for each of the last 7 days (or the next 7, if you're going to treat this as a log). Divide the circles into 24 hour clocks. Fill in sleeping, school, work, and other activities. Remember lunch hour and breaks at school are leisure time. All time not filled is leisure time!

    You might be surprised to see that you often don't actively choose how you use this time. Perhaps it just drifts by. Perhaps, after you've worked on this chapter, you will make active decisions about when and how you use your leisure time. Remember that you have even more leisure time during your Christmas vacation, spring break, and summer holidays! Let's explore the ways you can use this time, as well.

Using Leisure Time

As you leave school and begin to work full time, your leisure time may become even more important to you than it is now. When you look for work, you will probably want to find out how many weeks of vacation time come with a job. In some jobs, people can arrange their hours of work in different ways. They may be able to stop early on Friday afternoons. Others may work on "flex time," starting and stopping work when they want to, but completing a set number of hours. There is also a trend towards shorter work weeks, with some people already on four-day weeks. As people get more time for leisure and recreational activities, they will have to make more choices about how to use that time. Figure 7-2 shows the results of a survey of how some adults spend their free time.

You may have noticed that the percentages in this table add up to more than 100%. That's because each person may have taken part in many activities. The table can also be read in another way. If 95% of the people in the survey watched television, you can also say that 5% of them did not. If 83% of the people read newspapers, 17% did not.

FIG. 7-2 LEISURE TIME SURVEY (% of adults involved in the activity)

Activity		Activity	
Watching television	95	Visiting public libraries	21
Listening to radio	83	Art activities	13
Reading newspapers	83	Music activities	12
Reading magazines	58	Formal instruction	11
Listening to records or tapes	50	Going to popular music concerts	11
Participating in sports and exercise	47	Going to live theatre	9
Reading books	43	Going to classical music concerts	7
Visiting book stores	40	Visiting museums	6
Hobbies & crafts	33	Visiting art galleries	6
Going to movies	33		

Source: Atlas of Canada © The Reader's Digest Association (Canada) Ltd., Montréal. Reproduced with permission.

Investigation 7.2

SURVEYS

1. What percentage of people (a) never went to movies? (b) did go to art galleries? (c) did not listen to radios? (d) went to some music concerts?
2. (a) What are the 3 most popular activities?
   (b) What do they have in common?
3. Which activities would likely be (a) more popular with teenagers? (b) less popular with teenagers? (c) equally popular with teenagers?
4. Survey your classmates and find out what the 5 most common leisure activities are. Compare your results with Figure 7-3 (p. 142).

Rockin' Geography

In the book, *The Emerging Generation*, the authors show a survey of the leisure activities of people your age. The results are shown in Figure 7-3. You will see that music is ranked highest on the list. Beginning with this section on rock music, we will be looking at the arts in Canada. The case study of a real rock group (p. 143) is possibly the best way to see how geography plays a role in this type of cultural activity.

FIG. 7-3 LEISURE ACTIVITIES OF CANADIAN TEENAGERS (1984)

"How often do you...?"	% Reporting "very often"		
	Nationally	**Males**	**Females**
Listen to music	90	89	92
Watch television	57	61	53
Daydream about the future	51	43	59
Sit and think	44	35	54
Dance	44	32	56
Attend parties	40	40	39
Follow sports	43	58	29
Participate in non-team sports	40	44	37
Play team sports	39	50	29
Work out	37	40	35
Attend a sports event	27	32	22
Read the newspaper	37	41	34
Follow the news	35	41	29
Spend time on a hobby	34	36	34
Read magazines	32	29	36
Read books	29	19	39
Participate in a youth group	17	14	19
Go to a movie	17	15	19
Go to a video games arcade	13	20	7
Play video games in a home	12	17	7

Source: *The Emerging Generation*, Reginald W. Bibby and Donald C. Posterski, 1985.

CASE STUDY

Honeymoon Suite

In 1985, a rock band called Honeymoon Suite was rising to success in Canada. Here is a brief account of how that band started out to get songs and records played on "top hit" charts. By the time you read this, Honeymoon Suite could be totally unknown, a band of the past, or it could be very famous. Most bands have short-lived success.

Honeymoon Suite began as a cover band. A cover band starts out playing other groups' songs in small bars and clubs (50-100 people). Its main goal is to get work, experience, and exposure to an audience every week. Band members tend to travel in old vans and trucks filled with their equipment. They hope that their manager will make "block bookings" so that their shows are in one area. All successful bands need a managing agent and a booking agent to help them get started. These people try to get a recording company to offer the band a contract, what all bands dream of!

With a record deal and a disc on the market, two things happen. The band gets better and bigger club dates (500 people). More importantly, the band gets radio time for its songs. Honeymoon Suite's first record album got a lot of radio play in the Maritimes. So, the band, the manager, the booking agent, and the recording company (now 4 parties) planned an eastern tour. The band was to play in places like Halifax, Sydney, Saint John, and other centres where its music had been popular on the radio.

At the same time, the band continued to look for more exposure. One way to get it was to play opening acts. At this time, April Wine, Teenage Head, and Platinum Blonde were Canadian groups who could draw large crowds. Honeymoon Suite opened for them. The band also tried getting shows in cities like Toronto where there are many concerts.

While building a market at home in Canada, Honeymoon Suite was looking eagerly to the large US market. The band tried to get air time on such famous border stations as WMMS, a rock station in Cleveland. The band also recognized that American college campuses were good places to get bookings. As it got exposure, Honeymoon Suite began to play opening acts for popular stars and groups like Billy Idol and Aerosmith.

Then, the band hit some big spots. In Los Angeles, Honeymoon Suite played the Universal Amphitheatre and while there, made a successful rock video for wide television exposure. Canadian television exposure was helped by a prime-time special, shot in the jazz quarter of New Orleans.

Since that time the group has hoped for continued success. It plays to crowds of 1000 to 3000 on a regular basis and keeps high school dances as part of its bookings. The band recognizes that with their interest in music, students are a key factor in radio, record, and video market ratings.

FIG. 7-4 *The Canadian rock band Honeymoon Suite has a large following throughout Canada. Records, books, and t-shirts all contribute to the band's image.*

Investigation 7.3

1. In planning tours, bands have several factors to keep in mind:
   (a) population of the city and surrounding area
   (b) air play on local radio stations
   (c) distance from other cities (so block booking can be done)
   (d) weather (indoor or outdoor concerts)
   (e) concert facilities in the city
   (f) road and air connections to the city
   (g) history of sales in that city for other rock concerts
2. Hundreds of rock groups in Canada have worked hard to develop followings for their music. Coney Hatch might not be popular as you study this chapter. But the following itinerary shows how hard they worked and how far they travelled to become successful.

FIG. 7-5 CONEY HATCH ITINERARY

Date	Venue	Capacity of concert hall/ admission price
Feb. 18-19	Drive	
Feb. 20-23	Halifax, NS	1500 @ $4.00 & $5.00
Feb. 24-25	Drive	
Feb. 27	Cochrane, ON	TBA
Feb. 28	Drive	
March 1	Thunder Bay, ON	550 @ $8.00
March 2	Winnipeg, MB	850 @ $10.00
March 4	Brandon, MB	300 @ $8.00
March 5	Estevan, SK	200 @ $8.00
March 6-7	Regina, SK	300 @ $7.00
March 8	Weyburn, SK	200 @ $8.00

Mark the centres to be visited on a map on Canada. Show the route with a fine marker or coloured pencil.

3. (a) Plan a concert tour for a musical group of your choice. The tour should include visits to 20 cities in Canada and the US. What resources will you need to do this assignment?
   (b) Why did you select these cities?
   (c) Mark the cities on an outline map of North America, and show the route taken with a red marker.
   (d) Calculate how many kilometres the group would travel during its tour.

SKILL
BUILDERS
MEASURING
DISTANCES

The "Arts" in Canada

You have probably heard of the term "the arts." When people use this term, they usually have in mind certain types of activities. Classical music concerts, live theatre, ballet, museum exhibitions, and art gallery shows are among them.

FIG. 7-6 *Toronto's Roy Thomson Hall (left) is home to the Toronto Symphony Orchestra. Charlottetown's Confederation Arts Centre (right) hosts the long-running* Anne of Green Gables *musical every summer.*

Figure 7-2 (p. 141) shows that a relatively small percentage of people attend classical music concerts and live theatre. Nonetheless, many people and all levels of government recognize that the arts are important forces in our society. The arts help us define who we are. Because this is so, governments assist arts organizations through grants. The money for these grants comes from taxes paid by the Canadian public. Private citizens help ensure the success of arts organizations by taking subscriptions, or season tickets, and by making donations. Many businesses also support the arts through donations and sponsorships. The arts would have great difficulty in surviving in Canada without public support, but more and more people are appreciating how much they mean to our society.

Figure 7-7 shows examples of activities in the arts and their locations across Canada.

FIG. 7-7 CULTURAL FACILITIES IN CANADA

Province	Museums	Dance Co.	Theatres	Orchestras
British Columbia	233	5	10	7
Alberta	165	6	8	5
Saskatchewan	188	–	4	2
Manitoba	140	2	5	2
Ontario	581	12	30	55
Québec	262	4	24	9
New Brunswick	76	–	2	1
Nova Scotia	133	–	3	3
Prince Edward Island	23	–	1	1
Newfoundland	70	–	4	1

(Sources: Reader's Digest *Atlas of Canada*, Canadian Museums Association)

Investigation 7.4

SKILL

BUILDERS

GRAPHING

1. Using a map showing Canadian provinces, record the information from Figure 7-7 to get a map of Canadian cultural facilities. Use a separate colour for each of the 4 activities.

   Write the numbers for each activity on the map, province by province, using the colours you have chosen. Write the high numbers in large figures and the small numbers in small figures. You might also show a bar graph for each activity for each province. Try to come up with at least one more idea to show this information.

2. (a) What is the nearest museum to your school?

   (b) Make a class list on the chalkboard of all Canadian museums students in your class have visited.

   (c) What are some reasons for having museums?

   (d) How can museums provide information about the geography of a place in times past?

3. Most schools present live theatre, usually through their drama clubs. Some communities also have volunteer-based theatre groups, made up of people who wish to work on play productions during their leisure time. Fewer communities have professional theatre groups, which pay people for their creative or administrative work.

(a) Examine Figure 7-7 and your map of Canadian cultural facilities. Add up the total number of theatre companies in Canada. Then, calculate the percentage of theatre companies found in each province.

(b) Which province has the most companies?

(c) Suggest explanations for the pattern you found in (b). Think about the services needed to put on a successful show.

4. (a) Theatre can be a seasonal event. For example, Stratford, Ontario, and Charlottetown, PEI, host successful theatre events every summer. List some ways in which these events would benefit the economies of these communities.

(b) Make a list of events that have a similar effect on your community. In what season do they occur?

5. Something that is related to the arts but is more commonly available to people is Canada's library system. Your school certainly has a library or a resource centre. Refer back to Figure 7-2 (p. 141) to see how many adults use libraries after they leave school. Now read and look at the information in Figure 7-8.

(a) According to Figure 7-8, how many libraries are there in Canada?

(b) What factors influence the number of libraries that are found in a province?

6. (a) Find out where libraries in your community get their money to operate.

(b) Besides lending books, what other services do libraries in your community provide?

FIG. 7-8 LIBRARIES IN CANADA

Province or territory	Number of libraries [1]
Newfoundland	107
Prince Edward Island	26
Nova Scotia	82
New Brunswick	61
Québec	883
Ontario	1 012
Manitoba	89
Saskatchewan	321
Alberta	299
British Columbia	262
Yukon	7
Northwest Territories	21

[1] Includes permanent locations and mobile stations.

Source: *Canada Year Book*, 1988

Sports in Canada

Fitness

Sports include a wide variety of recreational activities. Some you probably play. Others you just watch. From a health point of view, participating in some kind of physical activity is much better than watching one!

Canadians are becoming aware of the benefits of exercise. The federal government has recognized the importance of fitness by sponsoring the National Fitness Test which you may have taken during your school career. In your school, a large portion of time, money, and effort may be spent on sports activities. Your community may also provide sports programs for all age groups.

Investigation 7.5

1. List the sports available at your school and estimate the number of people involved in each. Be sure to mention whether each sport is a team or an individual one, is played by both girls and boys, and is part of intramural or inter-school competition.
2. Which one of these 5 statements most accurately describes your own level of physical activity over the last 3 months? Do not include any job-related physical activity.
   - No deliberate effort to improve my physical fitness
   - Occasional moderate activity once a week or less (walking, cycling, tennis, recreational sports, swimming, etc.)
   - Regular moderate activity averaging 2 or 3 times a week
   - Frequent regular activity averaging 4 or more times a week
   - Regular training for a specific sport with 4 or more weekly workouts that produce a heavy sweat
3. Look at Figure 7-9, which shows the summary of a physical fitness survey taken across Canada by Participaction. (Note: The percentages don't always add up to 100 due to rounding.)
   (a) Assign a colour to each activity category from "regular training" to "little activity." Draw a bar graph for each region to see if there is a pattern to fitness in Canada.
   (b) Study the population groups in Figure 7-9. Are there any relationships between (i) fitness and age? (ii) fitness and occupation? (iii) fitness and income?

   Suggest 3 reasons for any relationships that you can find in these patterns.

FIG. 7-9 COMPARATIVE LEVEL OF PHYSICAL ACTIVITY (percentages)

	Regular training	Frequent activity	Moderate activity	Occasional activity	Little activity
Total: Canada	4	11	22	35	28
Sex					
Male	5	12	20	34	29
Female	2	11	23	37	27
Region					
Atlantic	2	8	17	39	32
Québec	5	10	20	38	27
Ontario	3	13	20	33	31
Prairies	2	11	27	33	27
BC	5	13	26	40	16
Age					
15-19	16	23	25	25	11
20-29	4	11	28	38	18
30-39	3	10	24	38	25
40-49	1	9	22	39	28
50-54	1	12	16	35	35
55-64	–	11	14	35	40
65 and over	–	9	15	34	42
Occupation					
Professional, managerial	3	14	27	33	22
White collar	4	11	24	39	22
Blue collar	3	8	20	36	33
Other/not working	4	13	20	34	28
Income					
Under $15 000	2	11	20	36	31
$15 000-19 999	1	11	21	41	26
$20 000-24 999	2	13	18	33	34
$25 000-34 999	5	10	24	37	24
$35 000 and over	5	13	26	35	21

Source: Participaction

Team Sports

"Hockey Night in Canada" is a long-standing sports tradition. At one time, Saturday nights meant the whole family sat around the radio listening to a game between the Toronto Maple Leafs or the Montréal Canadiens and one of the other four teams. Now many cities have professional hockey teams.

FIG. 7-11

Hockey is an important part of our culture. Canadian teams regularly play in hockey tournaments with other nations.

Investigation 7.6

1. Examine the following tables which list professional hockey and football teams in Canada.

FIG. 7-11 CANADIAN TEAMS IN THE NATIONAL HOCKEY LEAGUE (1988)

Québec Nordiques	Montréal Canadiens	Toronto Maple Leafs
Winnipeg Jets	Edmonton Oilers	Calgary Flames
Vancouver Canucks		

FIG. 7-12 CANADIAN FOOTBALL LEAGUE (1988)

Ottawa Rough Riders	Toronto Argos	Hamilton Tiger-Cats
Winnipeg Blue Bombers	Saskatchewan Roughriders	Calgary Stampeders
Edmonton Eskimos	BC Lions	

(a) On an outline map of Canada, label the cities with NHL and CFL teams. Use a symbol for each sport.
(b) Which cities in Canada have teams in both the NHL and the CFL?
(c) Is there a connection between a city's population and whether or not it has both CFL and NHL teams?

2. (a) Look at the chart on stadium sizes and city population (Fig. 7-13). Suggest 3 things a city must have in order to support a professional sports franchise.
(b) Identify 2 Canadian cities that could support future franchises in hockey or football.
(c) What other professional sports may seek to establish franchises in Canada?

FIG. 7-13 SPORTS FACILITIES

City	Hockey arena	Seating capacity	Football stadium	Seating capacity
Edmonton Population: 785 500	Northlands	17 308	Commonwealth	60 181
Montréal Population: 2 921 400	Forum	16 074		
Québec Population: 603 300	Colisée	15 264		
Toronto Population: 3 427 200	Maple Leaf Gardens	16 182	SkyDome	56 000
Vancouver Population: 1 380 800	Pacific Coliseum	15 753	BC Place	59 478
Winnipeg Population: 625 300	Arena	15 250	Stadium	32 946
Calgary Population: 671 300	Olympic Saddledome	16 825	McMahon	38 408
Hamilton Population: 557 000			Ivor Wynne	29 195
Regina Population: 186 500			Taylor Field	27 637
Ottawa-Hull Population: 819 300			Lansdowne Park	34 838

Television

Let's look in more depth at the leisure activity 95% of Canadians participate in...watching television.

Television is without a doubt our number one leisure activity. The kind of television network reception you get forms an interesting geographic pattern. The Canadian Broadcasting Corporation (CBC) is a government-sponsored network that has the responsibility of bringing television programming to all parts of Canada. In addition, large private Canadian networks, like CTV and Global, serve the more populated regions of the country. These networks provide a somewhat different style of programming than that of the CBC. However, some of the most popular shows come from the three largest, highly competitive American networks: NBC, CBS, and ABC.

In Canada, a government agency called the Canadian Radio-television and Telecommunications Commission (CRTC) regulates television broadcasting. The CRTC has rules on how much programming time *must* be devoted to Canadian content. It limits the number of minutes of commercials per hour. It also determines which channels appear on the cable's main listings and which ones are available only through a converter. Finally, it is concerned with the unauthorized reception of television satellite signals, picked up by some Canadians on "dish antennas."

FIG. 7-14

Even people in Arctic and other remote areas can have a wide choice of television programming through dish antennas. They no longer depend on the range of television transmitters.

Investigation 7.7

1. (a) List 4 benefits we get from television as a form of leisure activity.
   (b) List 4 ways in which television may be criticized as a poor form of leisure activity.
2. Write down the names of the educational television stations (including American PBS stations) that can be received in your community. What kinds of programs do they broadcast? How much time do you think an average person would spend watching these stations? Predict the future uses of this type of network.

FIG. 7-15

Canadians use computers in offices, at home, and in schools. These students are discovering information about animal life with the help of a computer.

Parks in Canada

People of all ages need recreational areas, but at different ages, people need different facilities. For example, what you would like to have at a park is different from what things a young family would like to have. Planners who create parks must consider the people who may make use of a particular facility. In some cases, planners may create a park that will appeal to a narrow range of users. In others, they may try to appeal to all ages.

Investigation 7.8

1. People need different things in a park. Name 2 facilities each of the following park users would probably want to find.

   - baseball player
   - chess player
   - child with pail and shovel
   - picnickers
   - person with a novel
   - active 10-year old
   - person in a wheelchair
   - person your age

As people have more leisure time to spend away from school and work, the planning of recreational areas becomes very important. Planners need good forecast methods to see trends and meet people's needs. The following two case studies will illustrate some of these concerns.

National Parks

Canada's national park system is one of the best in the world! Our national parks are run by Parks Canada, part of the federal ministry of the environment. With its headquarters in Ottawa, Parks Canada looks after national parks across Canada. Figure 7-16 shows park locations.

The double purpose of our national parks is to preserve some of the most beautiful and scenic areas of Canada and to mark important national heritage sites. Setting aside areas as national parks ensures Canadians can always enjoy special landscapes, seascapes, plants, and animals. We can also appreciate significant aspects of our history.

FIG. 7-16   National parks of Canada *Canada's national park system is more than 100 years old. This map shows where Canada's national parks are located. How many have you visited?*

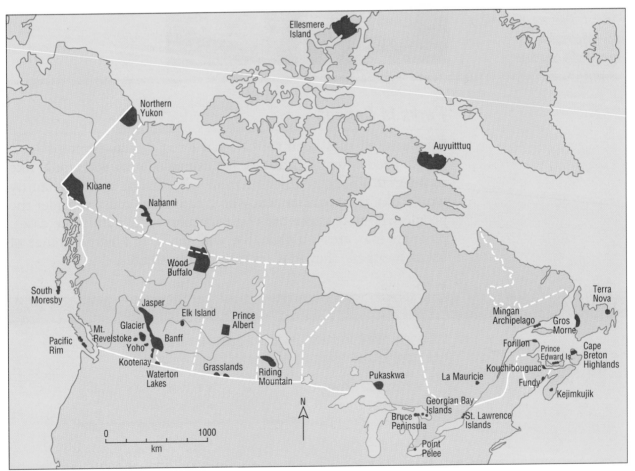

CASE STUDY
Prince Edward Island National Park

One national park is located in the province of Prince Edward Island. Referred to as PEI National Park, this park is a system of beaches about 24 km north of the capital of Charlottetown on the Gulf of St. Lawrence. It has some of Canada's finest white sand beaches, near Cavendish. It also has sands tinted red from the erosion of red clay. Along a 9 km stretch the beach is bordered by red sandstone cliffs up to 30 m high. In other parts, a boardwalk takes visitors through sand dunes 18 m high, dunes such as you might see in the Sahara Desert. This 40 km stretch of sand, bluffs, dunes, saltwater marshes, and freshwater ponds is one of the smallest national parks. Yet it draws more than a million visitors each year. This is one of the highest attendance figures for a national park.

People who are fans of Lucy Maud Montgomery's famous character Anne like to visit the Green Gables farmhouse in Cavendish. This is where the novel *Anne of Green Gables*, which was also made into a successful play and movie, is set. Naturalists like to watch the blue herons in the marshes of Rustico Island or to examine the marram grass which binds the sand into the huge dunes along the coast. Most visitors prefer to be where the sand is smoothed by the ocean surf and to swim where the waters are warmer than many places farther south.

Investigation 7.9

1. (a) Make a list of the natural features that make this a good area for a national park.
   (b) From the park map (Fig. 7-17d, p. 156), measure the length of PEI National Park and estimate its average width.
   (c) Name the beaches that are included in the park.
2. (a) Cavendish Beach is formed by a **sandspit**, a landform across the mouth of New London Bay.
   (b) What other bays have sandspits?
   (c) What 3 factors would create these sandspits?
   (d) How might local fishing fleets benefit from the sandspits?
   (e) How could the sandspits become an obstacle to them?
   (f) What advantages are provided by the beaches in front of the bays?
   (g) What problems could result from the location of these beaches?
   (h) What jobs would the permanent residents have along this coast?
   (i) List 5 ways in which the permanent residents benefit from the annual inflow of 1 million tourists.
3. Suppose a large company says it would like to buy 100 ha of land at Cavendish and build a factory there. The factory would employ several hundred people. Some local residents react by saying they think the additional truck traffic and large storage tanks would harm tourism in the area. What steps would you take in order to reach a decision to support building the factory or not?

SKILL BUILDERS

DECISION MAKING

a

FIG. 17-17d

FIG. 7-17a *Green Gables is the site of Lucy Maud Montgomery's famous novel,* Anne of Green Gables.

FIG. 7-17b *Parks Canada ensures that the beaches and capes of PEI National Park are accessible to all.*

FIG. 7-17c *PEI National Park is located along the northern shore of the island.*

b   **c**

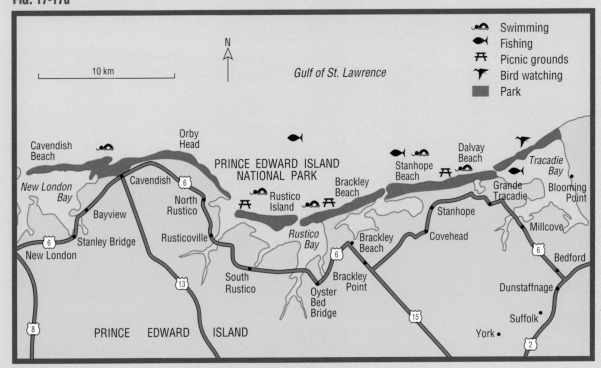

Theme Parks

Unlike national parks with their magnificent scenery, theme parks are totally "built" recreational environments. The most famous ones are the Disney theme parks in Florida and California in the US. Canada's first major theme park is Canada's Wonderland, situated north of Toronto.

Probably the largest theme park in Canada is the West Edmonton Mall. Read the description of the mall that follows and study the photos in Figure 7-18.

CASE STUDY

West Edmonton Mall

FIG. 7-18

"ENDLESS SUMMER AT THE WORLD'S LARGEST WATERPARK"

"EIGHTH WONDER OF THE WORLD"

These are just two of the press release headlines used by the West Edmonton Mall owners. Are these headlines only media hype to attract more shoppers? Or do they recognize that the mall is a forerunner of the city of the future? Will we all live in an enclosed, pleasure-dome environment some day?

The headlines have a basis in fact. The waterpark covers 4.5 ha in the year-round pool area. The size and attractions of Canada's super mall are what the owners claim make it the "eighth wonder of the world." In addition, there is a full-sized hockey rink where the Edmonton Oilers practice occasionally. There is also a wild game farm and bird aviaries.

What is the basis for their claim? To begin with, the West Edmonton Mall is in the *Guinness Book of Records* 4 times:

- world's largest shopping centre:
  - 830 stores + 11 department stores
  - 110 eating places
  - 19 theatres
  - 58 entrances
- world's largest indoor amusement park:
  - Fantasyland has 24 rides and attractions
  - Waterpark has white water rafting, hot springs, high diving, overhead gondola rides, and surf-making wave machine
- world's largest parking lot
  - 20 000 places
  - for 15 000 employees and up to 350 000 visitors on a weekend
- world's largest number of balloons released at an opening
  - 500 000 helium-filled balloons

The gigantic enclosed mall covers 28 city blocks, and would hold 115 football fields. It is a shopping centre and an amusement park designed to get shoppers into the stores and keep them there as long as possible. The shopping areas follow special themes. For example, Bourbon Street is patterned after the street of the same name in New Orleans, Europa Street after famous European shopping streets.

The mall's hotel, the Fantasyland, has 360 rooms designed on different themes. The Polynesian room has a South Seas atmosphere. The Arabian room is like that of a desert prince. The "truck rooms" feature beds in the back of antique pickup trucks!

The West Edmonton Mall isn't just a fantasy land. Despite the concerns of outside merchants that the mall would get all the business in Edmonton (population 785 500), the mall's share of local trade has levelled off at about 25%.

In order to build it, many zoning regulations and planning details had to be thought about. For example, the mall draws as much electrical energy as a city of 75 000 people. Mall security is difficult because of the many entrances and large area. Also, the volume of traffic and number of tourists flooding into that corner of the city meant that good public relations with neighbouring subdivisions were important.

These problems were tackled because of the project's tremendous potential. The West Edmonton Mall would be a major tourist attraction. People would come and spend money there. Fifteen thousand Edmontonians would get jobs.

The mall is a success. The businesses are making money. The people are coming in droves.

Investigation 7.10

1. (a) What are 4 reasons for calling this "the eighth wonder of the world"?
   (b) Give 3 advantages this mall brings to the city of Edmonton.
   (c) What are 3 problems that a giant mall such as this might create for a city?
2. The West Edmonton Mall is an example of a large, environment-controlled entertainment centre and mall. If you could build such a centre in your community, where would you put it and what facilities would it contain? Working with a team, plan and design a "liveable winter centre" for a particular place, such as your neighbourhood, your city, or a place in Canada that would benefit from your plan.
   (a) Select, describe, and give reasons for your group's choice of site.
   (b) (i)   Design a map of the centre and/or sketch of the building.
       (ii) Report on the features the centre will have.
       (iii) Outline the media campaign you will use to attract customers.

Travel in Canada

Prince Edward Island National Park and the West Edmonton Mall are only two of the many unique and interesting places you can visit in Canada. However, Canada is such a huge country that the factors of time, distance, and cost may seem to make planning a trip an overwhelming task. The benefits of travel can make it worth trying to cope with these problems, though. Through travel you can get a new and wider outlook on your life.

One way to overcome problems of travel in Canada is to use the resources of the Canadian Hostelling Association. The association aims to provide simple overnight accommodations through hostels, places where you can stay cheaply while you tour through an area. Hostels are open to people of all ages and backgrounds. However, they are heavily used by younger people. They provide great ways to meet people, especially young people from other countries. But they provide "no frills" accommodations and you should be prepared to pitch in with some of the chores.

In Canada, overnight hostels are cheap. They are graded according to the range and quality of facilities offered. Some have resident managers and hold up to 30 guests. Other, smaller ones operate more like self-serve places.

There are 70 hostels scattered between the Maritimes and British Columbia. In the Canadian Rockies there is a chain of hostels in Banff, Jasper, and Yoho national parks. Here you have excellent chances to hike, cycle, or in winter, to ski from one hostel to another. In these hostels, you usually prepare your own meals in the kitchens. Blankets, pillows, cooking utensils, and cleaning equipment are provided for your use. There are separate sleeping quarters for females and males.

If you can find accommodation through the Hostelling Association or other means, then your next main problem is getting where you want to go. Several options are open to young travellers, but hitchhiking, which is dangerous, is *not* a recommended one. Instead, you could ride a bicycle, or once you get your driver's licence, you might be able to take a car.

Consider the many types of public transportation. Trains can provide cheap fares if you are willing to sit up for a few hours. They also allow you to plan several stops along the way, and to carry skis and bicycles. Airlines have many features. You can also look out for special "youth fare" deals. Or you can take your chances by flying "stand by" and hope that someone cancels at the last minute. Another good method is the bus. This provides good service and flexibility at a reasonable cost. Sometimes, you can even get a bus pass which lets you travel for an unlimited distance for a fixed period of time. A little bit of effort, a few letters of inquiry, and some phone calls can give you a wealth of information.

Banff, Alberta, and Québec City, Québec, both attract many young visitors and seem to welcome people who are on the road. In Banff, the focus is on outdoor activities in the mountains. Many stores cater to hikers and backpackers. You can easily rent bicycles to get around. Nearby base camps outfit you so that you can get to and explore the great scenery. Banff thrives as much in the winter as a ski resort as it does in the summer with other activities.

Québec City is an exciting city for students to visit, and life there is youth-oriented. The boardwalk running parallel to, but high above the river is always crowded with people. Street musicians perform along this route, and the many nearby cafés are popular meeting places. Québec City seems to be full of life and activity 24 hours a day. It also has hostels and inexpensive rooms in and around the Old City of Québec where most attractions are found. Even in winter, especially in February during the Québec Winter Carnival which is an annual highlight, the city's pulse is strong. As a capital city, Québec has a variety of urban activities that are not available in Banff.

Investigation 7.11

SKILL
BUILDERS
MAPPING

1. (a) Locate Banff and Québec City in your atlas. Give the latitude and longitude for each place.
   (b) Using the text photos and descriptions, determine why tourists are attracted to Banff and Québec City. List 3 reasons for the popularity of each place.
   (c) What are 2 other places in Canada that young people seem to visit frequently? Suggest 2 possible reasons for the popularity of each place.

FIG. 7-19
The mountains tower over the main street of Banff, Alberta.

FIG. 7-20
Québec City's old-world charm attracts many visitors.

Investigation 7.12

SKILL

BUILDERS

BRAINSTORMING

1. Leisure and recreation activities provide many full- and part-time jobs for Canadians. Think about the leisure and recreation facilities in your area. Make a list of places or businesses that could provide part-time jobs for students. Beside each item, identify the kinds of jobs that students could do.
2. What leisure and recreation facilities could be developed in your area?
   (a) Work with 3 or 4 students to brainstorm a list of possible facilities that could be developed in your area. Remember in brainstorming the wilder the idea the better!
   (b) Examine your ideas to see which ones have the greatest potential. Think about these questions as you go through your list:
      • What facilities already exist?
      • What advantages does your area have?
      • What problems would have to be overcome?
      Select the 5 best ideas.
   (c) Develop one of the ideas further by designing a tourist brochure, drawing a sketch of the place's layout, writing a letter to a friend, or doing something similar.

Summing Up

Canadians have more leisure time than ever before and we're taking this time seriously. People fill their after school and after work hours with a variety of activities ranging from intense physical ones such as racquet sports to more leisurely pastimes like theatre going.

More and more Canadians use their leisure time to travel to other areas of the country. Tourism provides job opportunities for many people, especially for students. Jobs include those at national parks, restaurants, souvenir shops, and arts centres. Can you think of any tourism-related jobs in your community?

CHAPTER EIGHT

Housing and Shelter

YOU DON'T HAVE TO THINK TOO HARD or too long to realize how important housing is. You need shelter from the weather, privacy, and security from possible intruders. People often shelter pets and farm animals, as well. Most businesses also have some kind of protective housing. They must provide their employees and visitors with fairly comfortable environments and look after their equipment and products.

Our need for shelter is so basic that we spend more than one-third of our incomes on the places we live in, the energy needed to make them comfortable, their upkeep, and the furniture and appliances we use inside of them. In fact, you may have to spend more than one-third of your income on housing during your adult working years.

It's not surprising that Canadians think shelter and protection are vitally important needs. After all, temperatures can range from -63°C in winter to 45°C in summer. In this chapter, you will look at how Canadians have met these needs and how not only geography, but factors such as history, culture, and personal taste affect our housing choices.

Elements of Design

Our study of housing and shelter leads us into a closer investigation of buildings. As you have probably already figured out, it's through buildings that most of our needs for shelter are met.

The design of a building is influenced by many factors. To understand why a particular building looks as it does, let's examine briefly some of these influences.

FIG. 8-1 *A hockey arena, such as the Saddledome in Calgary, must contain a large open space inside for the ice surface and the spectators. Its roof must be wide and can't be supported in the middle. For that reason, hockey arenas usually have curved roofs.*

FIG. 8-2 *The dome shape of this building makes it easier to heat, an advantage in the Arctic.*

Function, **site**, **situation**, available materials and **technology**, and **culture** are design elements that architects consider.

Function Architects say that "form follows function." In other words, the design of a building is determined by what it's supposed to do.

Site This word refers to the immediate area of a building. When architects consider sites, they look at landforms, soil, wind patterns, cost of land, access to transportation, and any other important environmental factors they recognize.

Situation This factor is a broader version of site. Instead of local environmental influences, architects look at regional ones. Regional climatic patterns and regional transportation facilities are a few examples of what they consider.

Available materials and technology What you make depends on what you have to make it with. A house can be built out of logs. A skyscraper can't. The skyscraper requires special materials such as steel and reinforced concrete. Canadians have used the materials around them very successfully. They have made houses out of logs, stones, sod, animal skins, bricks, wood, and snow. Having these materials wouldn't have been enough though. You also need to know how to use them.

Culture Buildings usually do more than provide protection and shelter. They also reflect the culture in which they exist. Culture means a people's way of life. It refers to social customs, beliefs about what is important or beautiful, arts, and language. The style of our buildings therefore says something about us and our society.

FIG. 8-3 *Building skyscrapers wasn't possible until special materials such as reinforced concrete and steel became available.*

Investigation 8.1

Figure 8-4 shows 4 types of buildings: a gas station, warehouses, an igloo, and a church. Which design elements had the most influence on each of these buildings?

a

d

b

c

FIG. 8-4a *All gas stations need an open area in front of them so that cars can have easy access to the pumps. Gas stations should also be close to main roads to attract the most business.*

FIG. 8-4b *An igloo is an ingenious way of providing shelter during an Arctic winter.*

FIG. 8-4c *Warehouses are usually single-storey buildings for ease in moving items. They also have to be close to major transportation routes.*

FIG. 8-4d *The design of this church in Alberta follows a traditional Ukrainian style.*

Choosing a Home

Home is usually more than just a roof over our heads. It's the place where we *live* — where we relax, play, entertain our friends, and do things with our families. For most of us, home is a special place, and so we often go to much effort to make it comfortable and express our personalities.

Home can be many things. People often think of a home as a house, but, in fact, most Canadians live in other kinds of dwellings. In 1986, only about half of urban Canadians lived in **single-family detached dwellings** (the technical name for a house). The rest of us lived in apartments, townhouses, duplexes, and other kinds of dwellings. In this section, we shall look at the many different kinds of housing available in Canada and consider some of the things we should investigate when choosing a home.

Investigation 8.2

1. Let's look at the variety of homes available to Canadians. Many of you will be looking for a place of your own in a few years, and it's worth knowing what choices you will have. Here is a list of some common dwelling types in Canada.

   - detached house
   - semi-detached house
   - duplex
   - triplex
   - townhouse
   - mobile home
   - low-rise apartment
   - high-rise apartment
   - apartment above business

   (a) Either find pictures in newspapers, magazines, and real estate listings or make sketches of the dwellings listed above. Draw a chart like Figure 8-5 and fill in the appropriate spaces.

FIG. 8-5 HOUSING CHOICES					
Name + Picture	No. of units in dwelling	Own/rent	Special features	Relative (high-low) cost	Advantages/ disadvantages

(b) When you have completed the chart, identify which types of dwellings are available in your community.

(c) Try to classify the dwellings in other ways.

  (i) Classify them by location:

Urban	Suburban	Rural
(downtown city)	(city outskirts)	(agricultural or non-city area)

  Some dwellings will belong to more than one classification.

  (ii) Classify them by method of ownership:

Rent	Own	Condominium

  A condominium is a housing development in which various people own apartments, detached or semi-detached homes, or townhouses. They share in the ownership and upkeep of the common areas.

  Most dwellings in the list will fall into more than one of these categories.

2. In some Canadian communities, the cost of housing has increased so much over the past few years that some people cannot find affordable housing for sale or rent. Do some research on the cost of housing in your area. You will find information on the topic in local newspaper real estate sections and in reference materials in your resource centre. You could also contact real estate agents for information. Present your findings to the class.

Whether you rent or buy, your home will cost you a lot of money. In fact, choosing a home will be one of the most important spending decisions you make. If you make the wrong decision, you may find it costly and difficult to change. So be sure to investigate carefully before you commit yourself.

What should you think about before you choose a place to live? One thing, of course, is the cost. Can you afford the monthly mortgage or rent payments? Although housing costs in some places are extremely high, you must try to have enough money left over from your pay cheque to cover other expenses. If you're buying, you will have to think of taxes and heating and maintenance costs as well.

There are also many other considerations. You must decide if the home you're looking at is in the best possible location for you. You should know what condition it is in and whether it needs expensive repairs. You should also consider how safe and easy it is to live in.

Figure 8-6 lists questions that a smart consumer would ask when choosing a home to buy or rent. The list contains most of the important questions that should be asked about a home. It also contains a few questions that apply to some kinds of homes but not to others.

Investigation 8.3

The purpose of this Investigation is to turn Figure 8-6 into a decision-making chart that will help a person choose an appropriate home.

1. (a) Pretend you are looking for a home. Choose the type of dwelling that best suits your needs from the list at the beginning of Investigation 8.2. You may choose to live alone or to share with other people.
   (b) Read the questions in Figure 8-6. Make sure you understand what they mean and why they should be asked. Ask your teacher for help if there are any you do not understand.
   (c) Identify the questions that apply to your dwelling type.
   (d) Add any other questions that you think should be asked about your dwelling type.
2. (a) Create a scoring system that will help you make a decision between different homes. You will want to decide which questions about homes are most important. Show your scoring system in chart form.
   (b) Write a brief paragraph explaining how your chart will help you make a good decision.

FIG. 8-6 CHECK LIST FOR BUYING OR RENTING A HOME

Location

1. Is the building close to good roads?

2. Are there public transportation services nearby?

3. Is it easy for you (and anyone else living with you) to get to work or school?

4. Are there shopping and recreational facilities nearby?

5. How far is it to the nearest hospital, police station, and fire station?

6. Should you be concerned about any hazards, such as flooding, pollution, or crime?

7. What is the neighbourhood zoning plan?

Structure

8. How old is the building?

9. What kind of material covers the outside walls?

10. What are the main building materials in the basement? in the ceilings? in the walls?

11. What kind of material covers the roof?

12. When was the roof last replaced?

13. Is the building free of rot and insects?

Heating and air conditioning

14. How is the building heated?

15. Is it air conditioned?

16. How old is the furnace?

Energy efficiency

17. How well insulated are the ceilings and walls?

18. What kinds of windows does the building have?

19. Does it have any energy-saving devices?

Electrical and other services

20. Where is the fuse panel? How many amps is the electrical supply? (The average house today needs a 100-amp electrical supply to handle a full load of modern appliances. Older houses may have only 60-amp supplies. Houses with electrical heating will need 200-amp supplies.)

21. Are there enough electrical outlets in every room?

22. How old is the wiring? What is the wiring made of?

Security

23. Where are the emergency exits?

24. Does the building's construction provide adequate resistance to fire?

25. How is the building lighted?

26. How is the building designed to protect the inhabitants from intruders?

Plumbing

27. How is water supplied to the building?

28. How is waste water removed from the building?

29. What are the pipes made of?

30. Is the water pressure adequate?

Miscellaneous

31. Does the building appear to have been well looked after?

32. What facilities does it have for vehicles?

33. How is garbage removed?

34. Is the building equipped to deal with handicapped people?

35. How many floors are there? Are there any moving devices to get people or things from floor to floor?

36. Are there any businesses sharing the same building?
37. Who is responsible for maintenance?
Financial
38. How much are the monthly rental or mortgage payments?
39. How much are the taxes?
40. How much does the building cost to heat?
41. What is the monthly cost for electricity and/or gas?
42. Are there extra costs, such as condominium fees?

Buildings Across Canada

FIG. 8-7

Do you know where this house is located?

Suppose you woke up one morning in the middle of the picture in Figure 8-7. Would you know where you were? Perhaps. You would certainly know that you weren't in Canada. You could tell that from the design of the building. But how? What suggests that this building isn't Canadian? The materials it is made of? The age of the house? The design? Or a combination of these factors?

This building is, in fact, in England, and it clearly has many features that are not typical of Canadian houses. These differences reflect differences in culture, history, climate, available building materials, and so on.

Now suppose you were to wake up one morning far from home, but still in Canada. Would you be able to tell where you were by the appearance of the buildings around you? If you were in a modern suburb, you might find it hard. But if you were in an older area, you might find clues to your whereabouts in the design of the buildings. Differences in culture and environment within the country resulted in some distinctive styles of houses and other buildings. Although the influence of American styles has made regional differences less obvious, Canada still has many varieties.

In this section we shall look at various building styles found in different parts of Canada.

Investigation 8.4

1. Suppose you are an editorial assistant for *Canada's Architecture* magazine. The captions and photographs (Fig. 8-8) on page 174 are to appear in the next issue. But 5 minutes ago, your boss dropped the pictures and captions on the floor. Everything got mixed up. She has gone for lunch with a famous architect. You have been asked to match the pictures with the correct captions. In your notebook, write the letter of the picture and the number of the house description that matches it.

FIG. 8-8

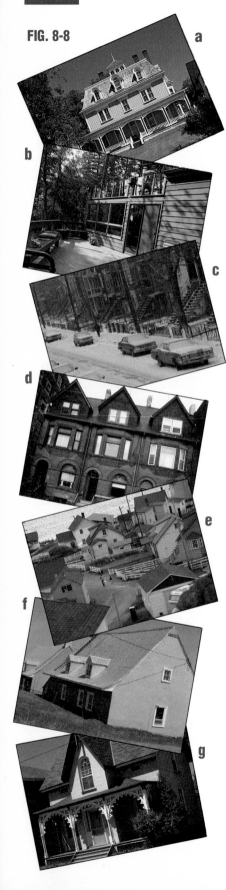

a
b
c
d
e
f
g

1. **Montréal townhouse (Montréal, Québec)**   The raised entrance and staircase of this house are typical of many houses in Montréal, even some recent ones.

2. **Gothic-style house (Peterborough, Ontario)**   This type of house has a gable over a centre doorway and windows with rounded or pointed tops. It was especially popular in southern Ontario in the last half of the nineteenth century.

3. **Québec farmhouse (Montmorency, Québec)**   The design for this seventeenth-century house near Québec City comes from Normandy in France. The house's steep roof lets snow fall off easily. The ladder on the roof is also a common feature. It makes it easier to clean the chimney and fight fires. Houses like this were made of both stone and wood. Many can still be seen in Québec today.

4. **Newfoundland salt-box house (Twillingsgate, Newfoundland)**   Sturdy houses such as this were built in the outports and towns of Newfoundland in the 1700s and 1800s. They are made of wood and have steep roofs with chimneys in the middle. They often have lean-tos built on to one side.

5. **Maritime colonial (Liverpool, Nova Scotia)**   This house, with its shuttered windows, overlapping wooden siding, centre doorway, and balanced proportions, is a typical example of an eighteenth century American design. Loyalists continued to use the design after they fled to the Maritimes during and after the American Revolution.

6. **Toronto brick house (Toronto, Ontario)**   Before the First World War, many houses in Toronto were built by English developers who tended to use English designs and brick construction. While wood is the most common building material in most parts of Canada, brick is the major one in southern Ontario.

7. **West Coast modern (Victoria, British Columbia)**   The design of modern houses on the West Coast reflects the use of local building materials, the mild climate, and the region's spectacular scenery. This house uses British Columbia cedar for siding and trim. The large windows provide a good view of the landscape. The second-storey deck makes it easy to spend lots of time outdoors.

2. Find or draw a picture of each of the following kinds of homes. Identify where in Canada you would find them.
   - houses built before 1800
   - houses with no basements (Hint: Houses in cold climates often have basements so that their foundations will be stable below the frost line.)
   - houses built on posts
   - floating houses

We often express our personalities through our homes. Similarly, governments, companies, and various businesses often have buildings that are intended to create certain images in the public eye. For example, the traditional design and heavy stone construction of our federal Parliament buildings suggest dignity, authority, and permanence. The design supports the idea that Parliament is an important place to Canadians.

More and more we are beginning to realize how much our thoughts and actions are influenced by our environment. If we work in relaxed and comfortable surroundings, we can be more productive than in an environment that makes us tense or prevents us from concentrating well. Many things inside a building can affect our mood: the quality of light, the colour of the walls, the level of noise, and the texture of carpets and furniture fabrics.

Architects and designers use such factors to create moods that will support the purposes of the space. You do the same thing in a temporary way when you decorate the school gymnasium for a dance. Of course, not all spaces are designed to create moods. Some of them, like warehouses or workshops, are functional only. Low cost and efficiency are the main design concerns.

Investigation 8.5

1. You are going to explore how different places within the same building affect the way you feel.
   (a) On the left side of a page in your notebook, make a list of these headings, allowing some space for notes to be added: **Name**; **Purpose**; **Main colours**; **Materials and textures** (walls, floors, furniture, etc.); **Ceiling height**; **Decoration**; **Lighting** (bright/dim; harsh/soft; etc.); **Size and shape of space**; **Noises**. Add any other headings that you think might be important.

(b) Choose 3 public places in your school that you can get to quickly and easily without disturbing other classes. Your teacher may need to make special arrangements.

(c) Visit the 3 locations and record important details about them in your chart. (Name the 3 places across the top of your chart.)

(d) Write a description of how each place made you feel. What was its mood? Was the mood pleasant? Did the place remind you of its purpose?

(e) What influenced your feelings about each of these places? Answer with a short paragraph for each one.

(f) Do you feel each place's purpose is supported by the feelings it creates? If not, suggest ways of redesigning the place so that its purpose would be better met.

2. Modern buildings are very different from those built about 100 years ago. That is because many things have changed since then, people's tastes, technology, materials, ways of living, and so on. The pictures in Figure 8-9 show 4 sets of buildings. Each set shows 2 buildings that perform the same function. One building is old. The other is fairly new.

In what ways are the buildings in each set different from each other? To help you analyze the differences, make a chart for each pair. Consider such things as the following:

Materials   What is the major material used in the construction of the building? Stone, brick, wood, steel, glass, and concrete are the most commonly used building materials in Canada.

Design   Consider shape, size, decoration, and prominent structural features such as pillars and windows.

Special technology   Does the building require special technology such as air conditioning or elevators?

Site/setting   Is there anything special about the building's location? Consider such things as whether it is downtown or in the suburbs, on a narrow or a wide lot, and near or far from the street.

Finally, add a column to your chart and give it the heading *Lifestyles*. In this column, write about the different ways of life represented by the buildings in each pair of photographs.

a

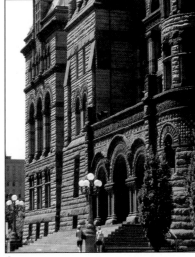

b

c

d

FIG. 8-9

Summing Up

Getting and maintaining good housing will occupy a large part of your life. Much of your pay cheque will be spent on rent or mortgage payments, appliances and furniture, and services like heat, water, telephone, and cable television. But you spend much of your life in your home, so it's wise to choose your residence carefully. We hope the information in this chapter has helped you understand housing in Canada a little better.

CHAPTER NINE

Energy

CANADIANS ENJOY A **standard of living** that would be impossible without vast supplies of cheap energy. If our major energy sources were to disappear tomorrow, our lives would change drastically. We wouldn't have electric lighting, televisions, stereos or most other household conveniences. We would miss air conditioning in summer and would have to find new ways to heat our homes in winter. The one-hour car trip to friends or relatives in the next town would probably take more than a day by foot, and the two-hour plane trip would turn into a two-week expedition. Most offices and factories would close, and with their closing would go many jobs and products we have relied on.

All advanced industrial countries, like ours, need large quantities of energy, but Canada uses more than most. Canada, in fact, uses more energy per person than almost any other country in the world. We also possess many major energy resources, but we have begun to realize that some of our best energy sources are being used too quickly. Because we use so much energy, it's getting more expensive. As a result, more of the money we earn goes to pay for our energy needs. We have also begun to realize that getting and using the amount of energy we do can cause environmental problems and even endanger our health.

Our energy needs present us with a dilemma. To preserve our standard of living, we need large quantities of energy. But if we continue to use so much energy, we will use up our resources and pollute the environment. Clearly, all of us have to think more carefully about our energy use.

In this chapter, we shall look at the different energy sources we use and consider their advantages and disadvantages. We will also examine some ways of using energy more efficiently.

Investigation 9.1

1. Figure 9-1 shows the amount of energy used per person in various countries in the world. Figure 9-2 shows how much energy is required for different kinds of uses in Canada.

   (a) Using this information, plus any other useful information from your atlas, write a short paragraph explaining why Canadians use more energy than people in most other countries.

   (b) After you've done (a), compare answers with other members of your class. See if you can agree on which reasons provide the best explanation of our heavy energy use.

   (c) As a class, discuss whether it is possible for Canadians to reduce their energy use.

FIG. 9-1 ENERGY USE PER PERSON IN SELECTED COUNTRIES

(Percentage of the world average)

World	100%
Australia	351%
Brazil	40%
Canada	505%
China	36%
Cuba	74%
West Germany	409%
India	14%
Japan	187%
Mexico	86%
Poland	243%
Portugal	68%
Sweden	250%
United Kingdom	274%
United States	493%
USSR	334%
Zambia	15%

Source: *United Nations Statistical Yearbook, 1986*

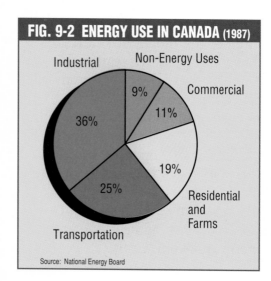

FIG. 9-2 ENERGY USE IN CANADA (1987)

Industrial 36%
Non-Energy Uses 9%
Commercial 11%
Residential and Farms 19%
Transportation 25%

Source: National Energy Board

FIG. 9-3

b *Transportation* Almost all of the energy we use for transportation comes from petroleum. About 80% of this energy is used for road transportation.

a *Residential* Heating and air conditioning account for about 85% of home energy use. Lighting and appliances account for the rest.

c *Commercial* About two-thirds of the energy used by offices, stores, hospitals, schools, and other public buildings is for heating and air conditioning.

d *Industrial* The biggest single energy use is for industrial purposes, but only a few industries use most of the energy. They are the pulp and paper, iron and steel, smelting and refining, and chemical industries.

e *Non-Energy Uses* Although petroleum is used mainly as an energy source, it can also be made into chemicals, lubricants, asphalt, and fertilizers.

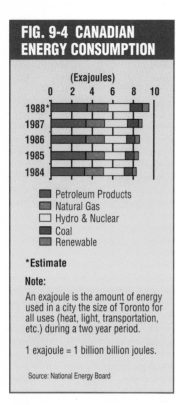

FIG. 9-4 CANADIAN ENERGY CONSUMPTION

(Exajoules)

Petroleum Products
Natural Gas
Hydro & Nuclear
Coal
Renewable

*Estimate

Note:

An exajoule is the amount of energy used in a city the size of Toronto for all uses (heat, light, transportation, etc.) during a two year period.

1 exajoule = 1 billion billion joules.

Source: National Energy Board

Energy Resources

Where do we get our energy from? Figure 9-4 shows Canada's major energy sources. It also shows our consumption of each of these sources. The graph doesn't show that almost 75% of our energy comes from petroleum, natural gas, and coal. These sources are called **fossil fuels**. They have been formed from the decayed remains of plants and animals that lived millions of years ago. These fuels are **non-renewable resources**. That is, once they are used they can't be replaced.

Our other major energy sources are nuclear power, which is used to make electricity in nuclear generating stations, and hydro-electric power, which produces electricity from the renewable energy resource of falling water. Approximately 19% of our energy comes from hydro-electricity. About 6% of our energy supply comes from other **renewable resources** such as firewood, garbage, and wood wastes from the forest industry.

Canada has large quantities of all the resources needed for producing energy — fossil fuels, nuclear fuels, and water power. But even with all these resources, we still import part of our energy supply from other countries. As Canada grows and our energy needs increase, we may have to import even more energy. Canadian governments have tried to cut down on the amount of imported energy, because they would rather see the money for these fuels spent inside Canada. If we didn't use so much foreign energy, we would avoid the danger of having supplies cut off because of wars or troubles elsewhere in the world.

Governments in Canada have tried to reduce imported energy by encouraging people to reduce the amount of energy they use. If we used our own energy resources more wisely, we could eventually stop buying energy from other countries. Different government programs have helped people add insulation to their homes and put in more efficient heating systems. As a result of such efforts, we are more concerned about energy and its wise use today than we were a generation ago.

Oil and Natural Gas

The most common forms of fossil fuels are crude oil and natural gas. Crude oil is the raw material from which we make gasoline and different kinds of oil, as well as various chemical products. It comes out of the ground as a liquid and must be refined before it can be used. Natural gas comes out of the ground as a gas. It, too, usually needs to be refined before it can be used as a fuel, but not as much as oil.

Petroleum companies employ **geologists** to help them look for new deposits of oil and natural gas. The geologists use their knowledge of how fossil fuels are formed to find clues that will lead them to oil or gas deposits. These are three clues they look for:

- Oil and gas are formed from the remains of ancient plants and animals. Parts of some plants and animals didn't decay, but survived as fossils. The most common fossils are the shells of ancient shellfish. Certain kinds of fossils serve as a clue to the presence of oil or gas.
- The decaying plants and animals were gradually covered by layers of sediment which eventually became compressed into **sedimentary rock**. Certain kinds of sedimentary rock can indicate the presence of oil or gas.
- Oil and natural gas are usually found in folded **porous rock** which is trapped between layers of **non-porous rock**. The porous rock acts like a sponge for these resources.

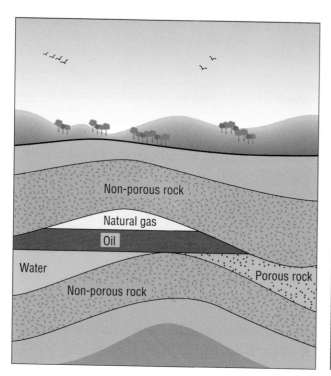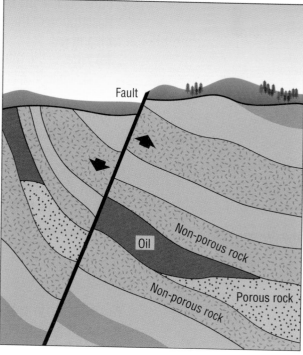

FIG. 9-5 Oil and gas trap *Liquids and gases can pass through porous rocks but not through non-porous rocks. Oil and natural gas are often trapped in porous rock that lies between two layers of non-porous rock.*

Finding oil and gas is one problem. Getting it to customers is another. Figure 3-5 (p. 35) shows that many of our major population centres are far away from fuel deposits. The fuels must therefore be transported long distances to reach most customers, and the best way of moving them is by pipeline. Most of the oil and gas used in Ontario and Québec, for example, comes by pipeline from western Canada. But pipelines are expensive to build. As a result, importing foreign oil by sea to the Atlantic provinces is cheaper than piping in Canadian oil from the West. When the oil and gas reserves off the Atlantic coast are developed, fuel imports may no longer be necessary.

Investigation 9.2

1. Figure 3-5 (p. 35) shows known oil and gas deposits in Canada. It also shows where deposits may be found in the future.
   (a) Which provinces have the most deposits?
   (b) What 2 areas may have the most deposits in the future?
   (c) What problems might we have in developing some of these potential sources of oil and gas?
2. Look back at the oil and gas trap diagram in Figure 9-5. Now reread the description of the 3 clues geologists look for when they are exploring for oil and gas.
   (a) What is the difference between porous and non-porous rock?
   (b) By selecting key words from the 3 clues, write 2 descriptive sentences about what geologists look for.
   (c) For each of the following items, write a sentence on how the item helps geologists in their search for oil and gas: (i) fossils; (ii) drilling; (iii) seismic surveying (explosions). Get help from a dictionary or other reference sources.
3. From which countries does Canada import petroleum? Use an atlas or other source to help you identify them.

Coal

Another important fossil fuel, both for the world and for Canada, is coal. Coal is a black or dark brown mineral that gives off heat when burned. There are different kinds or qualities of coal. The highest quality is anthracite, a hard coal that gives off less smoke than other kinds of coal. The lowest quality coal is lignite.

About 60% of the coal we produce is used in thermal generating stations to make electricity. This is called thermal coal and is generally of low quality. The remaining 40% is used mostly for smelting metals. Smelting is melting an ore to get the metal out of it. The coal used for this purpose must be high quality so that impurities are not added to the metal. Very little coal is now used for home heating.

Coal is plentiful in the three western provinces. Huge deposits in British Columbia have been developed to supply Japan and South Korea with coal for their metal industries. There are also large deposits in Alberta and somewhat smaller ones in Saskatchewan. In eastern Canada, the long-established mines of Nova Scotia have supplied coal to the Sydney steel mills. Some of these mines now extend far out under the ocean's floor.

For the first half of the twentieth century, coal was Canada's major energy source. It was used as a fuel for homes, industries, steam locomotives, and electric power stations. Coal is messy, however. During the 1950s and 1960s, coal was replaced by oil for home and industrial use. Oil was more convenient to handle, cleaner, and, at that time, cheaper. Coal continued to be used in thermal generating stations, but even for these users oil was considered a better fuel. Oil caused less pollution.

Not surprisingly, the demand for coal dropped, but since about 1970 it has grown stronger. Japan has been taking large exports of coal for its iron and steel industries. A huge increase in the price of oil in the 1970s also brought about greater coal use throughout the world. With its lower cost, coal is once again the fuel that heavy fuel-using industries, such as the electric power industry, prefer to burn.

FIG. 9-6

Coal being loaded at Roberts Bank, British Columbia

Coal also has another key advantage. It's plentiful. Coal has a major disadvantage, though. As we noted earlier, it causes pollution. The pollution can be controlled by putting devices called scrubbers in the smokestacks of coal-burning furnaces, but these scrubbers are expensive.

Investigation 9.3

1. Despite increased oil and natural gas prices, homeowners haven't gone back to using coal. Why might they be reluctant to use coal for heating their homes?
2. How would the greater use of coal affect the quality of life in cities? Why?

Hydro-electricity

Electricity makes our lifestyle possible. It heats and lights homes, runs appliances, heats water, and provides the energy for dozens of other tasks. Our use of electricity extends into almost every aspect of our lives.

Fortunately, Canada has a great deal of electrical power. Hydro-electric plants which rely on the energy of falling water meet about two-thirds of our electricity needs.

Figure 9-7 shows how a hydro-electric plant harnesses water to generate electricity. As you can see, there is a reservoir full of

FIG. 9-7 Hydro-electric plant *Why does the penstock become smaller before it enters the turbine?*

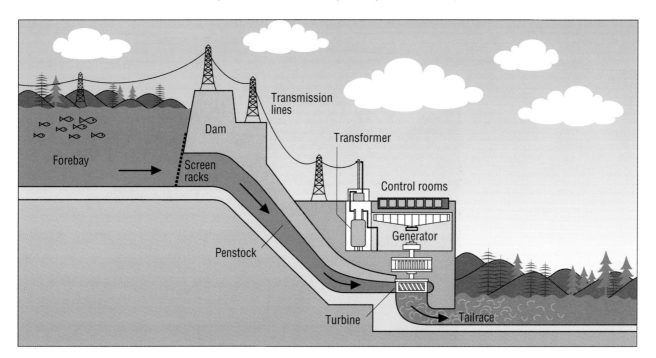

precipitation above the generating station. This reservoir stores extra water during wet periods to ensure that water is also available during drier periods. Water flows through a tunnel, or penstock, to a turbine. The force of it spins the turbine around, causing a generator to turn. The generator sets up an electrical current, and then transmission lines transport the energy to customers.

Investigation 9.4

FIG. 9-8 ELECTRICAL PRODUCTION BY PROVINCE (1985) thousands of megawatt hours

	Hydro	Thermal	Nuclear	Total
Canada	301 290	88 829	57 066	447 185
Newfoundland	39 648	1847	–	41 495
PEI	–	2	–	2
NS	914	6543	–	7457
NB	2289	3685	5427	11 401
Québec	133 696	152	3180	137 028
Ontario	41 376	31 950	48 459	121 785
Manitoba	22 410	367	–	22 777
Saskatchewan	1941	9897	–	11 838
Alberta	1411	32 021	–	33 432
BC	57 052	2072	–	59 124
Yukon/NWT	553	293	–	846

Source: Statistics Canada

1. Which provinces get at least 50% of their electricity from hydro generation? Which 3 provinces get less than 25% of their electrical power from hydro-electric generation?
2. Besides hydro generation, how else do provinces get electrical power?

Power stations can be built only where there is a large drop in the water source's level, such as at Niagara Falls in Ontario. The water must have enough force to spin the turbine. Most suitable sites in the populated parts of the country have already been developed. There are other possible locations available, but these are in remote parts of the country. Developing these remote sites is only practical if the sites can produce very large quantities of energy. Big projects make the expense and difficulty of constructing power plants and long transmission lines economical.

The James Bay hydro-electric power development is an example of a **megaproject** (a huge, expensive project) to get power from remote parts of Québec to customers in the southern part of Canada and in the US. Several smaller rivers that used to flow into James Bay were diverted to dammed reservoirs on La Grande Rivière. The Caniapiscau River was also diverted to form a huge reservoir, larger than any other lake in Québec. The development, expected to grow from one to seven generating stations, can produce more than 10 000 Mw of energy from all this water.

FIG. 9-9
James Bay-La Grande Project

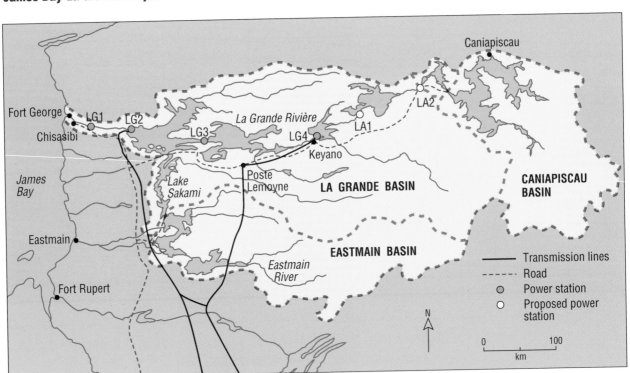

Some people opposed the project because of the environmental change it caused. The whole drainage pattern in a large part of Québec was altered. Wildlife suffered. The Native peoples of the area fought a long battle to defend their rights and way of life. They gained, among other things, the right to control the hunting, fishing, and trapping of all important species of game in northern Québec. Other people argued the power project was not really necessary because most of the energy would benefit Americans, not Canadians.

The James Bay power project is an example of the potential for hydro-electric energy that exists in the Canadian North. But, environmental groups oppose northern energy development because of the potential damage to the natural environment, and Native peoples criticize it for the disruptive effects on their way of life and culture. We may see more megaprojects using northern rivers, however. Hydro-electric energy remains a reliable, renewable source of power that is non-polluting.

Nuclear Energy

Nuclear energy, a recent form of energy, is also used to generate electricity. It supplies about 16% of Canada's energy needs, but may meet much more of our energy needs in the future. Nuclear power is cleaner than fossil fuels, but there could be some serious problems with using it. As a result, some people strongly oppose its use.

Nuclear power generation uses uranium atoms to provide energy. One type of uranium atom, uranium-235, is unstable, or capable of splitting into two or three separate atoms. When this splitting happens, some neutrons from the centre of the original atom fly off. If these neutrons hit another atom of uranium-235, that atom may split as well, sending off more neutrons and causing other atoms to split. This series of collisions is called a **chain reaction**. When this chain reaction is controlled, a tremendous amount of heat energy is given off. The heat from the splitting of the atoms is used to heat water to make steam. This steam runs a turbine and a generator to make an electrical current.

FIG. 9-10 Nuclear-power plant *Where do you think nuclear power stations should be located?*

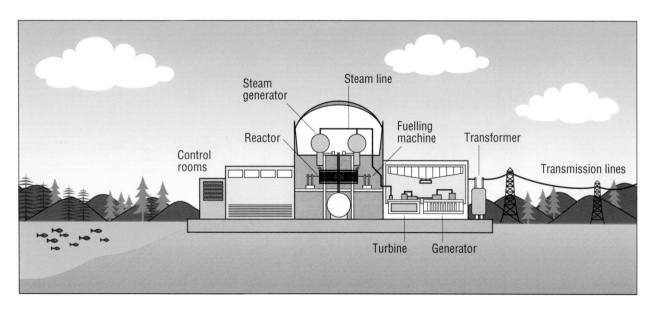

Uranium-235 is not found in a pure state anywhere in the world. It must be refined from impure uranium ore. The miners, such as those at Elliot Lake, Ontario, get about 1.5 kg of useful uranium from every 1000 kg of ore they dig up. The yellowcake they get from milling the uranium is sent to Blind River, Ontario, where it is further extracted from the impure rock. The uranium is then further refined at Port Hope, located on the shore of Lake Ontario. Here the uranium is prepared for use in nuclear reactors both in Canada and in other parts of the world.

Canada has huge quantities of uranium trapped in the ancient rocks of the Canadian Shield and the Western Cordillera. In fact, an estimated 559 000 t of recoverable uranium exist in Canada. In a typical year, about 11 000 t are refined. Between 80% and 90% of the uranium-235 produced in Canada is exported to buyers around the world.

This vast energy resource has the potential to supply Canada with power for many years. However, there are some serious problems that must be overcome. One of the most difficult is the disposal of **nuclear wastes**.

FIG. 9-11

Why are the technicians at this nuclear-power plant wearing protective clothing and equipment?

Nuclear wastes are the remains of the fuel bundles after the chain reaction has occurred inside the nuclear reactor. These wastes are highly radioactive and will remain that way for thousands of years. Radioactive materials give off rays or particles that can damage the atoms of living cells. Cancer is one result of the damage done by radioactive emissions.

To date, scientists don't have a process that will make nuclear wastes harmless. These materials must be put some place where they can't affect humans and other living things. The very long time necessary for storage means they can't be buried or dumped near the earth's surface where they can contaminate water in the ground. Some people have suggested that the wastes should be sealed in deep, no-longer-used mines or shot into space. Any plan seems to have many flaws that must be overcome. The wastes produced so far are stored in deep "swimming pools," large water-filled tanks. The water prevents the radiation from reaching people, but doesn't provide a long-term solution to the problem.

Other wastes are left during the refining stages. Some radioactive materials remain at the mine sites after the uranium-235 is separated from the ore. More wastes come from refining at the Port Hope plant. These wastes have low radiation levels and can usually be stored at dump sites. People are still concerned about the long-term danger of this radioactive material.

Another concern is the possibility of an accident in which a reactor is damaged and large amounts of radioactive material are released into the air. An accident of this kind occurred at Chernobyl, USSR, in 1986. More than 30 people were killed, 1000 injured, and more than 100 000 others were forced to abandon their homes. Over the years, a number of people will probably die from cancer caused by exposure to the radiation. At its worst, however, a reactor accident could lead to many thousands of deaths. Reactors have several safety devices to prevent such accidents from happening. However, the possibility of a major disaster still exists.

Despite these worries, many developed countries view nuclear power as a real alternative to burning fossil fuels to generate electrical energy. Uranium is plentiful, doesn't produce smoke or acid rain (which we'll discuss in more detail in Chapter 10), and the small volume of fuel is easily transported. Unlike hydro-generating plants, nuclear plants can usually be built close to the areas they supply. Unfortunately, these benefits must be considered against the potentially serious problems of waste disposal and reactor damage. The safety record of the Canadian nuclear industry is among the best in the world. Nevertheless, the decision to choose this clean, durable energy source or to reject it is difficult to make.

Investigation 9.5

SKILL BUILDERS

RESOURCE CENTRE

1. Compare nuclear power plants and hydro-electric power stations under these headings: **Energy Source**, **Equipment Needed**, **Location Considerations**, **Problems**.
2. Explain why it is important that nuclear wastes be disposed of carefully.
3. Work in pairs to prepare yourself for a debate on the topic, "Nuclear power is the best way of meeting Canada's future energy needs."

   Gather, organize, and write information that will either support or argue against the statement. While you may become aware that there are advantages and disadvantages that could be presented on both sides of the argument, prepare for only one side of the debate. Your teacher will ensure that the same number of students work on each side of the debate. Be ready to present your information to the class.

   You can obtain information supporting the use of nuclear energy from the Canadian Nuclear Association, 111 Elizabeth Street, 11th Floor, Toronto, Ontario, M5G 1P7. Get in touch with Energy Probe, 100 College Street, 6th Floor, Toronto, Ontario, M5G 1L5 for information against the use of nuclear energy.

Alternative Energy Sources

The five energy sources you've studied so far are the most important ones in the world's developed countries. But we know that not all these sources will be available or adequate in the future, and some of them present serious environmental problems. Fortunately, other sources of energy are available to us. Most of these are now used only in a small way or are just in the planning stages. But they could become important sources in the future. Let's look at several of these alternative energy sources in more detail.

Energy from biomass   Biomass refers to the plant and animal life on earth. Because we can replace what we use, **biomass** is a renewable resource. Firewood is an example of biomass that can be used to produce energy. Biomass energy can also be produced in other ways, such as through the collection of gases from decaying manure and through the production of alcohol from fermenting grain crops. Figure 9-12 shows some sources of biomass material. The chart also shows how much oil could be saved if we used biomass energy. Our total oil consumption for 1985 was about 80 000 000 m^3.

FIG. 9-12 POTENTIAL BIOMASS ENERGY

Potential resources	Millions of cubic metres of oil equivalent per year
Municipal garbage	2.7
Manure and straw	11.4
Forest and mill waste	30.2
Surplus wood and woodlots	11.7

With our vast forests and productive grasslands, Canada has tremendous potential for producing biomass energy. Forests, for example, could become plantations or large tree farms, producing fast-growing trees that could be turned into biomass energy. Biomass contains less energy by volume or mass than fossil fuels, so transportation would be more costly. Nevertheless, as non-renewable energy supplies get exhausted, this type of renewable energy could become extremely important.

Solar energy   The sun is the earth's original energy source. Fossil fuels are produced from the sun's energy which nurtured the plants and animals that became fossils long ago. The sun also makes hydro-electrical power possible. It causes water to evaporate from the oceans, to later fall as precipitation, then to swell the rivers used to produce hydro-electrical power. The sun's energy can also be trapped directly to help heat homes and businesses.

Solar panels are the most important means of collecting solar energy (Fig. 9-13, p. 194). These panels use the sun's energy to heat air or a fluid that can then heat the inside of a building. Think of the warmth you feel when you stand before a window on a bright winter's day. That is a good indication of how much energy is available.

Solar cells also collect solar energy. They are used in solar-powered calculators and watches. The cells transform energy from the sun into small electrical currents that run such electronic devices.

Unfortunately, solar cells are expensive, so they have not been used for major tasks such as providing electricity for a whole house. But within decades, it may be possible for every household to get all necessary electrical energy from a series of these cells.

FIG. 9-13
Trout Lake Indian Reserve has experimental solar panels.

Tidal energy   Oceanic tides result from the gravitational pull of the moon. The movement of this water is so powerful that there are plans to tap it to provide huge quantities of reliable energy. In fact, the Nova Scotia Power Corporation built a small tidal power plant on the Annapolis River, near Annapolis, Nova Scotia in 1984. It was constructed to demonstrate a new type of turbine generator. The Annapolis project was the first one in the Western Hemisphere to supply electrical power from tidal energy. However, the expense of tidal power projects means that schemes, such as the ambitious Bay of Fundy dam proposal, are unlikely.

The Bay of Fundy scheme calls for the construction of a massive dam across part of the Bay of Fundy between New Brunswick and Nova Scotia. This is because the bay has some of the highest tides anywhere in the world. The surge of water up the Bay of Fundy would spin turbines in the dam and generate electricity. The turbines would spin again as the tide water withdrew.

The Bay of Fundy tidal energy plan would result in much environmental change. The controlled movement of water past the dam would disrupt the normal flow of water. Plant and animal life would be affected. Also, the huge costs of building such a large dam and the technical problems that would have to be overcome would make the project difficult to justify. Tidal energy remains a possible energy source, but not one that will likely be important in Canada for a long time to come.

FIG. 9-14
Potential of tidal energy on the Bay of Fundy
The numbers on the map show the mean tidal range in metres. The areas are shaded from low tidal range (light) to high tidal range (dark).

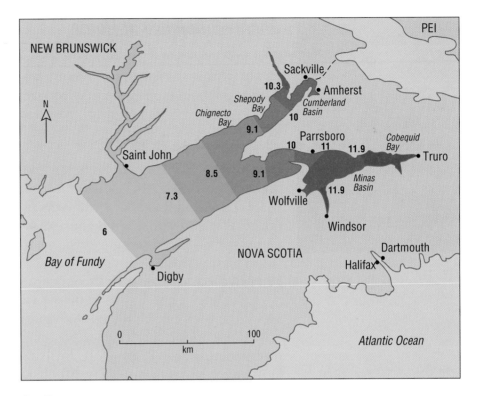

Investigation 9.6

SKILL BUILDERS
BRAINSTORMING

1. Figure 9-15 shows another alternative source of energy, the wind. With your classmates, brainstorm the advantages and disadvantages of wind power.
2. With your classmates, brainstorm other natural or human sources of energy that could be useful in the future for Canadians. Consider the advantages and disadvantages of these energy sources.
3. Create an alternative energy map of Canada. This map should show which areas of Canada could use the following alternative energy sources: solar energy; wind energy; biomass; tides. It should also show possible locations of the sources you discussed in Question 2.

   In preparing your map, do some research on related topics such as yearly hours of sunlight across Canada; wind speed, duration and direction across Canada; sources of biomass; location and heights of tides.

FIG. 9-15 *Wind turbines such as this can be used to generate electricity. By storing some of the electricity in batteries, the energy can be saved for those times when there is little wind.*

FIG. 9-16

Government agencies and environmental groups promote the wise use of energy.

Energy Efficiency at Home

One reason why we use so much energy in Canada is the coldness of our winters. Heating our homes is a major energy expense. Although there is no way to avoid this cost altogether, in recent years we have begun to think more seriously about how we can keep heating costs down. We have been trying to make our homes more energy efficient.

One of the most energy-efficient homes ever invented was the igloo (Fig. 8-4b, p. 167), the traditional winter dwelling of the Inuit. The igloo, made of snow, was usually heated by a small oil lamp. The snow insulated the igloo and kept the heat in. The dome shape helped to spread the heat evenly. The long entrance tunnel prevented the winds from blowing into the igloo and stopped the warm air inside from getting out.

Canadians, including most Inuit, would probably prefer not to spend their winters in igloos. And indeed they don't. Most houses are more comfortable than igloos, but many of them aren't economical to heat. They were built when energy was cheaper. Housing designers now pay much more attention to ways of keeping the heat in and the cold out.

Investigation 9.7

1. Two geographic factors must be taken into account when designing energy-efficient buildings in Canada:
   - The cold winds normally blow from the north and the west.
   - The sun's rays fall mostly on south-facing walls.
   (a) Suggest how a house could be built with these factors taken into account.
   (b) As a special project, research a home that has been designed to be heated by solar energy. Describe how the house gets its heat from the sun and how it is insulated to prevent heat loss.
2. One hundred years ago, most homes were heated with wood. Fifty years ago, most were heated with coal. Today, there are a number of fuels and heating systems that can be used, so it is sometimes difficult to decide which one is best for your home.

   Suppose you are buying a new home and the builder has asked you which heating method you wish to use. Rather than make a snap decision, you decide to do some investigating. You hope to learn which heating method gives you reliable service at the least cost. Here are some alternatives you might consider: natural gas; propane; oil; electricity. Are there any other alternatives you could add to the list?

SKILL

BUILDERS

DECISION
MAKING

(a) To make your choice you need to consider several factors about each energy source. The factors listed in Figure 9-17 will be useful in helping you to reach a decision. Copy Figure 9-17 into your notebook, and add any other factors you think might be important. If any of the fuels listed are not available in your community, leave them out of your chart.

(b) Now, do some research on each factor, possibly working with other students in your class. Rank the fuels from 1 to 4 for each factor, giving the highest number to the fuel that is best in terms of that factor. For example, the fuel that is most plentiful would get a score of 4. The one that is least polluting would also get a score of 4. You will see that the chart already shows how the fuels rank by relative cost. Once you have filled in the chart for the rest of the factors, total the fuel columns. The fuel with the highest total should be your most efficient fuel.

FIG. 9-17 ENERGY SOURCE FACTORS

Factors in determining energy source choice	Energy resources			
	Natural gas	Propane	Oil	Electricity
1. What is the relative cost of heating your home for a year with the fuel?	2	4	3	1
2. How much storage space is needed for the fuel?				
3. How much space is needed for the heating unit?				
4. How much does the fuel pollute?				
5. Is the world running out of this fuel?				
Total				

3. From our experiences in the 1970s, we know that we cannot depend on the availability of a particular energy source or on the stability of energy prices. Imagine that by the year 2025 oil and natural gas became so scarce that they were more expensive than solar energy. Using sketches, maps, and notes, show what effect conversion to solar energy would have on our communities, homes, cars and other forms of transportation, and where we live in Canada.

Summing Up

We rely on energy, especially fossil fuels, to make our high standard of living possible. But our reliance cannot continue forever. We are affected by changing world energy prices, and the petroleum and natural gas we consume in such huge quantities are non-renewable resources. Alternative energy sources are not yet practical and our need for reliable energy supplies has sometimes led to damage of the natural environment. All this suggests that we must manage our environmental resources. That is the topic of the next chapter.

CHAPTER TEN

Environmental Management

Until recently, we took our rich natural environment for granted. The resources of our lakes and forests seemed inexhaustible and indestructible. We relied on the **environment** for much of our wealth and recreation. But in the past few decades, all that has changed. We now recognize that there are major environmental problems. Some animals, once found in great numbers, are in danger of becoming extinct. Fish can't survive the pollution in many of our lakes. In some areas, people fear that the air they breathe and the water they drink may be harming their health. Many parts of our environment are endangered. And since we depend on the environment for our standard of living — and even our lives — we, too, are endangered.

Sometimes our problems have been caused by carelessness. Our cities and industries produce poisonous wastes that have passed into our air and water untreated. We have also used many of our resources wastefully, without realizing that they may one day become scarce.

Some problems have been caused because we haven't understood how complex and sensitive the environment is. Our environment is a complicated system in which living things depend on each other in many different ways.

If we know that problems exist, why don't we fix them? The environment's complexity sometimes makes that hard to do. For example, in trying to protect one part of the environment, we could accidentally destroy other parts. The fact that many people's jobs depend on environment-threatening activities also slows down problem solving. There is a dilemma. Do we sacrifice jobs to save the environment? Obviously, we must try to protect both the environment and the jobs. The only way we can do this is to manage our environment — that is, to constantly and carefully control the way we use it. If we manage it successfully, then we shall be able to use our environment without destroying it.

In this chapter, we will look at a few case studies that illustrate some of the dangers threatening our environment. We shall also look at some of the problems of environmental management.

Food Chains and Pesticides

Every living thing depends on something else in its environment. This is especially true in the case of food. Figure 10-1a shows a **food chain**. Each living thing depends on the thing ahead of it in the chain for its food. For example, the spruce trees provide food for spruce budworms. Budworms, in turn, provide food for woodpeckers and other small birds. These birds are then eaten by larger predatory birds, such as goshawks. When the chain is working properly, all the different creatures in it have enough food and enough of them survive at each stage to keep the system going.

But what happens if the chain is disturbed in some way? Suppose, for instance, that the woodpeckers and some of the other smaller birds die from disease or because of something people have done. What would happen to the chain's other parts?

The most obvious effect would be on the larger birds. If they couldn't find a food supply to replace the one that was depleted, many of them would starve. The number of these birds would decline.

FIG. 10-1   Food chain and Food pyramid

What can you tell about the budworm-woodpecker-goshawk system from this drawing?

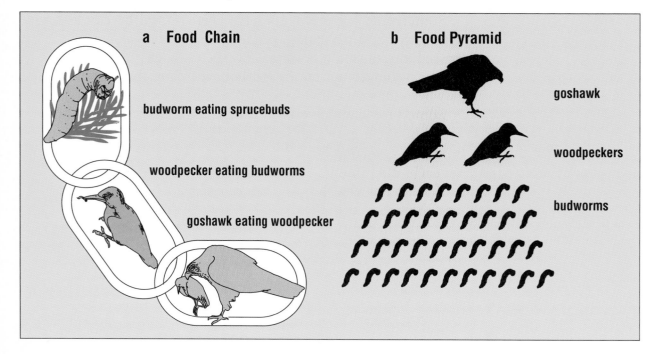

a Food Chain

budworm eating sprucebuds

woodpecker eating budworms

goshawk eating woodpecker

b Food Pyramid

goshawk

woodpeckers

budworms

What about the other side of the chain? With fewer birds eating them, the number of spruce budworms would increase. The budworms would destroy more spruce trees. Eventually, there might be so many budworms that not enough spruce trees would remain to feed them all. Then, many of the budworms would die. Although it is possible that a new balance might be achieved between the number of spruce trees and budworms, it is also possible that the budworms might destroy the forest. In that case, the whole food chain would be wiped out.

In trying to meet our own needs, we often change or destroy natural environments and food chains. Forests, for example, are often cleared to make way for housing developments. As a result, the homes and food supplies of many living creatures are lost.

In clearing the forests, people weren't destroying a natural environment deliberately. But that is what happens whenever we try to change a natural environment without understanding how its different parts work together.

Another common way in which we interfere with food chains is with pesticides. Pesticides allow us to increase the size and quality of our crops. They do so by destroying insects that feed on the crops. But insects are part of a food chain, so the use of pesticides often has unintended results. Take the case of DDT, one of the first modern pesticides. During the 1950s and 1960s, DDT was very popular with farmers. It gave farmers larger crops to sell in good years and saved their crops from being wiped out by insects in other years. Consumers were also happy. Higher crop production meant lower food prices for them. However, as the years went by, people discovered that some species of wildlife were disappearing in areas where DDT was being used.

As evidence built up that DDT was harming the environment, many people demanded that it be banned. Fortunately, newer and safer pesticides had been developed by the late 1960s, and farmers could switch to these. DDT is now restricted by law to just a few uses. It is no longer used in agriculture at all.

Investigation 10.1

1. Although pesticides are safety tested, many people remain concerned about their possible long-term effects on the environment and on people directly. The example of DDT suggests that it may be hard to predict the effects of pesticides. These effects may be indirect and take a long time to be noticed. Some people have argued that, because of possible health and environmental problems, we should stop using pesticides. Others have argued that if we did, we might face food shortages and job losses.

   In this activity, we will look at some of the arguments for and against pesticide use. Here are 5 typical opinions from people representing different sides of the issue.

   (i) Vice-president of a chemical company   "After one year without pesticides, insect damage would cause crop yields to drop by 30% and food prices to increase by up to 300%. The insect damage would also lower crop quality. Countries that rely on Canada for wheat and other grains might have to go without enough food or would have to pay much more for it. At the same time, Canada would lose millions of dollars that it now receives from wheat exports."

   (ii) Organizer for a conservation group   "One of the biggest problems is that insects gradually become resistant to the effects of manufactured poisons. Authorities estimate there are now about 400 species of insects that are not affected by most pesticides. In the long run, pesticides are not an effective way of dealing with the insect problem."

   (iii) Representative for a consumer group   "Traces of pesticides remain on food even after it has been cleaned. Exposure to even these small amounts for a long period of time could have harmful effects on people's health. Farmers and others who are in direct contact with the pesticides face even greater dangers. The World Health Organization estimates that pesticides cause up to 500 000 deaths or injuries throughout the world each year. Yet we are assured that these chemicals are harmless."

   (iv) Chairperson of a farmers' organization   "If pesticides were taken off the market, food production would drop by 25 to 30% within a year and 50% within 5 years. About $300 million worth of wheat a year would be lost in Saskatchewan alone! This would be a severe loss to the farmers, grain handlers, and farm equipment dealers."

   (v) Government official   "None among us would continue using these chemicals if they were proved to be hazardous to the lives of the farmers who use them or to consumers. However, certain hard choices have to be made. If we don't use them, some farmers are going to go out of business, and all Canadians are going to have to pay more for their food. Canada's ability to save people from starvation will be less too, because we may not always have surplus wheat to send to famine-stricken countries."

These arguments represent 5 strong points of view and should be read critically. Each argument may be true as far as it goes, but it may emphasize only one aspect of the whole problem. The arguments may also stress the worst possible outcomes of the problems they oppose.

FIG. 10-2 THE RANGE OF POSSIBLE OPINIONS ON THE USE OF CHEMICAL PESTICIDES

Totally opposed to any kind and under all conditions	Few kinds rare occasions	Neutral some kinds some conditions	Many kinds most conditions	Totally in favour of all kinds and under all condtions

SKILL
BUILDERS
COMPARATIVE
THINKING

(a) Draw the diagram in Figure 10-2 in your notebook. Use arrows and the roman numerals beside each argument (i.e. i, ii, iii, etc.) to indicate where the 5 spokespeople would be placed along the line.
(b) Summarize the arguments for and against the use of pesticides.
(c) Suggest possible solutions to the problems of whether or not we should use pesticides.

Acid Rain

Acid rain, a special type of air pollution, has been identified as a major problem. It wasn't noticed before because it couldn't be seen and didn't leave a layer of dirt when it fell. Only when plants and fish in many of our lakes and rivers began to disappear did we become aware of acid rain's quiet threat.

Acids are chemicals which, in their most powerful form, can dissolve or burn almost any solid substance they come in contact with. In a mild form, such as in vinegar and lemon juice, they have a sour taste. Acids in our stomachs help us break down food for digestion.

The opposite of an acid is a **base**. Bases and acids neutralize each other. In other words, we can remove the acid from a substance by mixing it with a base. We sometimes do this when we have stomach upsets caused by too much acid. To neutralize some of the acid in our stomachs, we drink solutions of baking soda, which is a mild base, or take commercially prepared antacids.

Pure rain water is normally halfway along the scale, neither acidic nor alkaline (basic). However, when certain airborne chemicals mix with the moisture in the air, they produce rain that is mildly acidic. Scientists say two kinds of chemicals are responsible for acid rain: **sulphur oxides** and **nitrogen oxides**.

Sulphur oxides are produced naturally when forest fires and volcanic eruptions occur. They are produced artificially when fossil fuels (coal or natural gas) are burned. The artificially produced sulphur oxides are especially a problem when burned in large quantities. This occurs at coal-burning electrical generating stations and in industries where coal-burning smelters melt down iron, copper, and other minerals.

Nitrogen oxides are produced by automobile engines and by some industrial processes. Most of the nitrogen oxides are produced in large cities. Both nitrogen and sulphur oxides can travel many hundreds of kilometres through the air before combining with the moisture to fall as acid rain.

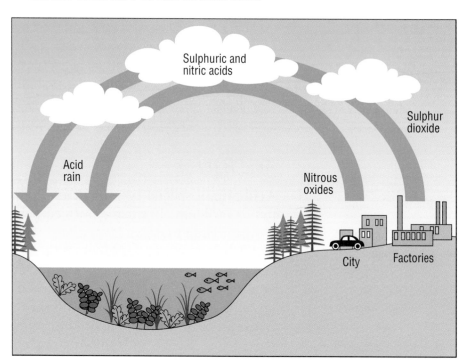

FIG. 10-3 Acid rain process

If this illustration shows the beginning of the acid rain process, what would a seriously affected area look like?

Acid rain has been falling for more than 100 years. Its effects are more noticeable now because the acidity has built up enough over time to cause problems. Our prosperity and growing population size have also led to a worsening of acid rain. There are now more cars, coal-fired generating stations, and other sources of sulphur and nitrogen oxides than ever.

What does acid rain do? First, picture an unharmed lake. It has plants, such as bulrushes or grasses, along its edges. It also supports a wide variety of insects, frogs, snakes, and fish. The lake's water is probably pure enough to drink, but if you looked at a glass of it you would notice a slight colour. The colour indicates the presence of tiny living organisms that exist in every healthy lake.

The first thing you would notice about a lake that is seriously affected by acid rain is the water's beautiful clearness. This is because the acids have removed those tiny organisms. An acid lake has fewer plants. It also has few of the small creatures that fish and other water life depend on. Many types of young fish, especially trout, can't survive in a lake that has been affected by acid rain. Ontario's 250 000 lakes are at risk of dying because of acid rain. In the Sudbury area, which has been affected the most by acid rain, all the lakes have low fish populations.

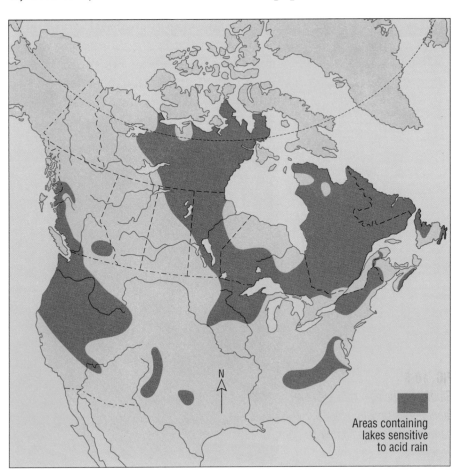

FIG. 10-4 Acid-rain sensitive areas

Some lakes in Canada are not sensitive to acid rain. These lakes contain high levels of calcium which form a base that neutralizes the acid in the rain. Acid rain-sensitive lakes lie in areas where the soil or rocks don't contain enough calcium to neutralize the acid.

Areas containing lakes sensitive to acid rain

Acid rain doesn't just fall in the area where it is produced. Coal-fired power plants and smelters usually have tall smokestacks to keep their smoke from falling on the communities around them. The gases from these stacks can be carried hundreds of kilometres by the prevailing winds. The higher the smokestack and the stronger the wind, the further the gases will be carried. As a result, areas downwind of the smokestacks are the most threatened by acid rain.

The effects of acid rain go beyond the killing of plant and fish life. As we know from our study of food chains, birds and animals will also die when an affected lake can no longer supply them with food. When the wildlife that attracts their customers disappears, businesses such as sport fishing and tourism suffer too. Tourism is an important industry in Canada, and the quality of our natural environments is one of the main attractions. If acid rain destroys some of these environments, many Canadians could be out of jobs.

Forests are in danger as well. In Germany, large areas of forest have already been ruined by acid rain. Canadian foresters fear the same thing could happen here. In Québec, far more sugar maples have been dying than usual, and many concerned people suspect acid rain is the cause. Some provinces, such as British Columbia and New Brunswick, are more vulnerable to acid rain, because much of their populations depend on forestry for jobs. If great numbers of trees were destroyed, serious human and economic problems would result.

FIG. 10-5

Studies are being conducted in laboratories to determine the harmful effects of acid rain on vegetation.

Our cities and towns are also not immune from the effects of acid rain. Building and statue surfaces wear down at faster rates. Cars rust more readily. As a result, we pay more to keep our buildings and cars in repair. Acid rain may also harm human health. Some doctors suspect that acid rain may increase the danger of lung disease.

Not everyone agrees on the causes, effects, or seriousness of acid rain. One major obstacle encountered by Canadian authorities is the American government's refusal to move quickly on the acid rain problem. Since a large proportion of the chemicals that create acid rain come from south of the border mostly from electrical generating stations, we need the Americans' full co-operation before acid rain can be eliminated. In the mid-1980s, Canada and the US formed some committees to look more closely at the situation. But progress in combatting acid rain will probably be slow. Reducing the pollution will be extremely expensive. Both American and Canadian companies don't like the high costs of the new equipment needed. So, acid rain will continue to be a difficult environmental problem for years to come.

Investigation 10.2

1. Compare the map of areas sensitive to acid rain (Figure 10-4, p. 207) with the map of Canada's landform regions (Figure 4-8, pp. 52-53). To what landform region does the sensitive area correspond? Why are lakes in this region at risk from acid rain?
2. Now that we understand the acid rain problem better, perhaps we can begin to solve it. Some suggested ways of combatting the effects of acid rain include:
   - adding calcium to lakes to neutralize the acid
   - burning fuels with less sulphur, such as natural gas. (The biggest source of acid rain is sulphur oxides from coal-fired generating stations and smelters.)
   - trapping the sulphur before it can be released into the air by installing scrubbers in the smokestacks of industries burning coal

   We must manage the environment so that we can continue to meet important human needs, such as electric power and transportation, while at the same time preserving our natural heritage. Finding a solution to acid rain will not be easy or inexpensive. Even if we do find a solution, much time will be needed before the problem is entirely solved.
   (a) Research the suggested solutions and find out how successful each one has been or might be in reducing the effects of acid rain.
   (b) What problems limit the usefulness of each method?
   (c) What additional solutions have been tried?

SKILL
BUILDERS
RESOURCE
CENTRE

Finding information on acid rain can be quite difficult. Here are some sources to try.

1. **Library**   Look under the catalogue headings of "acid rain," "environment," and "pollution."
2. **Government**   Use the telephone book to find the department that looks after the environment. Remember to look in the federal as well as the provincial government listings.
3. **Special groups**   Use the telephone book to find special interest groups that are interested in protecting the environment. Their names might begin with "Pollution," "Environment," "Nature," or the name of your province.
4. **Industries**   Many polluting industries are working on solutions to the acid rain problem. Their public affairs departments may be able to provide you with information on their approaches to pollution control.
5. **Individuals**   Ask a librarian or someone at your local newspaper to suggest other contacts for material on this topic.

Farmlands: Do We Have Enough?

Canada's open spaces and size often impress people from other parts of the world. Our country is, after all, second largest in area. But thinking of how large Canada is often makes people, including Canadians, overlook something—that only a small portion of our land can be used to feed the population.

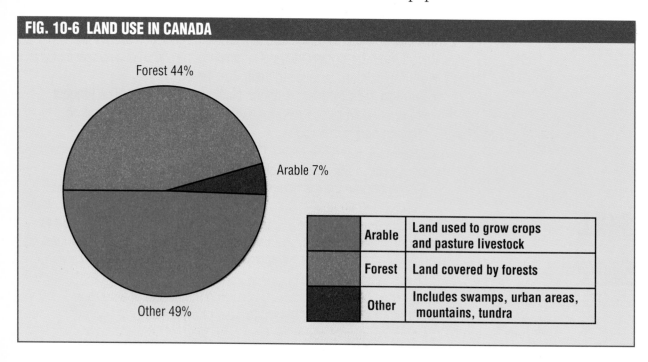

FIG. 10-6 LAND USE IN CANADA

Forest 44%

Arable 7%

Other 49%

	Arable	Land used to grow crops and pasture livestock
	Forest	Land covered by forests
	Other	Includes swamps, urban areas, mountains, tundra

When we look at Figure 10-6, the amount of land that we have available for food production doesn't appear to be very large. Let's calculate the actual size.

Canada's total area is 9 976 000 km^2
Food producing land is 7% of the total area.
Therefore, the total area of arable land is
$7.0 \times 9\,976\,000 \div 100 = 698\,320$ km^2

This food-producing land is almost twice the area of all of Japan. But Figure 10-7 shows a disturbing trend. Over the 30 years shown, much Canadian food-producing land has been lost. At the same time, our population has increased considerably. If this trend continues, we will have more and more trouble growing enough food in Canada to meet our own needs.

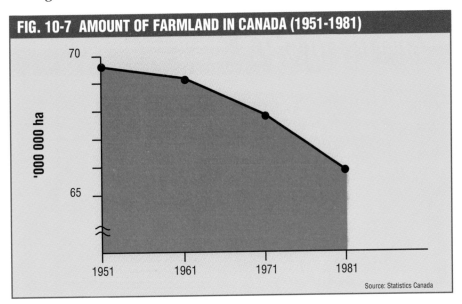

FIG. 10-7 AMOUNT OF FARMLAND IN CANADA (1951-1981)

Source: Statistics Canada

Most farmland loss is due to urban expansion, and the land being lost has usually been our very best farmland. Most of our population originally settled in prime farming areas. As these areas become built-up, only poorer quality soils will be left for food growing. It's estimated that for every 1000-person increase in the population, 70 ha of farmland has been lost to cities. Much of our most fertile and productive lands lie beneath city pavements.

The loss of farmland is especially serious in two unique areas of Canada: the Niagara Peninsula in Ontario and the Okanagan Valley in British Columbia. These are the only two places in Canada where tender fruit, such as peaches, cherries, grapes, and plums, can be grown successfully for the marketplace.

If scarce fruit land is taken out of production, there are only a few ways that we can make up for the decrease in our fruit supply.

• We can reduce our consumption of fruit that can't be grown elsewhere in Canada.
• We can try to develop specialized facilities, such as greenhouses, to replace the natural environments for growing these foods.
• We can import the fruit.

Since our population is increasing, it is unlikely that we could reduce the total amount of fruit we eat. We probably wouldn't want to build specialized fruit-growing facilities either, because that would be expensive and the fruit would cost more. So our only practical choice is to import even more fruit than we do now. Importing more fruit means spending more of our money outside the country and weakening our economy.

Investigation 10.3

FIG. 10-8
Niagara Peninsula, 1953

1. (a) Trace the borders of the air photo in Figure 10-8 onto a piece of tracing paper or acetate. Now, mark the following on your tracing paper: major roads and railways; major water bodies; wooded areas; farmland (including orchards).

FIG. 10-9
Niagara Peninsula, 1986

 (b) Compare Figure 10-9 with your sketch. Shade on your sketch the areas of farmland that have been lost between the times of the 2 photographs.

 (c) Determine from the photographs what land uses have replaced farming and fruit growing.

2. Figure 10-7 (p. 211) shows the amount of farmland in Canada from 1951 to 1981. You will notice that the graph starts at 65 000 000 ha.

 (a) Redraw the graph so that the axis showing the total amount of farmland starts at 0 instead of 65 000 000.

 (b) Compare the new graph with Figure 10-7. Although both graphs show exactly the same information, they don't look very similar, do they? Explain, in your own words, the difference between the 2 graphs.

 (c) Sometimes people use graphs to emphasize points of view. Which graph would someone use to stress the disappearing farmland problem? Which one would someone use to play down the problem?

Investigation 10.4

1. Figure 10-10 shows an area close to a major city. The land is valuable, and a builder wants to develop it. Dairy farmer Hans Vandenburg now owns the land, but he has decided to retire and sell the farm. The Blue Valley Development Corporation has offered Mr. Vandenburg $6500/ha for his 100 ha farm. The farmer thinks he will accept the offer, but he might be willing to take less if the land were to be kept for rural or park use.

Because the municipality in which the farm is located has an official development plan, change in the use of the land must be approved. Before approval can be given, a hearing must be held so that people can express their opinions about the proposed purchase. The corporation has said it plans to build expensive houses, a sports complex, and a park on the land.

One important fact that will affect the land's use is the flooding of the river nearly every spring. Once every 25 years or so, much of the valley suffers from heavy floods.

Four people, representing different interests, spoke at the public hearing.

Brenda Dawes, the Blue Valley Development Corporation representative, explained that the sloping land would make an attractive setting for luxurious homes, much in demand in the community. With the city's boundaries

FIG. 10-10   Blue Valley

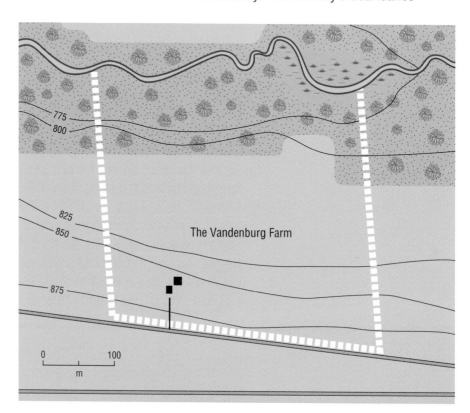

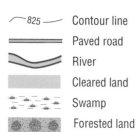

—825—	Contour line
≡≡≡	Paved road
〰〰	River
	Cleared land
✳✳✳	Swamp
🌿🌿	Forested land

already extending beyond the Vandenburg farm, it seemed natural to her to change the land's use from rural to urban. Ms. Dawes said that her company would cover much of the extra costs of expanding the sewage and water supply systems. Taxes paid by new home-owners would more than cover the rest. She explained that the occasional flood would not affect her company's plan, because no buildings were to be erected on the flood plain. She also mentioned that, with proper planning, most trees could remain and roads and houses could be designed to complement the natural setting.

Antonio Grilo, a farming corporation representative, said that he would like to purchase the farm for fruit and vegetable growing. The sloping land would be used for peach, cherry, and apple orchards. The flat land would be used for vegetable growing. Mr. Grilo said he planned to build drainage ditches in the lowland in order to reduce the water problem. But he wasn't worried about floods damaging crops because the floods normally occurred before the planting season. Mr. Grilo explained that his group couldn't afford to pay $6500/ha but could pay about $5000/ha. He reminded people at the hearing that Canadians have already lost much fruit land to urban development.

Irene Eisen represented the Blue Valley Conservation Authority which was trying to obtain the land for public use. She said the low-lying land along the river had not been farmed for several years, so it had grown back to its natural state. The conservation authority wanted to preserve the natural conditions there because few similar areas existed in that part of the province. Mrs. Eisen outlined her group's plan for a park that would include a wildlife preserve in the lowest areas, and sporting, camping, and picnicking facilities elsewhere. Flooding would be a natural advantage in the wildlife area.

Thomas Saito, the mayor of the city, expressed his approval for the housing plan. He pointed out that the town badly needed more homes to serve the growing population and to attract new people. The fact that the developer was willing to build a sports complex without using taxpayers' money was an added advantage. The mayor said he wasn't concerned about the need for new sewer and water facilities. The developer would pay most of the costs and any cost the city had to pay would be more than covered by the increased tax revenues from the new houses. The mayor concluded by saying the development would create more jobs for construction workers in the city.

(a) Use the following approach to help you decide which is the best use of the farmland.

Question: Which of the 3 land uses will I support?

Options:

- high-income housing and park
- fruit and vegetable farm
- wildlife and recreational park

Data analysis: Copy Figure 10-11 into your notebook. Now, for each of the given criteria, rank the land use options 3, 2, or 1, with 3 as the highest score or best solution. Which 3 of these criteria do you think are most important? Double the value of your scores for those 3 criteria. Your scores for these items will therefore be 6, 4, and 2.

FIG. 10-11 LAND USE OPTIONS

Criteria	Land use options		
	Housing and park	**Farming**	**Wildlife and recreational park**
Will provide the most taxes to the city			
Will cause the least damage to the environment			
Will provide the most employment over a long period			
Will be the most useful for the most people			
Will be the most attractive use of the land			
Will cost the city the least to build and maintain			
Total:			

(b) Are there other factors that have to be taken into consideration? If so, add them to your chart before arriving at a final answer.

(c) Total each column. The land use with the highest number of points should be the one that you support.

(d) Write a letter to try to convince the director of the Blue Valley Planning Authority to approve the land use you think is best. Be sure to include as many factors as you can think of. In real life, you can influence decisions in your community by writing letters or phoning government representatives.

Getting Rid of Garbage

Canadians are among the most wasteful people on earth. On average we produce about 2 kg of garbage per person per day — over 700 kg each year. This includes wastes from our homes, businesses, and governments. It has been estimated that we throw away $2 billion worth of food every year.

Our tremendous capacity to create waste comes out of our wealth. We consume a large number of products, many designed to be used for only a short time and then thrown away. But more importantly, we are so wealthy that we can afford to buy our goods nicely packaged in plastic, paper, or glass. The packaging is almost always thrown straight into the garbage. About 40% of our garbage is packaging material.

FIG. 10-12

Most garbage is buried in landfill sites, a relatively cheap way to get rid of the wastes. Until recently, only a very small part of our wastes were recycled.

Getting rid of garbage — **solid waste** is the more technical term — has been fairly easy up to now. Wastes have simply been put in **landfill sites**. Here, garbage is covered over with daily layers of soil and then left to decay naturally. The process is cheap and doesn't require special equipment. But a serious problem has developed: sites for landfill have become very hard to find. Those near large urban areas have been filled in and municipalities are facing higher transportation costs to move the garbage to more distant sites.

Even moving garbage greater and greater distances has not solved the problem for some large cities. Municipalities that are one to two hours away from large cities don't want to become dumping grounds for someone else's garbage. Such municipalities have taken on a **NIMBY**, or Not In My Back Yard, attitude. This has forced urban areas, such as Metropolitan Toronto, to consider such schemes as moving garbage by train to old mine sites in northern Ontario. It has also forced cities to start recycling programs.

FIG. 10-13
Recycling efforts have reduced the amount of garbage in many communities.

Recycling involves separating materials that can be reused from garbage which has no value to us at this time. Glass, plastic, paper, steel, cardboard, and aluminum are some of the materials that can be recycled. When this is done, the recovered material is made into new products and less solid waste ends up in landfill sites. Here are some facts about recycling:

- Recycling 1 t of material saves an average of 3 m³ of landfill space.
- Recycling aluminum cans saves 95% of the energy needed to make new aluminum cans.
- Recycling 1 t of newsprint saves 17 trees.
- Recycling 1 t of steel saves the energy equivalent of 3.6 barrels of oil and 1.5 t of iron ore.

Recycling alone won't solve the waste problem. Canada needs a proper waste management program that involves the "Four Rs." We must *reduce* the amount of material we produce; *reuse* materials as long as possible before disposing of them; *recover* as much of the waste as is possible; *recycle* the recovered materials into useful products. The only way to solve the problem of waste is to throw away only the minimum amount of materials.

Investigation 10.5

1. (a) How has your school tried to reduce the amount of garbage it throws away? Set up a research investigation to answer this question. In your conclusion, suggest 2 new waste-reduction methods that the school could start to use.
   (b) Create a poster, display, play, announcement, or the like, to encourage students to recycle more materials.
2. How does your municipality get rid of its solid wastes? Where will wastes go in 20 years? Research these questions and write a one-page summary statement.
3. Figure 10-14 shows 5 possible places for a new landfill site for the town of Richvale. Decide which site is the best choice by using a decision-making matrix. Begin by determining 5 to 7 criteria that should be considered in making this decision. When you have decided on a location, write the reasons for your decision in your notebook.

FIG. 10-14
Richvale's possible landfill sites

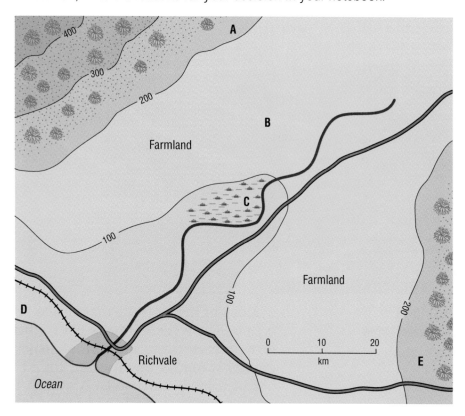

Railway

200 Contour line

Highway

River

Built-up area

Swamp

Forest

A - E Possible sites

4. Use newspaper and magazine articles to do a study on waste-management problems. Collect 5 articles that deal with the difficulties of getting rid of wastes in Canada. For each article, identify the problem being discussed, important facts, and possible solutions. Write a conclusion based on all 5 articles. Arrange your articles as a poster or make them into a booklet.

Water: The Next Crisis

Water is something most Canadians take for granted. Yet people in some parts of the world can't. They face shortages of fresh, clean water, even for cooking and drinking. Here's why Canadians have rarely had to deal with such problems:

- Canada has the largest reserves of fresh water in the world.
- Canada's total area covered by water is equal to the areas of East and West Germany, Austria, Switzerland, and Italy combined.
- Seven of the world's 14 largest fresh water lakes are in Canada.

Where does our water come from, and why does Canada have so much? Oceans surrounding Canada on three sides supply moisture that eventually falls on the land as rain. The diagram of the **water cycle** in Figure 10-15 shows how this moisture moves from the oceans to land.

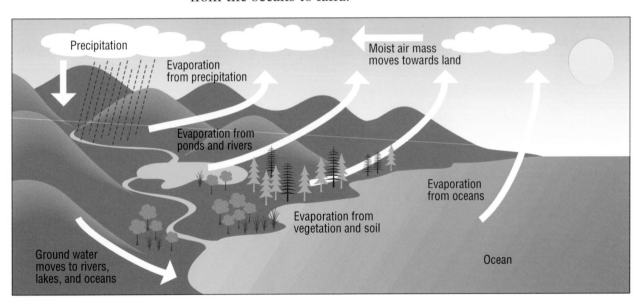

FIG. 10-15
The water cycle

Much of the moisture that falls as rain eventually returns to the oceans. The water that does not go there is either evaporated from lakes, rivers, trees, and soil, or soaks into the earth to become **ground water**. Ground water, found under the surface, can be obtained by drilling wells. Although it is difficult to know how much water is available underground, the estimate is that there is about 30 times as much as on the surface.

We may have lots of water, but we consume lots of it too. Water is important to our standard of living. The average Canadian uses about 450 L of water per day, equal to about two bathtubs full. In contrast, a person in the poorest and driest part of the world uses as little as 12 L per day.

Investigation 10.6

1. (a) Make a list of the ways you use water during an average day.
   (b) If, for some reason, you had to reduce your water use by one-half, what things would you do differently?
   (c) Suggest some ways in which you could conserve water but maintain your standard of living.

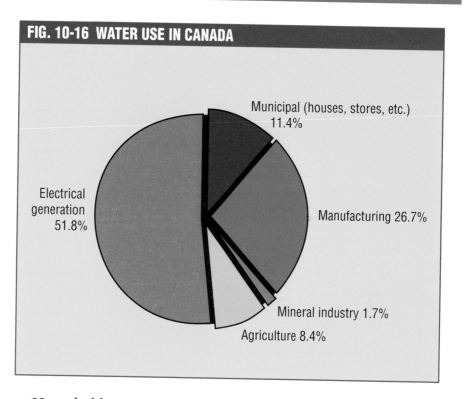

FIG. 10-16 WATER USE IN CANADA

Municipal (houses, stores, etc.) 11.4%

Manufacturing 26.7%

Electrical generation 51.8%

Mineral industry 1.7%

Agriculture 8.4%

Household water use represents only a small portion of all the water consumed in Canada. As you can see from Figure 10-16, manufacturers and electrical generating stations demand the most water.

Each time water is used, its quality is reduced in some way. For example, we use water to flush away dirt and grime from our clothes and dishes and to carry away our sewage. Industries may use water to carry away wastes or to dilute chemicals and other substances that are used in factories. Thermal and nuclear power stations use water to make steam for their generators and for cooling.

After use, water is channelled to a nearby lake or river, often still carrying its pollution. Even the clean water discharged from power stations can cause problems. It is warm enough to raise the temperature of the body of water it empties into, and the increase in temperature can seriously affect plants and fish.

Natural processes will purify most pollution from water bodies, but this takes time. Very often nature can't clean water as fast as we can pollute it. The polluted water isn't only a danger to wildlife; it can also be a danger to human beings. Even water that is cleaned can sometimes carry enough harmful chemicals to threaten human health over a period of time.

With so much water in Canada, do we really need to worry about our water supply? Unfortunately, we do, because much of the water is far away from our major population centres. The water that we use is usually the water that is closest to us. As our population grows, we put greater strain on our local water supplies, especially those for metropolitan areas. More people means that there will be more homes and more industries creating pollution that could threaten water supply safety. Greater populations will require additional sources of water.

Summing Up

You have seen in this chapter that different people have different views on what to do with our environmental resources. Lively discussions about environmental issues occur in communities across Canada frequently. When people argue about these issues, their emotions and feelings can become very important.

Emotions are a part of decision making, whether the decisions are about your personal life, your family or friends, or things around you. They also influence the way people who are making decisions about our environment think. As a class, find a local environmental or resource management issue and follow it for a time. You would soon be able to identify some of the issue's emotional aspects. Here are some ways to get information about an issue:

• Keep a scrapbook of newspaper clippings on the issue.
• Attend some public meetings or hearings about the issue.
• Have speakers from different sides of the issue talk to your class.
• Check out the resources of your local library.

Making effective decisions about managing our environment and our resources is important. Poor decision making means the waste or loss of our valuable sources of energy, water, minerals, and even fresh air. You are a decision maker, both now and in the future. The next generation is counting on you to manage all of Canada's resources wisely.

Not only do we have a responsibility to make effective decisions, we also have a responsibility not to be part of environmental problems. You might doubt that one person can make a difference. But, remember that if hundreds or thousands of individuals try, we can make cities and countrysides better places to live. Here are a few things we can do:

- Use natural gas instead of oil for home heating. Natural gas produces less sulphur oxide and therefore less acid rain.
- Drive cars that use less gas so that less nitrogen oxide and therefore less acid rain will be produced.
- Restrict the use of insecticides in our gardens and at our campsites, so there will be fewer poisons in the air, water, and soil.
- Be aware of decisions made in our communities about how land is used and where wastes are stored. This will allow us to identify harmful activities and to express concerns to political representatives.

Not all environmental problems begin in our community or even in Canada. Much of the acid rain that falls on Canadians comes from the US. Many poisons that are found in the Great Lakes can also be traced to factories in the US. Environmental problems are not just local problems, they are world problems. But if we in Canada can manage our own environment wisely, we will be in a better position to insist that others do so, too.

CHAPTER ELEVEN

Communications and Transportation

WE RELY ON SYSTEMS OF COMMUNICATION and transportation in many ways every day. Going to school, talking on the phone, listening to the radio, writing a letter, shipping a parcel...these are just a few of the ways.

As individuals, we want to be able to talk to other people and to visit them. As members of a community, we recognize that being able to meet and communicate with others is even more important. If we can't exchange ideas and discuss our plans and problems with each other, then we can't work together for our common good.

In a national community as large as Canada, communications and transportation are vitally important. Our country's great size, harsh climate, and often rugged landforms have sometimes made keeping in touch challenging. As a nation, we have always had to make a special effort to provide systems to tie us together.

In this chapter, we will look at different means of communications and transportation. We will see how these means have changed over the years. We will also study how they affect us personally and as Canadians.

Personal Patterns of Communication

Communicating is so much a part of our daily lives that we rarely think about the many different ways of doing it. In an average day, each of us might call someone on the telephone, send a letter, listen to the radio, watch a TV show, read a book, and take part in several conversations.

Some of these communication methods involve an exchange of ideas between particular people, a conversation between two persons being the best example. Person-to-person communication is called **direct communication**, because the communicators send their messages directly to each other.

Another kind of communication is one in which information is made available to a large number of people, such as through a newspaper. In this kind of communication, information travels in only one direction and not to anyone in particular. Such communication is called **indirect communication**.

Investigation 11.1

1. Copy the chart in Figure 11-1 into your notebook.
   (a) Sort the following communication **modes**, or methods, into the appropriate box in the chart. Add any other modes that you use.
   - computer information services (database)
   - computer bulletin boards
   - CB radios
   - newspapers
   - television
   - conversation
   - mail
   - AM/FM radio
   - magazines
   - telephone
   - notice boards
   - telegram

FIG. 11-1 MY COMMUNICATION MODES		
Type	Often used	Occasionally used
Direct (person-to-person)		
Indirect (person-to-people)		

   (b) What are your 5 most important modes of communication? What are some factors that affect your use of communication modes?

National Patterns of Communication

Cape Spear, Newfoundland, and the most western point of the Yukon/Alaska border are 5514 km apart. Nonetheless, we can communicate from one point to the other almost as if the great

FIG. 11-2

Communicating from one end of the country to the other has become much easier in recent years. This radio relay station, which sends the radio signal it receives onto the next station, has helped make this so. The station is part of a nation-wide system.

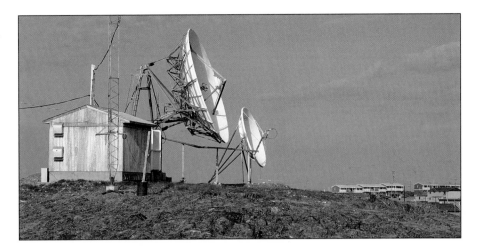

distance between them didn't exist. We are able to do this because Canada has one of the best communication systems in the world.

Canada needs to have a good system. Communicating between our cities is complicated not only by distance, but by natural obstacles, such as mountains and other rough terrain. Cultural differences also sometimes make communications difficult between us. To overcome these difficulties, we have laid thousands of kilometres of telegraph and telephone lines, built hundreds of radio relay towers, and launched satellites into space. We have also set up a national radio and television network, the Canadian Broadcasting Corporation, to inform us about what is happening throughout the country and to help us appreciate our cultural richness. Through such ambitious measures, we have sought to keep in touch with each other.

Our main communication systems are newspapers, books, magazines, radio, television, mail, and telephone. Businesses also communicate by telex, facsimile, and computer. In addition, many Canadians use two-way radios particularly when telephone lines aren't working. Each method has certain advantages and disadvantages.

The Telephone

The telephone is probably our most widely used communication system. Indeed, Canadians make more telephone calls than any other people in the world. We also have a long association with the telephone, dating back to 1876 when Alexander Graham Bell placed the world's first long distance call between the Ontario towns of Brantford and Paris. Communication systems have improved dramatically since then. Now you can pick up the telephone, dial 11 or so digits, and communicate with almost anyone in Canada or, indeed, in most other parts of the world.

FIG. 11-3
Times have changed! Most phone calls don't go through the operators anymore. Computers are widely used by telephone companies.

Investigation 11.2

1. Telephone companies work hard to produce accurate telephone directories so that people can communicate more easily and quickly. Using the information at the front of a telephone book, answer the following questions.
   (a) What are "area codes"? What is your area code?
   (b) Give the area code for each of these communities:
      i)   Summerside, Prince Edward Island
      ii) Yellowknife, Northwest Territories
      iii) Kenora, Ontario
      iv) Drummondville, Québec
      v)   Kamloops, British Columbia
   (c) Why are some telephone areas larger than others?
   (d) To find a phone number in Lethbridge, Alberta, what telephone number would you call for directory assistance?
   (e) What is a "toll" call?
   (f) Find the cost of a 3-minute phone call dialed directly (without operator assistance) from your community to Montréal, Québec.
   (g) During which time period can you get the lowest long distance rates?
   (h) What do the digits "1-800" at the beginning of a phone number mean?
2. We can find different patterns in the way people use their telephones across Canada. Look carefully at Figures 11-4 and 11-5. You will see that there are distinct regional differences.

FIG. 11-4 TOTAL TELEPHONE CALLS PER YEAR (1986) (In millions)	Local	Long distance	Total
Canada	34 673	1 959	36 632
Ontario (province with most calls)	10 657	705	11 363
PEI (province with fewest calls)	249	8	257

Source: Statistics Canada

(a) For both provinces in Figure 11-4, calculate what percentage of total calls were local and what were long distance, or toll. To get the percentage of local calls, divide the number of local calls by the total number of calls and multiply by 100. To get the percentage of toll calls, divide that number by the total calls and multiply by 100.

(b) Make a pie graph to show toll and local calls for Prince Edward Island and Ontario. Give your graph a title, colour each sector a different colour, and add a legend.

(c) What are 3 possible factors that could explain the difference between the 2 provincial patterns? Use an atlas to help you with your answers.

SKILL

BUILDERS

GRAPHING

FIG. 11-5 AVERAGE NUMBER OF CALLS PER TELEPHONE (1986)	
Canada	2 829
Newfoundland (most calls per phone)	10 062
Saskatchewan (fewest calls per phone)	1 871

Source: Statistics Canada

(d) Using the data in Figure 11-5, make a bar graph comparing telephone usage in Newfoundland and Saskatchewan to the average for Canada. Suggest reasons for the wide variation in number of calls per telephone.

3. Canadians can dial directly to most countries in the world, and many of us do. Whom do we talk to when we phone outside Canada? Figure 11-6 shows the countries we most often call.

Use the data from Figure 11-6 (p. 230) to show the pattern of Canada's international telephone communications on a world map. Draw arrows from Canada to each country, using the following scale to determine arrow widths.

Number of calls	Width of line
200 000-400 000	1 mm
400 001-600 000	5 mm
600 001-800 000	10 mm
800 001-1 000 000	15 mm
More than 1 000 000	20 mm

What patterns are there on your map?

FIG. 11-6 LONG DISTANCE CALLS FROM CANADA TO OTHER COUNTRIES	
United States	116 658 000
United Kingdom	4 724 000
Other European countries	7 782 000
Mexico	376 000
Bahamas	208 000
Australia	425 000
British West Indies	706 000
Jamaica	437 000
Total	135 946 000

Source: Statistics Canada

The Information Age

We live in what has sometimes been called the **information age**. Much information is available to us today because we have created the communications technology to handle vast amounts of it. The machine responsible for the information flood is, of course, the computer. The computer is a tool which can store vast amounts of information, process it in seconds, and communicate

FIG. 11-7

Computers have changed the way many people do their jobs.

it in a variety of ways. Using telephone lines, computers around the world can share information with each other. Other machines, such as photocopiers, tape recorders, and video recorders, have also made easy the communication of information in many different forms.

All the new ways of handling and sharing information are changing our world, especially our work world. There are now fewer jobs for bank tellers because automatic tellers do much of the work. There are also fewer jobs in factories, because robots and other computerized machines are doing work that used to be done by people. Fax machines, which can send copies of letters and other printed material over phone lines, are replacing the post office for some kinds of business communication. On the other hand, new jobs are being created. The expanding information industry needs people to plan and install new computer systems. There is also a demand for trained computer operators.

With all these changes, many people have had to learn new skills or new ways of doing their old jobs. It seems that change because of new technologies will continue to be part of our work world. More than ever, we must have appropriate training for both starting and continuing successful careers.

Investigation 11.3

1. Go through several newspapers and cut out job ads that ask for a knowledge of computers. You will probably find a demand for word processor operators, computer programmers, and people with other such skills. Prepare a display or short report titled: **Jobs That Use Computers**.
2. List all the ways you come into contact with computers. Your school might keep track of attendance by computer, for example. What impact have computers had on the way you do things? How will they probably affect your life in the future?

Transportation

Transportation serves two purposes — moving people and moving things. Transportation systems help us to get to places in our own communities and far from our homes.

These systems carry our food, sometimes from nearby farms, sometimes from other countries. Even in winter, we can enjoy fresh fruit and vegetables, shipped in from warmer climates.

Transportation systems also allow us to export our products to customers around the world. Because they enable us to reach more markets, these systems promote Canada's prosperity.

Transportation is especially important in Canada because of our country's large size. Our transportation systems haven't been easy to establish, though. Some parts of the country are difficult to cross, for example, the Rocky Mountains, or the rocks and forests of the Canadian Shield. Canadians have devoted much effort and money over the years to overcome such natural obstacles. Now computers are playing a part. Many companies rely on them to keep track of their transportation activities across our huge land. Because the transportation systems we have developed make it easy for people and goods to move within the country they, in effect, foster national unity.

FIG. 11-8
It took a lot of effort and money to build a railway across Canada.

There are many different kinds of transportation, each with its own advantages and disadvantages. In Canada the main modes of transportation are water, rail, road, air, and pipeline. We shall now look closely at transportation by water, rail, road, and air.

Investigation 11.4

1. Transportation probably lets you do a great many things in your life. To see just how much you depend on it, copy Figure 11-9 into your notebook, and fill in the necessary information. Some of the more common reasons for using transportation have been suggested. Add any others that you can think of.

FIG. 11-9 MY TRANSPORTATION NEEDS

Frequency	Reasons	Usual method of transportation
Daily	• school	
	• friends	
	•	
	•	
Weekly/monthly	• sports	
	• church	
	• entertainment	
	• shopping	
	•	
	•	
Annually	• medical appointment	
	• vacation	
	•	
	•	

2. Some modes of transportation are better for certain jobs than for others. Figure 11-10 shows how much Canadians use the different transportation modes for each of the 2 major transportation jobs, moving people and moving things.

FIG. 11-10 MODES OF TRANSPORTATION

Moving people		Moving things	
Road	84%	Road	44%
Air	12%	Rail	41%
Urban transit	2%	Water	13%
Rail	1%	Air	2%
Other	1%		

SKILL
BUILDERS
GRAPHING

Urban transit refers to the buses, streetcars, and subways in city transportation systems.
(a) Make 2 pie graphs to illustrate the information in Figure 11-10.
(b) Write 3 sentences to explain the differences between these graphs.

Water Transportation

Canada owes much of its early development to water transport. Our larger rivers and lakes connect with thousands of smaller waterways to form a natural highway across much of the country. The St. Lawrence River and the Great Lakes are the most important parts of this highway. They provide a water route from the Atlantic Ocean to the middle of the North American continent.

Native peoples, early European explorers, and fur traders relied on this network of waterways for transportation. By the early 1800s, fur traders had developed routes that crossed Canada from Montréal to the Pacific Ocean, mostly by water. Traders from Montréal used the Ottawa and French rivers to reach the upper Great Lakes. From there they followed lakes and rivers to Lake Winnipeg. Then they could either follow the branches of the Saskatchewan River as far west as the Rockies or head northwest to Lake Athabasca. Hudson's Bay Company traders paddled down rivers running into Hudson Bay, such as the Hayes, to reach the same areas. West of the Rockies, rivers such as the Fraser and the Columbia provided routes to the Pacific Ocean.

At a time when other forms of transportation were either poor or non-existent, water routes were invaluable. But they had some major disadvantages, one of the worst being their many gaps. The rivers and lakes didn't always connect with each other, and rapids or shallows sometimes prevented boats from getting through. These problems could be solved by portaging — carrying the boats and cargo to the next place where the boats could be launched. But portaging could be extremely hard work. There were 26 portages on the Winnipeg River alone. Portaging also meant that the boats and their cargoes had to be fairly small. The longest canoes were only 11 or 12 m.

Not surprisingly, Canadians soon started to improve these waterways. They built canals to by-pass rapids and other obstacles so they wouldn't have to portage or shift cargoes from one boat to another.

Water transportation still has limitations. Rivers and lakes can only be used for half the year, because they freeze in winter. They don't always provide the most direct route from one place to another. And boats are relatively slow. When new means of transportation, such as trains, were developed, the smaller and more difficult water routes went out of use.

FIG. 11-11 *Travel by canoe in the early days was hard work!*

FIG. 11-12 *Canals were a tremendous improvement over other methods of travel.*

Today, water transportation is centred on the Atlantic and Pacific coasts and on the St. Lawrence River and the Great Lakes. Because of the St. Lawrence Seaway, ships travelling across the Atlantic Ocean can sail all the way up the St. Lawrence and through the Great Lakes. As a result, cities on the Great Lakes have become important ocean ports. Thunder Bay, at the western end of Lake Superior, is one of our busiest ports. Here, grain from the Prairies is loaded into ships to be carried to eastern Canada and other parts of the world. Figure 11-13 (p. 236) shows the seaway system and some of the products that are shipped through it.

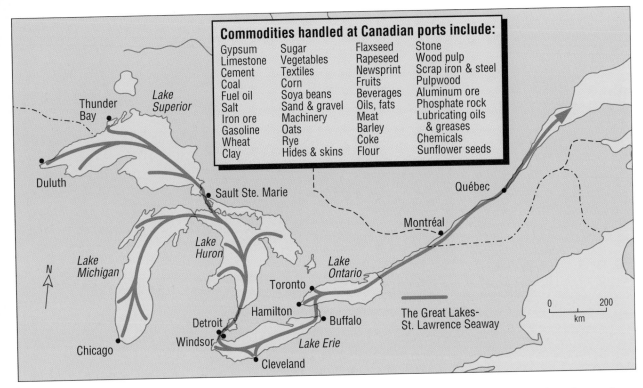

Commodities handled at Canadian ports include:

Gypsum	Sugar	Flaxseed	Stone
Limestone	Vegetables	Rapeseed	Wood pulp
Cement	Textiles	Newsprint	Scrap iron & steel
Coal	Corn	Fruits	Pulpwood
Fuel oil	Soya beans	Beverages	Aluminum ore
Salt	Sand & gravel	Oils, fats	Phosphate rock
Iron ore	Machinery	Meat	Lubricating oils
Gasoline	Oats	Barley	& greases
Wheat	Rye	Coke	Chemicals
Clay	Hides & skins	Flour	Sunflower seeds

FIG. 11-13
Great Lakes-St. Lawrence Seaway

Winter ice prevents the seaway from being used for about four months of the year. During that time, cargoes enter eastern Canada through the busy ice-free ports of Halifax, Nova Scotia, and Saint John, New Brunswick. Cargoes from the Pacific are unloaded in Vancouver, British Columbia, also a year-round ice-free port.

FIG. 11-14
Halifax is the major port in the Maritimes. The Halifax container terminals (right) serve all of Canada.

Investigation 11.5

1. Only 2 Canadian provinces lack ports for ocean-going ships. Which provinces are they? Using your atlas and an encyclopedia, list the main ocean ports for the other 8 provinces. Identify one major product or resource that is shipped through each port.

2. The St. Lawrence Seaway system allows ocean-going ships to travel inland 3700 km. To find out how long a 3700 km distance really is, do the following. Obtain a blank world map showing political boundaries and give the map the title **How Long Is the St. Lawrence Seaway?** Now get some coloured thread. Cut off 6 pieces to represent 3700 km lengths according to your world map's scale. Select 5 long journeys between different places in the world. Then tape the threads down to show how far a 3700 km distance is on the journeys you selected. For example, would 3700 km cover the distance around the British Isles or the distance from Japan to Australia? Label the start and end points for each string. Use your last piece of string to mark the St. Lawrence Seaway journey which will end at the western edge of Lake Superior.

Rail Transportation

Railways were invented in the early 1800s, with the first Canadian one built in 1836 near Montréal. When roads were few and rough, railways provided a quick, reliable way of moving goods and people over long distances. For many decades, the train was not only the best way of getting from one place to another, it was often the only way.

Now, other transportation systems compete with railways for passengers and freight. Trucks can penetrate far more areas than trains can and offer cheaper, more readily available service for sending small shipments. Airplanes, which travel much faster than trains, are more convenient for long distance travel. All this competition has changed our use of trains.

Many people who once travelled by train now prefer to go by air, or bus, or private car. In 1945, the railways carried 55.4 million passengers. By 1987, they carried about 6 million. The number is still falling. Most of the passenger business for VIA Rail, our national passenger railway, comes from the area between Québec City and Windsor. This part of Canada has the greatest concentration of population. Commuter services in the Toronto and Montréal areas also draw many train passengers. In other areas, few people tend to take trains.

Many arguments have been waged about whether we can still afford a passenger rail system. In 1989, the federal government announced drastic cuts in VIA Rail's budget. Some people believe this will end passenger-rail service in Canada. Many communities are upset because they don't want to lose their train services. Other people believe the federal government should improve train services. They think people should be encouraged to travel by rail because trains use much less energy and cause far less pollution per passenger than either cars or airplanes.

When it comes to moving cargo, there is no argument about trains being best for the transportation of large, bulky materials. Today, most railway business involves moving such freight as grain, coal, potash, iron ore, chemicals, and cars. Railways often transport the freight in **unit trains**, large trains, sometimes 1.5 km long, which carry only one kind of product.

Determining the best way of using our railways will be difficult. People seem to disagree more about rail transportation than about any other transportation mode, and will probably continue to do so for some time to come.

Investigation 11.6

1. (a) How would you describe the train service to your community? Use these questions to help gather information about rail transportation in your area.
   (i)   Where is the train terminal?
   (ii) What railway(s) serves your community?
   (iii) How often do trains arrive and depart?
   (iv) What are the trains' destinations?
   (b) List major cities that are within a 24 hour radius of your community by rail.
2. (a) On an outline map of Canada, shade those parts of the country that have high population densities. Turn to Figure 5-12 (p. 84) to see the distribution of the Canada's population.
   (b) Mark on your map all the provincial capitals. Add these key cities as well: Vancouver, Calgary, Hamilton, Montréal, Saint John.
   (c) Now, plan a rail transportation network across the country. Your goal is to serve the greatest number of people possible over the shortest distance.
   (d) Compare your rail network to the network that now exists in Canada. (You will need to use an atlas.) What differences do you see? How can you explain these differences?

Air Transportation

Airplanes are possibly the twentieth century's greatest transportation invention triumph, and speed is what sets them apart from other transportation methods. Unaffected by obstacles on the ground, airplanes can cross oceans and continents in hours.

FIG. 11-15

High speed air travel has changed transportation throughout the world. It's easier and faster to travel between two points by plane.

Air transportation plays a particularly valuable role in a country like Canada because its speed helps us overcome the problem of great distances. Business people who travel a lot appreciate this. They can spend more time working and less time travelling. Vacationers find that air travel opens up many more holiday destinations to them. And Canadians living in the country's remote areas now enjoy more comfortable living standards and more security because airplanes can bring them supplies and provide emergency transportation to distant hospitals.

Air transportation's main disadvantage is that it is expensive compared to other transportation means. As a result, airplanes tend to be used more for business than recreational travel. They are best for travelling medium and long distances where the time saving makes the higher ticket price worthwhile. The longer the distance, the greater the advantage of air travel. That is why almost all intercontinental travel is now by air.

Airplanes move mainly people, because getting people somewhere quickly is usually more important than moving goods quickly. Also, the costs of moving large amounts of freight by airplane are high. Some kinds of freight have to move quickly, though. If goods are perishable or needed in a hurry, it makes sense to ship them by air. Mail also has to move quickly, and in Canada, most of the mail addressed to distant places goes by air.

Investigation 11.7

SKILL BUILDERS

GRAPHING

1. (a) Using a reference book, make a list of the 10 busiest airports in Canada. Beside each airport name, record the number of flights into and out of the airport in one year.
   (b) Use the statistical information you gathered in (a) to make a bar graph. What title will you give your graph?
2. Look at Figure 11-16. Decide on a way to show this information in a visual form. You might graph it, draw it, or chart it. Make sure you give your work a title.

FIG. 11-16 TRAVEL TIMES IN CANADA

Method	Time period	Montréal to Vancouver
Steam-powered trains	1890s	115 h
Steam-powered trains	1930s	90 h
Diesel-powered trains	1970s	60 h
Automobile	1970s	75 h
Propeller-driven aircraft	1940s	18 h
Jet aircraft	1970s	5 h

Road Transportation

Canadians love them. Making them is one of our most important industries. Whole buildings are designed to shelter them. Their pathways consume millions of dollars of tax money and millions of hectares of valuable land. People spend large portions of their incomes buying, operating, and maintaining them. For some people, they are the biggest single expenses of their lives. We are, of course, talking about the car.

Why is the car so popular? The main reason is that no other transportation method offers as much convenience. The car is ready whenever we need it. There are no timetables to study, no contacts to be made for pick-up and delivery. And our network of roads allows us to travel quickly to many different destinations.

Until the coming of the car in the early 1900s, roads in Canada were poor. Outside the cities, they were rough, narrow, and unpaved, and travel on them was slow and uncomfortable. But, as Canadians began to buy cars, they began to demand better roads.

As a result, many roads were built and improved during the twenties and thirties.

Canada's first superhighway, the Queen Elizabeth Way between Toronto and Niagara Falls, opened in 1939. Yet it was not until 1946 that the first coast-to-coast trip across Canada was made by car, and many of the roads taken were bad. We didn't really begin to develop a good system of roads across the country until the fifties and sixties. The opening of the the Trans-Canada Highway in 1962 represented a major improvement in our road system, but 3000 km of the 7821 km highway were unpaved. The highway wasn't completely paved until 1970! Nonetheless, Canada now has one of the best road systems in the world.

Investigation 11.8

SKILL
BUILDERS
RESOURCE
CENTRE

1. (a) Go to a library's reference section, and find out how many kilometres of highways and other roads Canada has. Make a list or chart by province or by type of road.
   (b) Divide this total by the population of Canada to calculate the number of kilometres of road per person.
   (c) Find out the same information for 4 other countries, and make the same calculations in each case.
   (d) Create a bar graph of your results from (a), (b), and (c).
   (e) Write a sentence on how Canada compares in the number of kilometres of highway per person with the other 4 countries.
2. Think of all the different kinds of cars, trucks, recreational vehicles, motorcycles, vans, and snowmobiles that are available. Each is designed to meet travel needs, but each in its own unique way.
   (a) Choose a kind of vehicle that interests you. Find pictures and specifications for it using newspapers, magazines, and brochures to help you.
   (b) Imagine a specific trip where you could use the vehicle you chose. A camping trip is an example. Describe the trip briefly in writing.
   (c) Draw a sketch map of your route and explain the details of your trip so that your choice of vehicle makes good sense. Around your sketch map, glue your pictures and specifications in place. You could use a piece of Bristol board to display your work.

Making Transportation Choices

Sometimes, there is only one way to get to your destination. Other times, you have a choice. When making a choice between transportation systems, what should you consider? Certainly, the factors of time and cost will affect the decision you make. Comfort, convenience, and safety will also influence your choice.

You may also have to choose between transportation systems when you have something to ship. The choice you make here will depend on what you have to ship, where it has to go, and how soon it has to get there. Cost, of course, will be an important factor. Some transportation systems are best for moving large bulky items over long distances as long as the items don't have to arrive at their destinations quickly. Others may be best for fast deliveries of small or medium-sized items.

Our individual transportation choices influence the decisions that politicians, business people, and planners make about transportation systems. Suppose more people decide that they want to travel by air instead of by train. Plane services would have to increase while train services would probably decrease.

Transportation planners also have to consider factors that don't always affect our individual choices. These are social factors, important to us as a group of people or as a society. Some social factors that planners look at are energy consumption, pollution, amount of land used and where, cost, adaptability to changes in usage, and businesses and jobs created or protected. Taking factors such as these into account helps planners work out new transportation systems or change old ones.

Investigation 11.9

1. Copy Figure 11-17 into your notebook. Put check marks in the spaces to show the transportation mode you would choose for each of the distances in the chart and give reasons for each of your choices.
2. Copy Figure 11-18 into your notebook and identify the transportation mode most likely to be chosen for moving the product or good. Give your reasons for selecting that mode.
3. Figure 11-19 shows the relative energy efficiency rates of different transportation systems. The figures are based on fuel consumption per passenger for a 1000 km journey.

    In terms of saving energy, which is the best transportation system? Why do we sometimes prefer those transportation systems that use more fuel? How could we encourage people to make more use of these transportation systems that are the best fuel conservers?

FIG. 11-17 COMPARING TRANSPORTATION MODES

Mode	Distance				Reasons
	0-5 km	50-150 km	250-500 km	500+ km	
Walking					
Bike					
Bus					
Car					
Train					
Plane					
Other					

FIG. 11-18 MOVING GOODS

Product	Distance	Transportation mode	Reasons
Cattle	800 km		
Machine parts	250 km		
Fresh lobsters	1500 km		
Motor oil	50 km		
Light bulbs	300 km		
Iron ore	1500 km		
Fresh milk	75 km		
Wheat	1500 km		

FIG. 11-19 FUEL CONSUMPTION PER PASSENGER *

Train	9.4 L
Bus	13.2 L
Car (4-passenger)	30.4 L
Plane	65.4 L

* for a 1000 km journey

Summing Up

Communication and transportation systems have been particularly important to Canada. The country's vast size has made it necessary for distance to be overcome cheaply and easily. As a result, Canadian businesses have become leaders in the development of communication and transportation technologies. The linkages that these systems have created have helped tie the country together through good times and bad.

CHAPTER TWELVE

Canadian Diversity

I T'S DIFFICULT TO DEFINE PRECISELY what a Canadian is. The easiest and safest thing to say is that a Canadian is a person who lives in Canada. But that doesn't tell us very much.

So far in this book, you've seen Canadians in many situations and you probably have a pretty good idea what countries we have come from, where and in what conditions we live, what we do for a living and for recreation, and how rich we are in areas such as natural resources, human resources, and standards of living. The picture that is likely forming in your mind is that Canadians are quite different from one another. And that picture is perfectly accurate. A Maritimer is not a Torontonian; an Albertan is not a Québecois. A Vancouverite is not a Winnipegger. We differ greatly across this vast country and we also differ greatly within our own communities. We are a diverse people.

Diverse means being different. You've already seen that, as far as our landforms, climate, resources, and many other non-human features are concerned, Canada is highly diverse. In this chapter you will concentrate on the diversity of our people.

Chapter 5 introduced some basic ideas about our population. You will remember that it asked three major questions: Where did we come from? How many of us are there? and Where do we live? In this chapter there are only two major questions:

How different are we?
What are the results of our differences?

These two questions should be kept in mind and asked again and again all through the chapter.

Investigation 12.1

1. To begin your study of Canadian diversity, look at the diversity within a small community — your classroom. By this time, you've done some Investigations that are short, some that are long, and some that require you to obtain a lot of details before you can reach a conclusion. Now you're ready to organize a survey on your own. It might be helpful if, as a class, the work is split up the same way it was in Investigation 5.13 (pp. 101-02). You might also check other Investigations you've done to get more ideas on how to proceed. Here are some topics to deal with. (Feel free, of course, to think up some of your own.)

- places of birth
- languages spoken at home
- favourite music
- favourite foods
- hobbies

Once your information has been gathered, it should be organized, presented to the class, and discussed. Then conclusions should be drawn that show what you've learned about diversity in your classroom.

Canada's Ethnic and Cultural Groups: A General Study

There are several ways of grouping people in order to study their outlook on things, their lifestyles, and what they value. One way is by looking at ethnic and cultural groups.

An **ethnic group** is a group of people who are similar to each other in their language, customs, and background. The meaning of **cultural group** is very close to that of "ethnic group." Often the two terms refer to the same group of people — for example, the Hungarian ethnic group or the Hungarian cultural group. The same people are included in each case. In referring to a group's culture, however, artistic expressions through, music and other art forms are usually considered as well.

As you can see from Figure 12-1, Canada has a rich variety of ethnic groups. You will recall seeing a graph like this in Chapter 5 Figure 5-5 (p. 78). It shows the places from which immigrants came to Canada in 1986. Figure 12-1 is different, however. Most of the people represented in Figure 12-1 have likely lived in Canada for a long time, some of them for all of their lives. When asked by the census taker, however, they reported that they belonged to a particular ethnic group. That is, because of their backgrounds, customs, and languages spoken (sometimes more than just one), they placed themselves in one ethnic group or another.

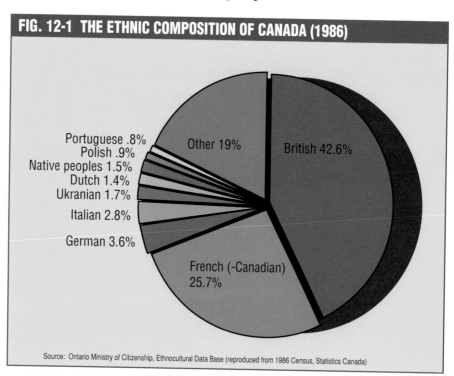

FIG. 12-1 THE ETHNIC COMPOSITION OF CANADA (1986)

Portuguese .8%
Polish .9%
Native peoples 1.5%
Dutch 1.4%
Ukranian 1.7%
Italian 2.8%
German 3.6%
Other 19%
British 42.6%
French (-Canadian) 25.7%

Source: Ontario Ministry of Citizenship, Ethnocultural Data Base (reproduced from 1986 Census, Statistics Canada)

This graph shows the ethnic composition of Canada's population. Name two other ethnic groups that would be included in "other."

Investigation 12.2

1. Starting with the gazetteer (which is a geographic index) look up in an atlas the locations of the regions, countries, and continents from which the ethnic groups listed in Figure 12-1 come. From which hemisphere, the northern or southern, do most ethnic groups come? What does this suggest to you about our ethnic customs and traditions?
2. (a) Compare the ethnic pattern in your class with the ethnic pattern for Canada. Use the ethnic groups listed in Figure 12-1. Set up your chart like this:

FIG. 12-2 ETHNIC PATTERN IN YOUR CLASS

Canadian ethnic groups	Ethnic groups in our class
British	Yes
French	Yes

(b) How does your class compare to Canada as a whole? Do you have most of, several, or only a very few of Canada's groups represented in the class? What is your largest group?

FIG. 12-3

There are many ethnic groups in Canada. These photographs show some of them. Can you identify the goups?

Now, let's look at another way of identifying ethnic and cultural groups. This way is by first language. A person's **first language** is the one that he or she first learned in childhood and still understands. For example, you might speak both English and Italian. If Italian is the language you first spoke when you were a child and you learned English later, then your first language is Italian. A person's first language, because it's strongly related to such things as culture and customs, is one indicator of ethnic characteristics. Figure 12-4 shows selected first language groups in Canada for 1941, 1961, and 1981.

FIG. 12-4 SELECTED FIRST LANGUAGES (1941, 1961, 1981)

	1941	1961	1981
Total Canadian Population	11 506 655	18 238 247	24 343 180
English	6 488 190	10 660 534	14 750 495
French	3 354 753	5 123 151	6 176 215
Chinese	33 500	49 099	224 135
Croatian, Serbian, etc.	14 863	28 866	88 230
Danish	18 776	35 035	25 695
Finnish	37 331	44 785	32 755
German	322 228	563 713	515 510
Greek	8 747	40 455	123 230
Hungarian	46 287	85 939	83 275
Icelandic	15 510	8 993	5 155
Indian and Inuktitut	130 939	166 531	140 975
Indo-Iranian	N.A.	N.A.	116 735
Italian	80 260	339 626	531 285
Japanese	22 359	17 856	19 735
Dutch	53 215	170 177	160 100
Norwegian	60 084	40 054	18 980
Polish	128 711	161 720	127 395
Portuguese	N.A.	18 213	164 615
Swedish	49 547	32 632	16 650
Ukrainian	313 273	361 496	285 115

Source: Statistics Canada

Investigation 12.3

1. (a) For each of the 3 years shown in Figure 12-4, rank the 10 largest first language groups in Canada. Draw a chart like Figure 12-5 (p. 252). English and French have been completed for you as examples.
   (b) Which groups held almost the same ranking from 1941 to 1981? Which group wasn't in the top 10 in 1941 but showed up in 1961 and rose in rank considerably from 1961 to 1981?
   (c) In your notebook, list the groups that have risen steadily in numbers from 1941 to 1981. What might the reasons be for these increases?

FIG. 12-5 THE TOP TEN FIRST LANGUAGE GROUPS

Rank	1941	1961	1981
1	English	English	English
2	French	French	French
3			

2. At this stage, let's stop and consider how a person might report herself or himself to a census taker. Angela was 18 years old in 1981. When the census taker asked about ethnic groups and first languages in her family, Angela reported that her ethnic group was Italian and her first language was English. How is this possible?

3. Note that there are decreases in numbers for some first language groups from 1941 to 1981. Which groups are they? Might the way people reported to the census taker in 1981, as compared to the way people reported in 1941 and 1961 have anything to do with these decreases? Explain your answer.

4. Write a paragraph on the 3 or 4 main ideas that you've formed about Canada's ethnic patterns.

Canada's Native Peoples

Now that you've considered the diversity of Canadians in general, let's take a closer look at Canada's **Native peoples.** You may gain some understanding of their lives, attitudes and values, and problems.

When the first European explorers arrived on the shores of eastern North America, they found people already living here. These people had come to North America approximately 27 000 years ago. Most probably starting from northern Asia, they crossed over what is now the Bering Strait between Asia and Alaska, at the time a land bridge. Then, over a period of thousands of years they migrated southward and eastward, settling most parts of North and South America. It's back to those original settlers that the present-day Native peoples trace their ethnic roots.

The total population of Native peoples in Canada is over 700 000. There are four main groups.

- Status or Registered Indians
- Non-Status Indians
- Métis
- Inuit

Status or Registered Indians are those who are registered with the Canadian government. The government grants them certain rights under the Indian Act. They may live on reserves, or land set aside for them, and they are allowed to trap and hunt on government land.

Non-status Indians are people of Indian ancestry who haven't registered or aren't qualified to register. They don't live on reserves and don't have the rights granted by the Canadian government to Status Indians.

Métis are of mixed Indian and non-Indian blood. This means one or more of their ancestors was non-Indian. Many Métis have joined with Indian associations in recent years. The Métis were officially recognized as a separate people by the Canadian government in 1984.

Inuit were formerly called Eskimos. They live mostly in the far north and form the smallest group among the Native peoples.

It has been impossible to calculate the exact numbers of people in each of these four groups. Figure 12-6 is based on government estimates.

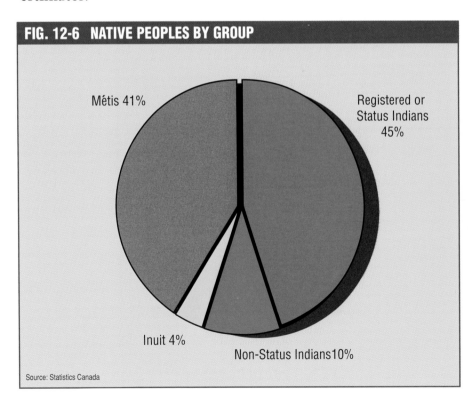

FIG. 12-6 NATIVE PEOPLES BY GROUP

Métis 41%

Registered or Status Indians 45%

Inuit 4%

Non-Status Indians 10%

Source: Statistics Canada

Investigation 12.4

1. Figure 12-7 shows the locations of Native language groups in Canada. In pairs, consult some outside reference materials to find out the status of Native languages in Canada today. Present your findings to the class.

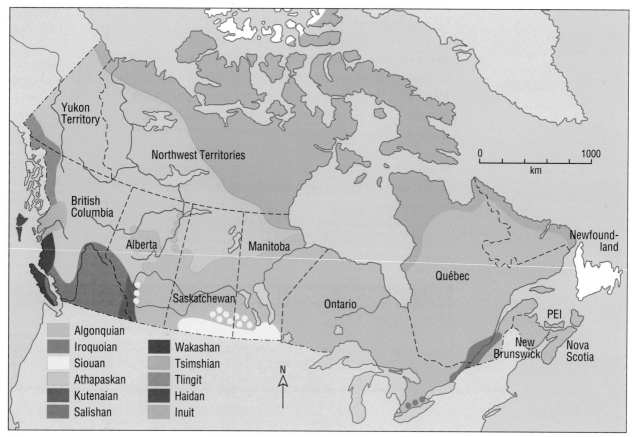

FIG. 12-7   Location of Native language groups

2. (a) Why might some Indians choose not to register and, therefore, give up certain rights? Why are some people of Indian ancestry not entitled to register as Indians?

   (b) Why might the Métis want to join Indian associations?

Now, let's look at cases of some actual people and groups who are of Indian and Métis origin.

CASE STUDY

The Regina Native Communications Centre

This centre is located in the city of Regina, the capital of Saskatchewan. Regina is in a part of Saskatchewan that has a high concentration of Native peoples. In fact, Regina itself has the highest percentage of Native persons (including Métis) of any major city in Canada.

As you saw earlier, it's difficult to count the exact number of Native persons. The low estimate in Regina for 1984 was 11 000. The high estimate was 30 000. Regina's total population was approximately 172 000.

Warren McLeod works at the Native Communications Centre in Regina. He prepares a radio show that is aired Sunday morning on 2 local stations. Warren's radio show deals with social and political concerns, provides information for Native peoples, and presents successful Native persons as role models

Warren talked a bit about being a Métis.

"I grew up in Fox Valley, Saskatchewan. It was a white German-Catholic community. I only really found out I was a Métis 2 years ago. For 18 years I thought I was a Non-status Indian; now I know I am a Métis person.

"I am still wrestling with what it means to have Native blood in my veins. I see myself as not simply a Native person nor as a Métis person, but as an individual.

"My father is Cree, Ojibway, French, and Scottish; my mother is English and Irish."

Marlyn Obey also works at the Native Communications Centre. She has travelled widely in North America and studied for a year at George Brown College in Toronto.

Marlyn talked about how well she did in elementary school on the Piapot Reserve near Regina. She found it very hard when she came to Regina at age 12. "I was very concerned about what white people thought of me.

"I had problems with teachers and counsellors. They told me to try harder, to do better, or I would have to go back to the reserve; some teachers joked about Indian people.

"Now as an adult, I know there is still prejudice but much of it is individual. It's like fruit, some people don't like some kinds of it and neither do I.

"I know the prejudice is there, but I can live with it and deal with it."

FIG. 12-8 *At the Native Business Summit, The Blackfoot Band of Alberta presented its idea for a resort on the Bow River. Many Indian bands have commercial enterprises on their reserves to create jobs.*

Investigation 12.5

1. (a) Calculate the low and high estimates of Native population as percentages of Regina's total population. Here is how the calculation can be made.

   Low estimate:

   $$\frac{11\,000}{172\,000} \times 100 = \underline{\hspace{2cm}} \%$$

   High estimate:

   $$\frac{30\,000}{172\,000} \times 100 = \underline{\hspace{2cm}} \%$$

   (b) Refer to Figure 12-1 (p. 249) and compare the 2 percentages (high and low) of Native peoples in Regina to the percentage of Native peoples for all of Canada.

   (c) Do you suppose that Native associations in Regina, such as the Native Communications Centre, are the *cause* or the *result* of the high percentage of Native peoples there? Give 3 reasons for your answer.

You learned about the Northern character of Canada in Chapter 4. Now, let's look at Inuit life in the Canadian Arctic. This story took place many years ago.

CASE STUDY

An Inuit Community

Sugluk is a small Inuit village at the extreme northern tip of Québec. (In some atlases it's spelled Saglouc.) The Inuit and their way of life over the last 30 years have changed a lot. Contact with the non-Native population to the south has been responsible for most of those changes.

The following is a brief story told by one of the older men of the Sugluk community. It is a true story.

"There were many hard times when food was scarce. Like the winter when the seals disappeared. Our supplies had been almost used up and we decided to go inland to hunt for Caribou. At last we got up over on to land. We burned the sleds to cook the dogs on as our supplies were now all gone. My brother and his wife had a little Caribou meat at their house and he brought us a few bits.

"My brother left his wife to come with us to hunt for food. My oldest sister and her husband brought us a few bits of food and then left us to go look for food. Since we had no sled we used a polar bear skin as a sled and dragged it along over the snow. Two more days and nights went by and all we had to eat was one ptarmigan [bird]. People were abandoning their own children. Mother was cutting up her own clothes to eat and the skin we were dragging was not large enough for a qaa [bedding sheet] because we were always eating it. In the end there was nothing left except the bare, flat ground!

"Then after two sleeps we saw four Caribou. My brother, who was a great hunter, would never miss the sighting of a Caribou but he was so weak from hunger he did not even notice them. We made motions like a Caribou in order to get close enough to shoot our arrows. One was wounded and the others ran away. If we had not been so weak, we would have gotten at least three of them. In the morning we were able to get two more. Although we had plenty of meat for a short time this soon ran out and we were hungry again. As we moved along we finally came to Sugluk when the snows were beginning to melt and we were not starved anymore. We stayed in Sugluk and that is where I grew up."

Source: A.C. Bennett, W.E. Flannigan, and M.P. Hladun, *Inuit Community*, Fitzhenry and Whiteside, 1972

Investigation 12.6

1. (a) What does the story tell you about the conditions of life in the Arctic in past years?
   (b) What do you think the storyteller means by saying "after two sleeps"?
   (c) Do you see any advantages to this kind of life compared to your own? If so, what are they?

FIG. 12-9

The community store is often the centre of activity in many northern communities.

FIG. 12-10   TYPES OF FOOD

Type of food	Seasonal availability	Method of getting food	Location of food
Caribou	Main hunting season — summer	Hunting	Migrating herds
Seal	Year round	Hunting	Coastal waters
Arctic hare	Winter	Hunting	Arctic region
Arctic char	Spring and summer	Fishing	Coastal waters
Mussels	Spring and summer	Gathered at low tide	Coastal waters
Clams	Spring and summer	Gathered at low tide	Coastal waters
Lake trout	Spring and summer	Fishing	Inland lakes and rivers
Sea sculpins	Spring and summer	Gathered along shore	Found along the shoreline
Seaweed	Summer	Gathered	Along shoreline
Berries	Summer	Gathered	Scattered Arctic regions

2. (a) Based on the types of food listed in Figure 12-10, in which seasons would food have been most plentiful? least plentiful?

   (b) The types of food tell a great deal about Inuit daily life. Is this an easy or difficult life compared to what you are used to? What are the things that you think you would like or dislike? For what reasons?

3. To end this study of Native peoples, read the following poem by a Native person, George Kenny. It appeared in his book of poetry and short stories, *Indians Don't Cry*.

The Bullfrogs Got Theirs (as now I do)

AS A BOY, I would go out with my friends
and spear bull-frogs.
It didn't matter if each frog might someday
be turned into a prince
by some little girl's magic capable mind,
nor did it matter if the bull frogs
had feelings to feel
our jack-knife sharpened stakes
through their hearts;
as boys will do without caring
for small animal life,
my friends and I would launch our wooden
spears, yelling
like the warriors we imagined
ourselves to be...

And as I'm older now, often I see people
with word-spears cut me down.
It doesn't matter if someday I might
become a prince
by the power of some woman's love,
nor does it matter if I
have feelings to feel
their verbal spears sharply
through my heart;
as people will act without caring
about others,
people, even now, spit their word-
spears, sneering
like the gods they imagine
themselves to be.

Reproduced with permission from *Indians Don't Cry*, by
George Kenny, published by NC Press Limited, 1982.

(a) When the poet was a boy, what did he imagine himself to be when he and his friends went out to spear bull-frogs? Why would they imagine these things?

(b) When he grew older, what kind of "spears" pierced his heart and hurt his feelings? Who do you suppose cut him down and why would they do this?

(c) What does the poem suggest about the lives of Native peoples in Canada today?

Canadian Policy: What Has the Government Done?

In this and earlier chapters you have seen that, from the very beginning, much of Canada's population came from a variety of countries around the world. Waves of immigrants came from Europe, mostly from France in the early years and then from Britain. After Confederation more immigrants arrived, especially during the first decades of this century. During these years, the Canadian government actively encouraged immigration in order to open up the west (see Fig. 5-4, p. 77). People from all parts of Europe arrived by the hundreds of thousands. After the Second World War another major wave of European immigrants arrived, made up largely of Italians, Greeks, Hungarians, and Portuguese. Immigrants from Asia, especially the Chinese, and from the Caribbean, particularly Jamaica and Trinidad-Tobago, further diversified our population.

FIG. 12-11
Many immigrants in the early part of the twentieth century came from Europe. This photo was taken at Québec City, an important entry port.

Figure 12-12 gives you some idea of where people with different cultural backgrounds have concentrated. It shows the distribution of people by first language in six major cities across the country and for Canada as a whole.

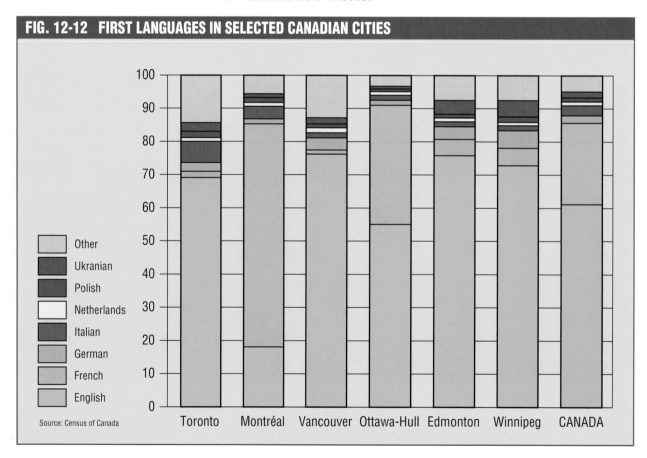

FIG. 12-12   FIRST LANGUAGES IN SELECTED CANADIAN CITIES

Legend:
- Other
- Ukranian
- Polish
- Netherlands
- Italian
- German
- French
- English

Cities: Toronto, Montréal, Vancouver, Ottawa-Hull, Edmonton, Winnipeg, CANADA

Source: Census of Canada

Investigation 12.7

(a) As you can see from Figure 12-12, English is the most widely spoken first language in all but one of the cities. Which city is the exception?

(b) State which cities have the highest percentages of people who speak each of the following languages: Ukrainian; Italian; German; Dutch (Netherlands); Polish.

Canada has a richer, more colourful society than ever before. And we have learned to live together, with all our different customs, traditions, beliefs, and languages with very little trouble and very few problems compared to many other countries. This is something about which Canadians can be proud. It hasn't happened automatically, however.

The government is aware that racial, political, cultural, and religious differences can create tension if groups get the impression that they are being treated unfairly. The government, therefore, has adopted policies to recognize the special characteristics of our ethnic and cultural groups. The policies encourage groups to continue to speak their languages and follow their customs, and to do so as loyal and responsible Canadian citizens.

Let's look briefly at two policies that show the government's intention to do something positive about Canada's diversity.

Bilingualism

French Canadians, all through their history, have been very concerned about preserving their culture. In 1963, the federal government asked a group of people to look into the well-being of the French language and culture in Canada. This group was officially called the Royal Commission on Bilingualism and Biculturalism. It took the commission eight years to do its work. Think of how many words in English have the prefix "bi" in them. Bicycle is a good example. The prefix always refers to something that has two things — a bicycle, of course, has two wheels. **Bilingualism** and **biculturalism** refer to two languages and two cultures: French and English.

The members of the B and B Commission, as it was nicknamed, made several recommendations. Here are four of the most important of them.

• Canada was to become a bilingual nation. It was to have two official languages, English and French. (This is now the case.)

- Students in all provinces were to be given a chance to study both English and French. (Some provinces agreed and did this, some did not.)
- More French Canadians were to be employed in the government. (This has been done.)
- Ontario and New Brunswick were to declare themselves officially bilingual. (New Brunswick did, Ontario didn't.)

In 1969, the government passed the Official Languages Act. It stated that English and French would be equal official languages of the Government of Canada.

Investigation 12.8

1. (a) With which recommendations of the B and B Commission do you agree? disagree? What are your reasons?
   (b) Does it seem to you that the Commission was recommending that *all* Canadians become bilingual? Do you believe that they should? What are the reasons for your answers?
   (c) Are ethnic and cultural groups other than the English and French likely to support bilingualism? Why might they? Why might they not? What groups might be more likely to support bilingualism than others? For what reasons?
   (d) Some French Canadians opposed bilingualism. What reasons can you think of for this?
   (e) What message do you think Figure 12-13 is trying to make?

Source: Produced by the Public Legal Education Society, Vancouver for the Department of the Secretary of State.

FIG. 12-13

2. Québec isn't the only province that contains considerable numbers of French Canadians. The following newspaper column shows the French-language rights was a hot issue in Manitoba in 1984. (And still is today.)

Manitoba NDP abandons bill on French rights

By Jeffrey Simpson
Globe and Mail Columnist

WINNIPEG The New Democratic Party Government of Manitoba abandoned its controversial French-language rights bill yesterday, ending a legislative session that had been brought to a standstill by opposition from provincial Conservatives.

The Government decision, taken after the Conservatives had walked out of the House for 12 consecutive sittings, probably means the issue will go to the Supreme Court of Canada.

A spokesman for the province's Francophones greeted the news that the language package was dead with chagrin.

"I'm disappointed, I'm frustrated and I'm very tired," said Leo Robert, president of Société Franco-Manitobaine, adding that he had already discussed the possibility of a direct reference of section 23 of the Manitoba Act dealing with languages going to the Supreme Court.

The Conservatives, however, were delighted that the NDP Government had been foiled in its attempt to get parliamentary approval for its French-rights package. That package would have enshrined French and English as official languages in Manitoba and provided a modest number of services for the 60 000 Franco-Manitobans, who represent about 6 per cent of the province's population.

"I think that I, along with the majority of Manitobans, heave a collective sigh of relief," Conservative House Leader Harry Enns said, dismissing concerns that the failure of the Legislature to extend French-language rights might be used by separatists in Quebec, as Premier Pawley warned.

The Tories and citizens' groups have labored intensely against the French-rights package since it was first announced by the NDP Government.

Source: Adapted from *The Globe and Mail*.

(a) What evidence do you find that Manitoba was unable to settle the issue of French-language rights?
(b) What do you think "Société Franco-Manitobaine" means? Who was its president? Why would he be tired and frustrated?

Multiculturalism

The policy of bilingualism was intended to recognize the French fact in Canada and to improve relations between our two major language groups. **Multiculturalism**, recognizing the rights and needs of many groups, is a policy of the federal government that has been designed to encourage the cultural life of all our peoples.

Investigation 12.9

Here are 2 questions relating to multiculturalism in Canada. Read them carefully and answer the following questions.

Quotation 1

The Department of the Secretary of State of Canada contributes to the development, among present and future Canadians, of a sense of belonging to the nation and encourages full participation of all groups and citizens in a society with a bilingual and multicultural character.

Quotation 2

Multiculturalism Canada is dedicated to working toward equal opportunity for all Canadians, in the economic, social, political and cultural life of Canada, with particular responsibility for those of other than French or English background.

Multiculturalism Canada does this by directly advocating changes in Canadian institutions and attitudes and by working with community organizations and interested individuals to ensure fair and equal treatment for Canadians of every cultural heritage.

Quotation 1 is taken from an annual report of the Secretary of State of Canada. Quotation 2 is taken from a booklet published by the Multiculturalism Canada division of the Secretary of State.

1. (a) What do the 2 quotations tell you about the role the Canadian government plays in the cultural life of our country?
   (b) How does Multiculturalism Canada help people?
2. Of all the major cities in Canada, Toronto is the most multicultural. Let's take a brief look at some changes that have occurred in that city. Figure 12-14 is a set of bar graphs showing Toronto's ethnic groups and how their pattern has changed over a period of 40 years.

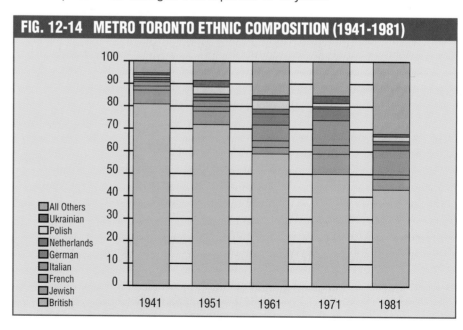

FIG. 12-14 METRO TORONTO ETHNIC COMPOSITION (1941-1981)

(a) What percentage of Toronto's population was British in 1941? in 1981? By how many percentage points did the British population decrease in 40 years?
(b) Approximately what percentage of Toronto's population was Italian in 1941?
(c) Toronto has experienced relatively few racial problems over the years. What do you think the reasons might be for this excellent record?

3. Figure 12-15 is a collection of photographs taken in Toronto.

FIG. 12-15

(a) Work with 2 partners and make a chart that lists all of the evidence in the photographs that suggests something about ethnic or cultural groups in Toronto.

(b) What evidence is there that Toronto, like the federal government, has encouraged multiculturalism among its cultural communities?

Regions

Canada, as you now know, is vast and diverse. We have seen that people in the north live in an environment that is quite unlike that found in the south; that people on the east coast make their livings in other ways than people on the Prairies; that people in big cities have different jobs from those who work in mining towns. Put simply, we don't all think the same way, and where we live has helped to form our views.

Let's look briefly at six divisions of our country and their various points of view. These divisions are called **regions**. A region is simply an area that has its own special character and can be distinguished from all other regions.

Figure 12-16 shows the main regions of Canada that have, over the years, developed different points of view from one another.

FIG. 12-16 The regions of Canada

The regions are based on a combination of physical, social, and economic characteristics.

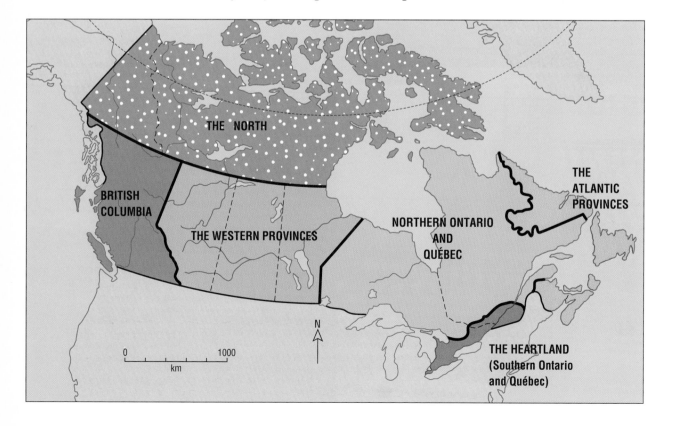

Investigation 12.10

1. Check Figure 12-16 against maps of Canada in an atlas. Draw a chart organized like Figure 12-17, in your notebook. In point form, fill in the details for each region under the proper headings.

FIG. 12-17   REGIONS OF CANADA

Region	Names of large cities	Type of land surface for most of region	Pattern of population distribution *
British Columbia			
Western Provinces			
Northern Ontario and Northern Québec			
Heartland			
Atlantic Provinces			
The North			

* See pp. 84-85 (ch. 5) to help you with this.

Having done this Investigation, you'll have a better general idea of what each region is like.

2. Let's look a little closer at the **Heartland** in particular. It contains the greatest number of people, the highest percentage of manufacturing, and the greatest number of head offices, financial institutions, and communications systems (radio, TV, magazines, etc.) in the country.

  (a) How many of Canada's 10 largest cities are located in the Heartland? (Look back to Figure 5-16, p. 88.) Which ones are they?

  (b) Why is "Heartland" a good term to describe this region?

3. Figure 12-18 (p. 268) is a collection of photographs of the 6 regions of Canada. For each region there is 1 photo. Each photograph has been numbered so that you can easily refer to it.

FIG. 12-18

Below are 12 statements about the regions of Canada. They're not in any particular order, but there are 2 statements for each region. Each statement has been given a letter so that you can easily refer to it. Read each statement carefully, keeping in mind what you already know about the regions, what you learned in earlier chapters about the economy of Canada, and what you know about Canadian diversity.

Statements

A. Farming on a big scale is a way of life that has been practised since the region opened up near the end of the last century and accepted immigrants from many parts of Europe.

B. A disappearing way of life on a vast, barren landscape.

C. Besides big cities and heavy industry, there is rich, gently rolling, attractive farmland.

D. Thousands and thousands of lakes and rivers and almost unending forests. Cottage country for many Canadians.

E. Many residents feel that the rest of Canada looks at them as people living in a beautiful landscape but one that has been tacked on to the end of the country, isolated by great distances and a barrier of great mountains.

F. Once, in the days when forests produced wood for building ships, the region was very prosperous. Today, it is off to one side of the country's centre of business and industry and relies on assistance from Ottawa.

G. Many of the people here trace their roots back to the original inhabitants of North America. They live in a harsh environment with long winters.

H. The westernmost province of this region became rich from oil resources, and its 2 major cities grew rapidly as a result. The great prosperity led to a sense of independence.

I. Approximately half of all Canadians live here—Canadians from all parts of the world. The region is split by a major difference in culture and language.

J. Most of the people are tucked into a little corner of the region. The rest live in small towns strung along valleys.

K. Mining, lumbering, and small cities and towns scattered over a huge area of low rocky hills characterize this region.

L. This is where the explorers first caught a glimpse of the New World, and where a prosperous fishing industry began.

(a) Working in groups, design a chart that matches each photograph in Figure 12-18 to Canada's 6 regions. Next, decide which two statements refer to each region. In other words, you will match one photograph to each region and two statements to each region. Remember the statements have been given a letter and the photographs are numbered so that on your chart the only words should be the names of the regions.

(b) When all the groups in the class are finished, the charts should be posted, explained, and then compared by the class as a whole. As a class, reach a consensus about the match-ups. Your teacher can confirm whether or not they are correct.

4. (a) It should now be apparent that Canada's diversity has many advantages but some disadvantages. List these in your notebook.

(b) Tension is the process of being stretched or pulled apart. When this happens feelings of stress and strain result. Working with a partner, list in your notebooks all the reasons for tension that there seem to be among Canada's regions.

Summing Up

Canada's population has much diversity because the citizens of Canada have come from many different countries. Over the years, the federal government has encouraged multiculturalism in Canada. Our cultural and physical diversity has contributed to the development of distinct regions.

CHAPTER THIRTEEN

The Miracle of Canada

MIRACLES HAPPEN RARELY. But, whether you know it or not, you are part of one.

Throughout this chapter, keep two questions in mind.

Is Canada's diversity threatening to pull it apart as a nation?

What has been done and can be done in the future to preserve Canada's unity?

These questions suggest that it hasn't been easy to keep Canada together as one country. Not only its diversity works against unity, but also its vastness, its undeveloped north, its division into provinces and territories, and, as we have seen, its regional tensions.

For over 120 years, however, the country has held together in the face of these challenges. How it has managed to do so is a long and complicated story about many struggles and even gambles against heavy odds. What it all adds up to is something so unusual, so surprising, and so remarkable that it can be called a miracle.

Unlike most miracles, however, the miracle of Canada did not just happen. Over the years, people fought hard for the idea of one nation and set up many systems and links to keep it all together. Today, there are just as many problems working to pull us apart as a nation as there were in 1867, at the time of Confederation — maybe even more. As responsible citizens, we must keep the *idea* of Canada clearly in mind and work toward promoting our unity if we are to continue as a nation.

In this chapter, you will look first at how the business world works to hold us together. Secondly, you will look at the important role that the government plays in national unity. Finally, you will consider how feelings of independence can bring Canadians together.

Our Business World: The Canadian Economy

In earlier chapters you learned much about Canada's economy —
its businesses and industries. You learned about the way the
country's economy works to produce goods and services and meet
Canada's many needs. Now it would be helpful if you surveyed
those chapters from a new point of view. This time, through the
following Investigation, concentrate on identifying ways in which
the economy works to help keep the country together — to help
create the miracle.

Investigation 13.1

1. This Investigation requires considerable research and organized,
   co-operative group effort. You should work in groups of 4. There are 3
   main sources of information that you can consult:

   - all the illustrations, maps, photographs, tables, and charts in this book
   - the written information in this chapter, especially sections that refer to
     the illustrations and help to explain them
   - sources outside this textbook, such as other books, atlases, pictures, and
     magazines that your school library or other libraries may have available.

   (a) As a group, brainstorm the following question:

      **What are the ways in which Canada's economy works to
      hold the country together?**

      Record your group's brainstorming in point form on a large sheet of
      chart paper. Be sure to keep this record for later reference.

   (b) Decide, as a group, what kinds of information you need to check out
      the points recorded in your brainstorming step.

   (c) Divide your group into 4 individual "consultants." Decide:

   - who would be good at checking out other references outside of this
     book, in the classroom and the library. This person becomes the
     "outside reference consultant."
   - who would be good at reading the maps, photographs, and the
     statistical tables in the earlier chapters of this book. This person
     becomes the "illustrations consultant."
   - who can see the main ideas in the book's text (the words) quickly and
     efficiently. This person becomes the "reading consultant."
   - who would be good at using the index and table of contents of this
     book to locate information. This person could help the other 2 who are
     working just with this book to get started. She or he becomes the
     "index consultant."

**SKILL
BUILDERS**

BRAINSTORMING

While the outside reference consultant is checking on the references, the other 3 can be doing their research. Each consultant should make brief notes of her or his findings and report them to the group. These notes can be in the form of sketches, sketch maps, charts, or other kinds of illustrations, as well as words. Remember, using words is not the only way of presenting information.

(d) The outside reference consultant should report back to the group first. She or he should direct each of the other 3 researchers to information in the outside sources to add to their findings. The outside reference consultant is now free to pair up with another consultant, depending on his or her interests, to continue the investigation.

Note: It's likely that not all researchers will finish at the same time, since some tasks take longer than others. Those who finish early should assist the others to help speed things up.

(e) When every task is completed, the group should get together, compare notes, and consider what everyone has discovered. This step can be organized as follows.

(i) Decide what points or ideas merely repeat each other and combine them into one main idea.

(ii) List all the main ideas (no particular order is necessary) on a sheet of chart paper. Be sure to include any sketch maps, charts, or other kinds of illustrations that people have made to present their ideas.

FIG. 13-1

These 4 consultants are using classroon resources to find an answer to this Investigation.

(iii) Organize the main ideas into major headings and subheadings. For example, you will probably have noted that railways have played an important part in holding Canada together. "Railways" could be a subheading under the major heading of "Transportation."

List your organized ideas clearly on a fresh sheet(s) of chart paper, ready for presentation as your group's answer to the question. Then examine the points that you recorded in your brainstorming session and compare those points to your organized main ideas.

- How close did your brainstorming come to what you found out in your investigation?
- What differences are there between the results of these 2 steps? What are the reasons for these differences?

(f) Discuss in your group what you have learned about finding answers through organized investigation or research.

(g) Choose a spokesperson to present your group's findings to the class as a whole.

(h) Under the direction of your teacher, the class as a whole should have an open discussion of the question stated in (a).

The Royal Bank of Canada

One of the largest financial institutions in the country is the Royal Bank of Canada. Figure 13-2 shows the distribution of the bank's branches across the country. As you can see, the Royal Bank forms a huge network across a vast nation. Because this institution is so widespread and because it must keep every part of the network quickly and efficiently in touch with every other part, we use it as an example or a case study to show how large companies help to bind the country together.

The following Investigation will show you how the Royal Bank's business activities help to link all parts of the country.

FIG. 13-2 THE ROYAL BANK NETWORK IN CANADA (1987)

Province	No. of branches	Province's population
Newfoundland	20	580 000
Prince Edward Island	6	128 000
Nova Scotia	83	888 000
New Brunswick	31	721 000
Québec	203	6 558 000
Ontario	621	9 273 000
Manitoba	102	1 083 000
Saskatchewan	119	1 022 000
Alberta	159	2 386 000
British Columbia	179	2 926 000
Yukon	1	24 000
Northwest Territories	3	50 000
Total	1500	25 738 000

Number of Personal Touch Banking machines   2000

Source: Royal Bank of Canada and Statistics Canada

Investigation 13.2

1. Work with a partner on this Investigation. On an outline map of Canada that shows the provinces and territories (provided by your teacher), show the distribution of the Royal Bank's branches across the country. Because there are so many of them and there is no indication in Figure 13-2 of exactly where they are, it will be impossible for you to use one dot to represent each branch. You must figure out a way, therefore, to show their distribution in a less detailed way.

2. Draw up a statistical table in your notebook organized like Figure 13-3.

FIG. 13-3 POTENTIAL CUSTOMERS PER BRANCH	
Province	**Persons per branch**
Newfoundland	
Nova Scotia	

The method for calculating how many people each Royal Bank branch could serve in each province is as follows (using Newfoundland as an example).

$$\frac{580\,000 \text{ (population)}}{20 \text{ (branches)}} = 29\,000 \text{ persons per branch}$$

This calculation tells you that for every 29 000 people in Newfoundland, there is one Royal Bank branch available for use. It does *not* mean that 29 000 people use each Royal Bank branch. There are many other banks for people to choose from.

3. When your map and statistical table are finished, analyze them to answer the following questions. (Leave out the Yukon and the Northwest Territories for these questions, since they have such small populations.)

   (i) Which province has the greatest number of Royal Bank branches? Would you describe the distribution pattern shown on your map as *even* or *uneven* across the country? What do you think is the main reason for such a distribution?

   (ii) Which 3 provinces have the highest concentration of branches? Which 3 have the lowest? Suggest some reasons why a big banking institution would concentrate its business in some parts of the country rather than in other parts. (Hint: Consider factors such as what economic activities might need bank assistance, in what places there are likely to be many banks in competition with each other, and so on.)

Now, let's meet two Royal Bank officials, Brian Deakin and Andrea Mayor (not their real names). By knowing what each of these persons does and how they communicate with each other, you can get a personal glimpse into some of the ways a banking system works in today's business world.

Brian works in the Montréal head office and is responsible for the Royal Bank's electronic banking in Canada. Andrea works in the bank's regional office in Regina, Saskatchewan, as manager of commercial and independent business marketing for the province.

Why do they communicate with each other, and how? Let's look at an example of what happens for Brian and Andrea on a typical business day.

A company in Saskatchewan gets in touch with Andrea Mayor asking her for help in handling tricky financial transactions. Andrea informs the company that the Royal Bank will design a "tailor-made" electronic money collection system for it using the bank's national network. She then gets in touch with Brian Deakin in Montréal and provides him with details about the company. Once the system is designed in Montréal, it becomes available, through computer technology, for use in Regina.

The Royal Bank system, then, through the contact between Andrea Mayor and Brian Deakin, provides the Saskatchewan company with two important things:

FIG. 13-4 *Computers haven't completely replaced the need for paper in modern offices.*

- Financial services to move the company's cash from one place in Canada to another.
- Detailed information about financial transactions such as how much money was involved, where the transaction was made, when it was made, and so on.

Investigation 13.3

1. How would the work of Brian Deakin and Andrea Mayor make the work of their customers easier and more efficient?
2. Write a short paragraph explaining how a company like the Royal Bank of Canada helps to tie the country together.

Government

There are three levels of government in Canada, as you know from studying Chapter 3. They are

- local or municipal government
- provincial government
- federal or national government

The local or **municipal government** is concerned with the running of your city or town. Its responsibilities include fire protection, parks, public transportation, schools, water and sewage, streets, law enforcement, urban planning, and so on.

The **provincial government** looks after broader matters such as industry, tourism, resources, agriculture, and education (the broad, province-wide matters).

In this chapter, the emphasis is on the **federal government** in Ottawa, so that you can get some idea of the role government plays in tying the country together — in creating the miracle.

How the Federal Government Works

How a government works is really a complicated story. Here is a simplified version of it because there is no need for a detailed study of government in this chapter.

First of all, let's examine the basic role that is played by our federal government. Figure 13-5 shows how Canada and its government work together.

FIG. 13-5

The basic role of government

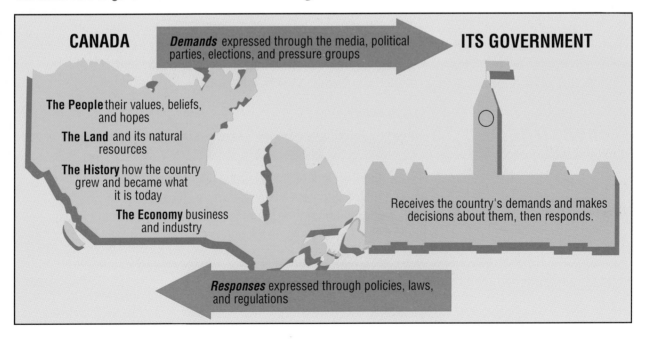

CANADA

Demands expressed through the media, political parties, elections, and pressure groups

ITS GOVERNMENT

The People their values, beliefs, and hopes

The Land and its natural resources

The History how the country grew and became what it is today

The Economy business and industry

Receives the country's demands and makes decisions about them, then responds.

Responses expressed through policies, laws, and regulations

Investigation 13.4

1. (a) Think of an issue or problem that the federal government should be made aware of. (Keep in mind the issues it deals with.)
   (b) How might each of the following be used to make the government aware of your issue?
   - the media (newspapers, television, etc.)
   - political parties (such as the New Democratic Party, the Progressive Conservatives, the Liberals)
   - elections
   - pressure groups (business groups, citizens' groups, etc., that wish to put forward their particular interests and desires)
   (c) Where do you, as just one individual, fit into all of this? How can the government be made aware of what your concern is?

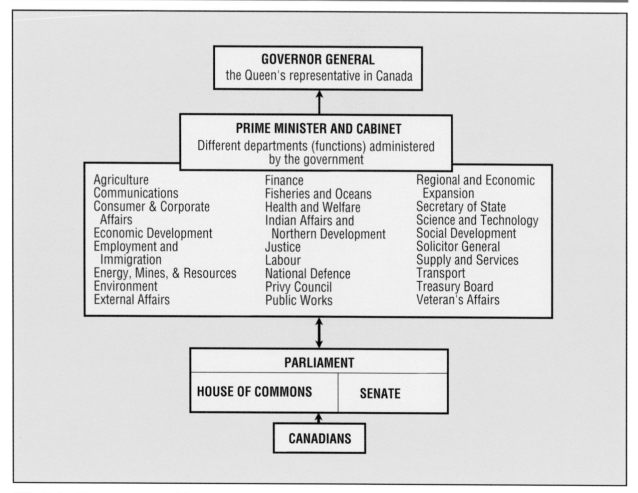

FIG. 13-6 The government of Canada

Figure 13-6 (p. 281) shows how the Canadian government is organized. Begin reading the chart from the bottom up. Canada is a democracy and in a democracy the people of the country decide, through elections, who will represent them to form their government. These elections decide who will go to Ottawa to serve in the House of Commons.

The **Parliament of Canada** is the branch of the government that passes the country's laws. It is made up of two sections or chambers: the House of Commons and the Senate.

FIG. 13-7

Canada's Parliament Buildings. They contain the House of Commons, the Senate, MPs offices, and meeting rooms.

The House of Commons has 295 elected representatives or members of Parliament (MPs) from across the entire country. The area that each represents is called a **riding**. Members of the Senate — senators — are not elected. At the time of Confederation, it was believed that a group of wealthy people in the government would be a good check on how the House of Commons runs the nation's business. Today, you don't have to be wealthy to be appointed a senator, but you must be at least 30 years old and have property worth $4000.

FIG. 13-8
Inside the House of Commons

1. Speaker
2. Clerk
3. Mace
4. Hansard Reporters
5. Sergeant-at-Arms
6. Government Benches
7. Opposition Benches
8. Prime Minister
9. Opposition Leader
10. Translation Booths
11. Press Gallery
12. Public Gallery
13. Official Gallery
14. Reserved Gallery
15. MPs' Gallery
16. Special Gallery
17. Diplomatic Gallery
18. Public Gallery
19. MPs' Gallery
20. Speaker's Gallery
21. Senate Gallery

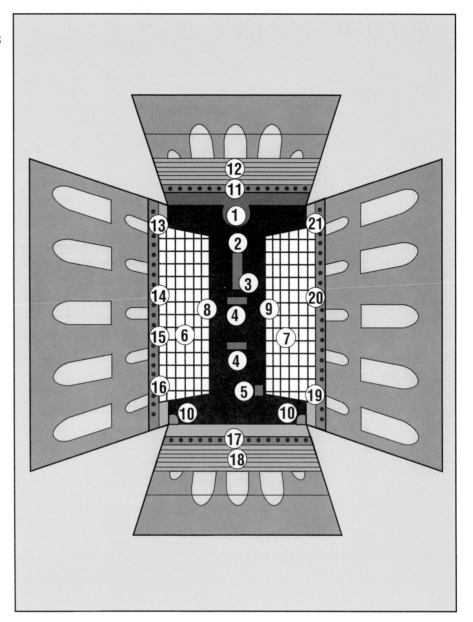

Source: National Capital Commission

The prime minister is the leader of the political party that has been elected to power and is the head of the government. The prime minister selects certain members of Parliament from his or her own political party to run the different departments of the government. Each selected member is called a minister and the department she or he runs is called a ministry. Together, this group of ministers is called the **Cabinet**. The Cabinet of Canada directly runs the affairs of the country as a whole.

Investigation 13.5

1. Work with a partner on this Investigation.
   (a) Refer to the Cabinet section of the chart in Figure 13-6 (p. 281). With the guidance of your teacher, complete a chart that states one way in which any 10 of the government ministries might play helpful roles in the country's affairs. For example, under Agriculture the role might be "organize the way wheat is sold overseas" or "provide financial help to farmers whose crops have suffered from bad weather conditions." Ideas could be used from earlier chapters to help you in this. Your chart should be organized in your notebook as follows.

FIG. 13-9   ROLES OF 10 MINISTRIES

Ministry	Role
Agriculture	
Communications	
Consumer and Corporate Affairs	

FIG. 13-10
How does the government work?

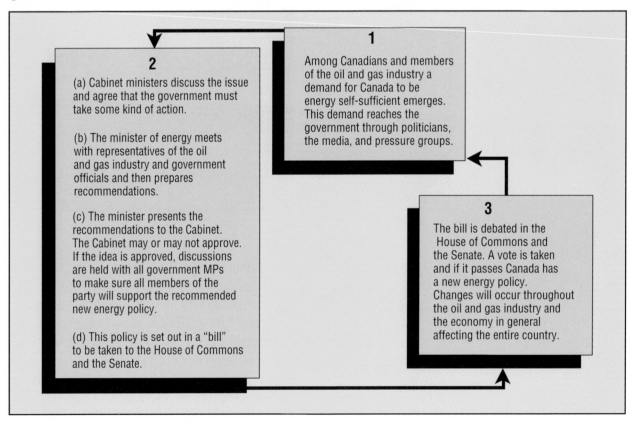

1 Among Canadians and members of the oil and gas industry a demand for Canada to be energy self-sufficient emerges. This demand reaches the government through politicians, the media, and pressure groups.

2
(a) Cabinet ministers discuss the issue and agree that the government must take some kind of action.

(b) The minister of energy meets with representatives of the oil and gas industry and government officials and then prepares recommendations.

(c) The minister presents the recommendations to the Cabinet. The Cabinet may or may not approve. If the idea is approved, discussions are held with all government MPs to make sure all members of the party will support the recommended new energy policy.

(d) This policy is set out in a "bill" to be taken to the House of Commons and the Senate.

3 The bill is debated in the House of Commons and the Senate. A vote is taken and if it passes Canada has a new energy policy. Changes will occur throughout the oil and gas industry and the economy in general affecting the entire country.

(b) Figure 13-10 demonstrates how people and businesses in Canada make the government work for them. The example used is the oil and gas industry, one of the largest industries in the country and one that greatly affects our daily lives.

(i) State 2 examples of how the oil and gas industry affects your life.

(ii) What does "self-sufficient" mean? Why is it important for a country to be as self-sufficient as possible in oil and gas?

(iii) In a big complex system such as the government, how could your individual needs and wishes be met?

(c) Consider the chart that you completed in (a) and your answers to (b). How does the federal government help to tie the nation together?

2. Most of the goods and services in Canada are produced by privately owned businesses. The government, however, plays an important role in business as well through a number of companies called **Crown corporations**. Crown corporations are owned by the government but are given a great deal of freedom to operate much like private businesses.

FIG. 13-11

Many corporations are identified by their logos. This is the CBC logo.

The following is a list of some of the best known and most important Crown corporations:

- Canadian National Railways (CNR)
- VIA Rail
- Canadian Broadcasting Corporation (CBC)
- Atomic Energy of Canada
- Petro-Canada
- Canada Post

Using references in your school library, briefly describe the role played in Canadian affairs by each Crown corporation in the above list. Be sure to emphasize how each corporation works to help keep the country together.

SKILL

BUILDERS

CARD
CATALOGUE

The Constitution Act and the Canadian Charter of Rights and Freedoms

Many democratic countries have a set of major principles, laws, and regulations that form the basis on which they are governed. These ideas form the country's **constitution**.

In Canada's case, our written constitution was signed into law in Ottawa on 17 April 1982, by Queen Elizabeth II. One section of the Constitution Act sets out the rights of Canadian citizens and is called the Canadian Charter of Rights and Freedoms. The following, which are some of the most important clauses of the Charter, promote a sense of being Canadian and a sense of togetherness among all of the nation's citizens.

Fundamental Freedoms

2. Everyone has the following fundamental freedoms: (a) freedom of conscience and religion; (b) freedom of thought, belief, opinion and expression, including freedom of the press and other media of communication; (c) freedom of peaceful assembly; and (d) freedom of association.

Democratic Rights

3. Every citizen of Canada has the right to vote in an election of members of the House of Commons or a legislative assembly and to be qualified for membership therein.

Mobility Rights

6. (1) Every citizen of Canada has the right to enter, remain in and leave Canada. (2) Every citizen of Canada and every person who has the status of a permanent resident of Canada has the right (a) to move to and take up residence in any province; and (b) to pursue the gaining of a livelihood in any province....

Legal Rights

7. Everyone has the right to life, liberty and security of the person and the right not to be deprived thereof except in accordance with the principles of fundamental justice.

8. Everyone has the right to be secure against unreasonable search or seizure.

9. Everyone has the right not to be arbitrarily detained or imprisoned....

Equality Rights

15. (1) Every individual is equal before and under the law and has the right to the equal protection and equal benefit of the law without discrimination and, in particular, without discrimination based on race, national or ethnic origin, colour, religion, sex, age or mental or physical disability....

Investigation 13.6

1. You may find some of the statements in these clauses a little hard to follow. Most of them, however, tell us clearly what our rights and freedoms are in these important matters. In your notebook, write the statements in these clauses that appear to encourage togetherness among Canadians. For each statement, explain just how it encourages togetherness.
2. Working with a partner, discuss the question: "What are the main ways in which the federal government helps to support the 'miracle of Canada' and keep it going?"

   Then write a letter to your federal member of Parliament, suggesting what the Canadian government might do, in addition to what it already does, to help promote Canadian unity.

Independence

Independence means being free to be yourself and to make your own decisions without having to depend on or be told what to do by someone else. This is true for you as a person, or even for a whole country, like Canada. Being independent doesn't mean, of course, that you're free to do absolutely anything you want. There are laws for the protection of everyone that we all must follow. But it does mean that, within those laws, you are able to decide your own future and how you are going to create it.

When you hear discussion about Canadian independence, you almost always hear about our independence in relation to one country in particular — the United States. The US is our most important trading partner, and our economy depends a great deal on its economy. Seventy-eight percent of what we export, in dollar value, goes to the US, and 70% of what we import, in value, comes from the US. Most of the time we are very friendly with the Americans. The border between our two countries is easily crossed — no passport is needed for a Canadian to enter the US and vice-versa. There is no military patrol of the border. The kind of relationship we have with the US is rarely found between two countries anywhere else in the world.

FIG. 13-12
The bridge at the St. Stephen, New Brunswick, and Calais, Maine, border

There are certain facts, however, regarding the differences between our neighbour and ourselves, that we can't ignore when we think of Canadian independence. Consider the enormous difference between Canada and the US in population. The US has about ten times more people than does Canada. Former prime minister Pierre Trudeau once said to the Americans:

> Living next to you is in some ways like sleeping with an elephant: no matter how friendly and even-tempered is the beast, if I may call it that, one is affected by every twitch and grunt. Even a friendly nuzzling can lead to frightening consequences.

Investigation 13.7

1. Draw a cartoon or a picture to show the great difference between Canada and the US in population and in economic and military strength. You might wish to use Mr. Trudeau's image to start with. Or you may wish to invent one that is completely your own.

FIG. 13-13
Was this cartoonist for or against free trade with the United States?

The idea of free trade between Canada and the US was hotly debated in the late 1980s. The idea was not new, however, as it has been considered a number of times throughout our history. **Free trade** means that products can be exported from one country to another without **tariffs** (taxes) being added by the importing country to the costs of the products. The 1988 federal election was based on this issue. In the end, the Progressive Conservative party under Prime Minister Brian Mulroney won the election and almost immediately finalized a free trade agreement with the Americans. Figure 13-14 presents some of the more important arguments for and against free trade that were presented during the free trade debate.

FIG. 13-14 SOME CANADIAN ARGUMENTS FOR AND AGAINST FREE TRADE	
For free trade	**Against free trade**
Canadian businesses would be able to sell their products tariff-free (therefore at lower prices) to the largest and richest market in the world.	American businesses would be able to sell their products tariff-free in Canada and would create too much competition for Canadian businesses.
The Canadian and the US economy would be even more closely tied together. As a result, Canada would get more advantages than it does now from American growth and development	Being closely tied to the United States is not necessarily good for Canada. If the US has problems, those problems will be felt in Canada even more than they are now.
Many countries are forming trading blocs. If Canada does not join a trading bloc, it will be left out of the global economy.	If the US gets more control over Canadian resources and businesses (and it has enormous control over some of them already), then it could reduce the ability of Canadians to make decisions about their own economy. Canadian social programs would be "down sized" to make us more competitive in the US.

Investigation 13.8

1. Discuss these 2 questions with a partner.
   (a) What are your feelings about the arguments in Figure 13-14 (p. 289)?
   (b) Do you think Canada's independence will suffer if it is more closely tied to the US? Give reasons for your opinion.

2. Canadians can be proud of Canada's colourful history, its ability to grow and stay together as an independent nation, its richly multicultural society, its high standard of living and its great natural beauty. As you've seen, however, it's in some ways an "underdog" in its relationship to the US.
   (a) What is an "underdog"? How does being the underdog lead to stronger ties among teammates in sports and help to develop team spirit and unity?
   (b) In what ways would the "underdog" relationship with the US stimulate feelings of independence among Canadians? How might such feelings of independence help to strengthen our feelings of togetherness as a nation?
   (c) "Canadians are the same as Americans. They play American sports, watch American TV shows, and read American magazines and books."

   How do you feel about this quotation? Do you agree or disagree with it? For what reasons?

Summing Up

At the beginning of this chapter we asked you to keep two questions in mind.

Is Canada's diversity threatening to pull it apart as a nation?

What has been done and can be done in the future to preserve Canada's unity?

In Investigation 13.9, you will reconsider these matters. This time in the light of the ideas that you have encountered and the knowledge you have gained by studying this chapter.

Investigation 13.9

1. Work in groups of 4 for this Investigation.
   (a) Skim this book and make a point-form list of
       (i)   those things that tend to pull Canada apart or destroy its unity
       (ii) those things that tend to reduce Canada's independence as a nation
       (iii) those things that help to unify the country
       (iv) those things that could be done to help unify the country.
   (b) At the beginning of this chapter, we made the statement that Canada's development is "so unusual, so surprising, and so remarkable that it can be called a miracle." Do you now agree with this statement? Give reasons for your opinion.

CHAPTER FOURTEEN

Forming an Image of the World

Y OU HAVE LEARNED THAT Canada is a large, diverse and complex country. The world, which is made up of many different countries, is of course, much more so. Nevertheless, just as you did for Canada, you can build some mental images of the world that will help you understand it better.

Let's begin by making some connections between you and your community and the rest of the world. In Chapter 3, you did the **Connections** Investigation that helped you see links between different parts of Canada. Here you'll try a similar Investigation. It's best to work on this task in groups.

Investigation 14.1

Step 1 Collecting the Information

Each person in the class needs to collect information from his or her household.
(a) As a class, design a chart so that you can record information about
  (i)   the location of friends and relatives in the rest of the world;
  (ii) names of places people in your immediate family have visited;
  (iii) the number of things in your home that you can identify as made in another country (e.g., Japan — 1 car, 1 stereo, 2 radios = 4).

You should set up the chart so that people, places, and things can be separated and counted. Copy the chart so that everyone collects the data in the same way.

(b) When all the data is collected, cut the charts up so that separate groups can work on different countries. Each group should tally the people, places, and things that are connected to each of their countries.

(c) Use coloured yarn to show the linkages between Canada and other countries. People, places, and things should be shown by different colours. Figure out the number of pieces of yarn you need for each country by using this scale:

> 1-5 connections of people, places, or things = 1 strand
> 6-10 connections = 2 strands
> 11-15 connections = 3 strands

and so on.

Step 2   Making the Map

(a) Using an overhead projector, trace a large world map onto a piece of chart paper. Make sure the boundaries of each country you identified in Step 1 are neatly drawn. The scale should be clearly marked.

(b) Label each country that has been included in your data and mark its capital city.

(c) Label major oceans, seas, and inland bodies of water.

Step 3   Making the Connections

(a) Make a chart that lists all the countries your class had connections to in Step 1. Also add these headings: ***Number of Strands of Yarn, Colour of Yarn, Length of Yarn Needed***.

(b) Using a metre stick, measure the distance on your map from Ottawa, the capital of Canada, to the capital city of each of the countries on your list. Carefully record the distance on your chart.

(c) As your chart is being completed, other members of your group can begin cutting yarn to the needed lengths. Be sure to put labels on each strand or you'll become confused and have to start over again.

(d) Use pins to put your yarn in place on the map.

Step 4   Studying the Connections

(a) In sentence form, describe the pattern made by each colour.

(b) For each of the 3 categories, list parts of the world to which your class is closely connected.

(c) List areas of the world to which your class is not closely connected.

(d) Suggest some factors that influence the connections people have to other parts of the world.

Forming Images

People living outside of Canada often view our land as very cold and difficult to live in. While those impressions are true for some parts of the country, they don't give an accurate image of Canada as a whole. But Canadians probably have correspondingly incorrect images of other countries. Unless you've lived in a country or visited it often, you can't know it very well.

Why do we have these inaccurate views? To answer this question we must ask another, from what do we get our impressions of other parts of the world? For the most part, they come from TV, radio, newspapers, magazines, and from talking to other people.

When do we hear about other countries? Usually we hear about them when something goes wrong, such as riots, wars, earthquakes, floods, drought, or starvation. These are all negative events that give a one-sided impression of any country.

We also learn about other countries when we are planning our vacations. We read travel brochures that describe the places we want to visit. These, too, give a one-sided view of any country, though this time the view is positive. The following description (p. 296) might be what you would find in a travel brochure.

This description is honest because everything the writer describes exists. However, it isn't complete — because it doesn't show any negative aspects of the place. It isn't balanced. Don't disbelieve everything that you read, but do be cautious or critical. Everything is written with a purpose.

Investigation 14.2

Read the travel brochure on page 296 and then answer Question 1.
1. (a) What is the purpose of the brochure on Oiratno?
   (b) List 3 words or phrases in the description that are facts.
   (c) Now, list 3 other words or phrases that are opinions (Opinions are statements that cannot be proven to be true or false.)
   (d) Why are there no negative comments in the description?
2. Use the knowledge you gained while studying the travel brochure to help you with the following.
   (a) Write 2 descriptions of your home, each between 25 and 50 words in length. The descriptions are for the following purposes:

   Description 1: The house or apartment is going to be sold or rented. You're in charge of writing an advertisement for it. You want to make your home sound as appealing as possible so that many people will be interested in it.

Oiratno

A D A N A C ' S   W O N D E R L A N D

The enchanted land of Oiratno awaits your visit! This lovely province has a huge variation in climate, from its sunny south with gorgeous beaches, marvellous cities, theme parks, and conservation areas, to its vast northern wilderness of untouched forests and lakes.

In the south, expressways, rapid transit and wonderfully inexpensive hotels make travel from the miracle of Aragain Falls to the capital city of Otnorot, located on the north shore of Lake Oiratno, to the Adanac's capital of Awatto, a mere flick of an eyelash.

In the north, private helicopters and planes will zoom you to beautiful, clear lakes and uninhabited forests to hunt and fish to your heart's delight. For surprisingly low rates, guides and equipment, for short and extended trips, can be arranged.

The people of Oiratno will welcome you with open arms. They will share their highways, their beaches, their hotels, and their wonderful parks, and will treat you as a guest in their homes. Gasoline prices are quite reasonable; there is a modest sales tax on the goods you will want to take back home with you.

Special rates are available from September to May. Call now and enquire about Oiratno's wonderful vacation packages.
They are unequalled anywhere in Adanac!

Description 2: The government is giving special grants of money to people to make repairs or additions to their homes. You want to apply for a grant. Write a description that will make officials agree that you should get some of the money.

When you are finished, read your descriptions over carefully. Then, revise and prepare final versions.

(b) Share your final versions with a classmate. Have the classmate list all the positive features in Description 1 and all the negative features in Description 2. Are there parts of the house or apartment that are mentioned in both descriptions?

The two descriptions you wrote in Investigation 14.2 are different because you selected only one point of view in each description. If you had put them together, you would have had a more balanced description of your home. You should always remember that what is *not* said or written is often just as important as what is. This is true whether you are talking about advertising or about news reports.

Let's apply what you have learned to news reports and see how they influence the views we have of other countries.

There is so much happening every day in the world that the journalists must choose what they're going to cover. Editors decide what stories and pictures to use and what to leave out. Reporters and editors usually make their choices based on what they think people are most interested in, as well as what important events are happening. Unfortunately, much of the news that is chosen is "bad news." As a result, your information about other countries from the news media is often influenced by the negative views. Look at the headlines on page 298.

The impressions that you get from the headlines are all negative. They are honest in that turmoil, drought, and starvation exist in Africa. However, they are misleading because these events aren't taking place all over Africa. You have to remember that Africa is a larger continent than North America and that it is made up of 48 separate countries. Africa is often written about as if it were one large country that is the same all over. But Africa has great variety in its peoples, climate, wealth, and technology.

Travel brochures tend to give positive reports of places, while news stories often highlight negative situations. When you study the geography of a continent or a country you want to find out what the place is really like. You want a balanced view. Let's see if you can establish one for Africa.

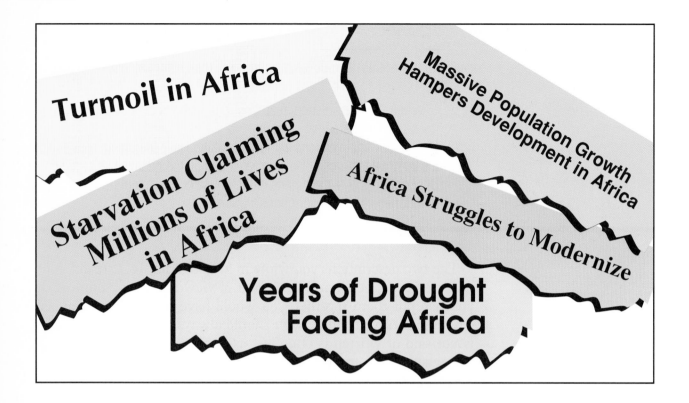

Investigation 14.3

1. (a) Work with a classmate. Each of you take one set of photographs (p. 299) and write a paragraph describing the way of life that you can see in the photographs. Describe the tools, animals, and other items that help show how the people live. You can include opinions as well as facts in your paragraph.

   (b) Exchange your paragraph with your partner. Check to see that each of you agrees with what the other has written. Make any changes you think are necessary after your partner has commented on your paragraph.

   (c) Now, with your partner, write a balanced description about the 2 sets of pictures. Use information from all 6 pictures in your paragraph.

Set A

Set B

FIG. 14-2

You've seen that advertisements and news stories help shape your image of other countries. You've also seen that the ideas created by both these sources are often not balanced ones. Let's look at some other factors that affect the images that are created.

- In some countries, political parties, the military, or a dictator control the media, and they decide what news gets reported.
- Sponsors or advertisers may not want certain facts made public. They might hide this information from the media and the public.
- Powerful countries such as the USSR and the US can put economic or other pressures on sources of information. They do this to influence the images in people's minds.

So, you might say, "How do you ever know that something is the truth?" The answer is simple — in any reporting of events, there is no *simple* truth! For all the reasons we have discussed, any report represents someone's image of what he or she saw or recorded at one point. Sometimes, as in travel descriptions, it's easy to detect bias. **Bias** is a deliberate attempt to give only one side of the picture. In other cases, bias is much harder to spot. That is why you should always consider carefully what you read or hear.

Investigation 14.4

SKILL BUILDERS

BRAINSTORMING

1. A few years ago, the Americans sent a spacecraft out beyond our solar system. On board it had a video disc with pictures of earth—the landscape, human activities, and so on. It was sent so that if any other life form found it, it would have images of our planet.
   (a) As a member of a project team, it is your task to select one theme and collect pictures of the earth that illustrate your theme. Possible themes are
      - the earth's cities
      - how people on earth make a living
      - people who live on earth
   (b) Brainstorm all the kinds of pictures you could use to give a range of images about your theme.
   (c) Carefully evaluate your list and narrow it down to 10 ideas.
   (d) Cut pictures from newspapers and magazines to show the 10 ideas you have decided on.
   (e) Write a tapescript titled ***Why These 10 Pictures Give a Balanced Image of the World***. Be sure to defend your choice of pictures.
   (f) Use your pictures and diagrams to create a collage on poster paper, using words and titles where necessary.

Mapping the Earth

Now that you have an idea how images of the world are created, you can make maps of the world. Figure 14-3 shows a map of the world you are probably familiar with. Notice that the land and water areas are not evenly shaped or evenly spread over the surface of the planet. This makes it difficult to set an image in your mind about what the world really looks like. The following activity will help you get an image of the shape and size of the earth.

FIG. 14-3

This is a typical world map. It shows the Mercator projection. In North America, we most often see world maps with North and South America on the left and Asia on the right.

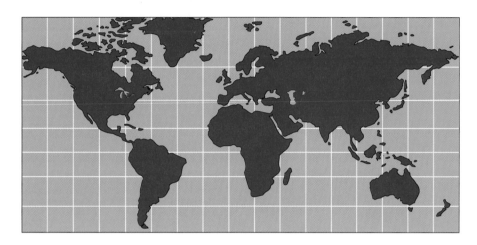

Investigation 14.5

In this activity, you will make and analyze a map of the world.
1. (a) Cut the following shapes out of white, unlined paper.
   - a 11 cm x 5 cm rectangle
   - a 4 cm x 6 cm rectangle
   - a 3 cm x 3 cm square
   - a 6 cm x 10 cm x 10 cm triangle
   - a 4 cm x 9 cm x 9 cm triangle
   (b) Colour each shape a different colour.
   (c) Compare the shapes you have cut out to the world map in Figure 14-3. Identify each shape by lightly pencilling one of the following names on the back:
   - Eurasia (Europe and Asia)
   - South America
   - North America
   - Australia
   - Africa

2. (a) Draw the equator and prime meridian on a blank sheet of paper so that the paper looks like Figure 14-4.

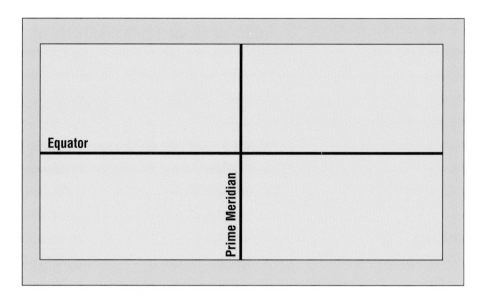

Equator

Prime Meridian

FIG. 14-4

(b) Arrange the continents you have cut out in the correct position on the sheet of paper. When they are all in the proper position, glue them down. Label the continents and oceans.
(c) Draw the line that separates Canada from the US. Label Canada.
(d) Sketch in the boundaries of a country in the world with which you have family ties or in which you are interested. Label that country.
3. (a) List the continents in size from largest to smallest.
(b) Estimate the size of the oceans, and list them from largest to smallest. Check your estimates using an atlas.
(c) List the continents that are located mostly in the Northern Hemisphere. List those that are mostly in the Southern Hemisphere.

Map Projections

It's impossible to make maps that accurately show the whole world. All world maps have some error because of the problem of flattening a globe to make it into a flat map. Imagine that you have a tennis ball or a tangerine and you try to make it lie as flat as a piece of paper. What would you have to do to get it as flat as possible?

Any change that results from trying to flatten a globe onto a piece of paper means that the map will have to have some feature that is different from the way the globe really is. Map makers try to make the errors as small as possible.

How a map is adjusted to reduce the errors depends on what the map is suppose to show. Sometimes it's more important to keep distances accurate. Other times, shapes of continents must be correct. The different ways of drawing the round earth on a flat piece of paper are called **map projections**. The use of a map will help you decide which projection is the best one to use.

Maps usually are drawn according to surface areas. The greater the area of a continent or body of water, the larger it appears on the map. But there are other ways of making maps. For example, you could make a map that is based on the number of people in a country, rather than the area of the country. On this kind of map, the size of the country would represent the number of people in the country. This is called an **isodemographic map**.

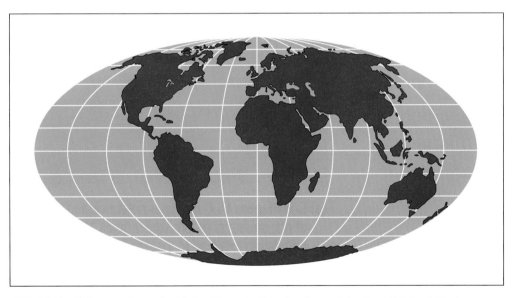

FIG. 14-5 *This map shows the Mollweide projection. It reduces distortion at higher latitudes.*

Investigation 14.6

1. (a) Carefully study the maps in Figures 14-3 (p. 301) and 14-5 (p. 303) by
   (i)   identifying the width and shape of Greenland on both maps;
   (ii) identifying the space covered by the entire Atlantic Ocean on both maps;
   (iii) measuring the width of Africa on each map.
   (b) Draw conclusions about how the maps are different.
   (c) Compare the 2 maps to a globe. Which one is the more accurate way to show the earth? Why is this method not used all the time?

Investigation 14.7

1. Let's make a simple isodemographic map of the world using population data on the continents. You'll need graph paper, scissors, paste, and paper.

FIG. 14-6 THE POPULATION OF THE CONTINENTS (1987)		
Continent	**Population in millions**	**Number of squares**
Africa	601	600 ÷ 10 = 60
Asia	2985	
Australia	25	
Europe	680	
North America	407	
South America	277	

(a) Copy Figure 14-6 into your notebook and then complete it. Use a scale of one square of graph paper equals 10 million people. Round the population totals off to the nearest 10 million. The first continent, Africa, has been done for you.

(b) Using the graph paper, count out the number of squares that you need for each continent and then cut them out in the rough shape of the continents.

(c) Plan your map on a large sheet of paper. Place your continent shapes in their approximate places on the map. Decide where the title, legend, and scale should go on your map.

(d) Complete the map by gluing down the pieces, shading the squares on the map, and lettering the title, legend, and scale.

(e) Write a paragraph of 4 or 5 sentences to someone who has never seen an isodemographic map, beginning with: "You would really be surprised if you saw a map of the world based on population instead of land shape!"

Summing Up

In this chapter you considered sources of information that people use to form images about other parts of the world. Often our images are distorted or inaccurate because we don't have a balanced view of places. The problems of mapping the earth also make it difficult to form an accurate image of its varied geography. Flat maps can't be drawn of the round earth without some distortion. To truly understand the world, therefore, you must seek as much knowledge about it as possible.

CHAPTER FIFTEEN

Understanding Global Problems

IN OTHER PARTS OF THIS BOOK you have read about the way people live in Canada. Finding a satisfying job, travelling for enjoyment, and living comfortably are some of the goals that everyone strives for. Most of the people in Europe, Japan, Australia, New Zealand, and the US are trying to achieve similar goals. These are the wealthiest parts of the world, with the highest standards of living.

For many people in other parts of the world, however, more basic needs take priority. Food, shelter, and a peaceful existence are the most urgent matters in these less-developed countries.

In this chapter, you will look at some of the more important global problems — the need for food and water and the need for environmental security.

Food and Water

Good food and water are crucial to a high quality of life. Here is something to think about. Suppose your class decided to try an experiment on the quality of food and water. All you may eat each day is two bowls of rice — plain, ordinary white rice with nothing added. All you can drink is water dipped out of a stream near your school. You have to record how you feel at the end of each day. Let's start. How do you feel at the end of the first day? second day? (Remember now, you may eat only rice. Stay away from chocolate bars and the french fries in the cafeteria.) How do you feel at the end of a week? Maybe in your records you have included something about the amount of energy you have, and how much you enjoy all your activities.

Here it is a year later. How is it going? Has life been good to you? Have you got everything done you wanted to do? How do you think you will feel after another year? after 10 more years?

Obviously it wouldn't be wise to try an experiment like this. Your health could easily be hurt by the dirty water and the unbalanced diet. But can you imagine how people who have lived on poor food and water all their lives feel? Think about the amount of energy it must take them to do the things you take for granted. Think about how they must feel about their lives and their futures. A properly balanced diet and clean fresh water are important if people are to meet the challenges of day-to-day life.

The energy you get from food is measured in **kilojoules**. The number of kilojoules per person in a country is a good indicator of the amount and quality of food its people have. Figure 15-1 shows the daily food intake in kilojoules for every country. The average teenager requires 9020-11 480 kilojoules per day.

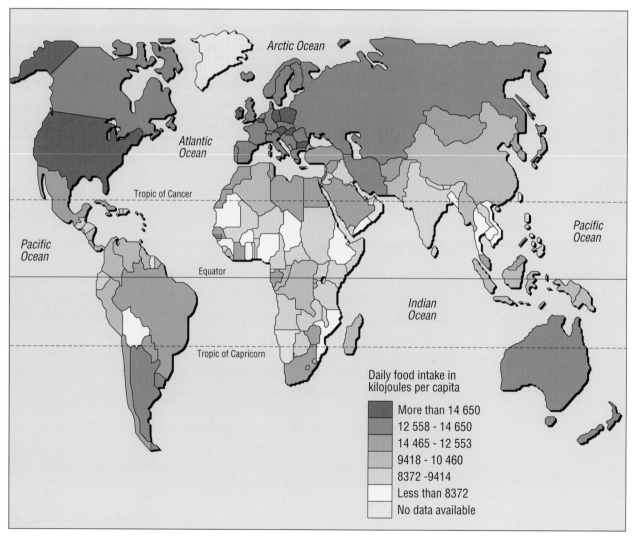

FIG. 15-1   World Kilojoule Supply

Investigation 15.1

1. (a) Using other resources, such as an atlas, find and list the 7 most populated countries. Beside each country in your list, record its kilojoule supply. What observations can you make from your list?
   (b) Which continents have the lowest kilojoule supply?
   (c) From your study in other subjects, explain why kilojoule supply alone isn't necessarily an accurate indicator of good or poor nutrition.

Poor nutrition and starvation are two of the world's most serious problems. Poor nutrition means that people don't have a healthy, well-balanced diet. It's a problem throughout the world, even in countries like Canada and the US where there is an excess of food. Starvation, however, is a problem in countries where people can't get enough food, not even of poor quality.

Why are people starving in the world when some countries have tonnes of food that are going to waste? Why is it so difficult to reduce the amount of hunger and starvation in the world? As with most difficult questions, the answers aren't easy to find. They're hidden in a combination of many factors. Here are some of the reasons.

Agricultural potential   The world's food supply is dependent on many factors. In areas where the ability to produce crops is poor, people won't be able to harvest food for themselves or their animals. Plant growth may be limited by temperature, rainfall, length of growing season, thickness of soil, and the lack of nutrients and minerals in the soil. In addition, misuse can make even the best soil useless over time.

Capital   With enough money (capital) and technology, deserts can be made very fertile and lands formerly under water can be drained and used for agriculture.

Money, or the lack of it, influences the amount of food people can buy. Even in countries that are poor, having money usually means that you can get enough to eat. Sometimes poor people in wealthy countries face starvation simply because they haven't enough money to buy the food that is available. The need for food banks in Canadian cities shows this is happening in Canada.

FIG. 15-2
Even wealthy countries, like Canada, have people who can't afford food. Many cities have food banks to provide basic foods.

Transportation and distribution   Food may be grown in large quantities in some parts of the world. In fact, there may be a surplus of food in one place, while elsewhere, people may be starving. **Transportation systems** are needed to get the food to the areas that need it. **Distribution systems** are needed to make sure the food gets to the hungry people. Many poor countries don't have any systems, or have inadequate systems, for moving food.

Technology   Technology refers to the skills and machines we use to make things. For example, some people use agricultural technologies such as fertilizers, pesticides, and machinery to produce more food. Without these resources, the amount of food grown from a piece of land would be smaller. Adopting new technologies tends to be expensive, however.

Pollution and erosion   Many parts of Europe and North America that used to be fertile have now been damaged by careless use. Industrial pollutants have drained into creeks and ground water and contaminated the soil. Improper working of the land has allowed erosion to take place. This causes soils to wash away into streams and rivers.

Rapid population growth   Places where enough food once grew to feed all the people can no longer produce enough because the population has increased faster than food supplies. There are more mouths to feed and so food doesn't go as far as it did.

Because Canada is so large and we have a relatively small population in world terms, this is a difficult situation for us to imagine.

Growth of cities onto farmland   One result of rapid population growth is the loss of farmland. Cities grow and expand outward onto farmland. Land that has houses and factories built on it obviously can't produce food.

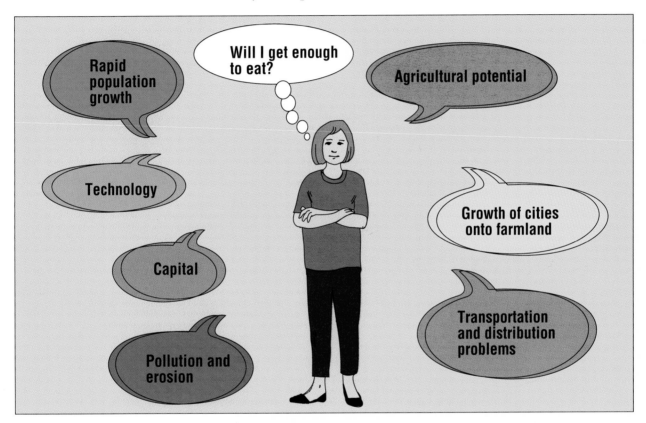

FIG. 15-3

All these factors influence the food supply.

Each one of the factors in Figure 15-3 could, of course, be dealt with in some way so as to produce more food. For example, dry regions could be irrigated and better systems might be devised for distributing food. New types of crops could be planted, better machinery could be bought, or food could be imported. Yet, often none of these things are done. Why?

There are many sides to this difficult problem. It may be that people don't have enough money to buy the things they need, like fertilizers, seeds, and tractors. It may be that governments in some poorer countries can't afford new or better technology. It may also be that people don't want to change or don't understand how new ways will help them. Food shortages and starvation are serious and difficult problems that no one has yet solved.

Investigation 15.2

1. What factors make Canada a "have" nation in terms of food production? (Hint: Look back at the section "Rich," pp. 63-67.)
2. (a) Suggest 2 ways that the Canadian government might help to reduce the amount of starvation in the world.
   (b) What problems might each of your solutions create?
3. There are a number of groups or agencies in Canada that try to help undernourished people. Using newspapers and magazines, find out the names of 3 of these groups. In what ways do they try to help starving people?

Water is essential for all life. Fortunately, Canada is very well supplied with drinkable water. However, many parts of the world don't get enough water to support all the people who live there, or their crops and animals. India has one of the largest populations in the world, and yet it is poorly supplied with fresh water. Many parts of Africa have similar conditions.

Some other parts of the world get adequate amounts of moisture and have large rivers. However, these areas are often centres of population and industry, and water supplies are becoming dangerously polluted. Some parts of Europe, Canada, and the US fall into this category. Still other areas get enough rainfall, but don't support many people because the environment is too difficult to live in. In these cases, large amounts of fresh water aren't being used.

Water is necessary for life, but it can, in fact, carry harmful diseases and pests and lower the quality of human life. When bacteria and micro-organisms which live in the water are transmitted to people, they can cause illnesses, blindness, and even death. In warm climates, these pests grow particularly quickly and are hard to control. Sometimes chemicals are added to the water in an attempt to kill them. However, these chemicals also hurt humans.

In order to live well, people must get enough nutritious food and drinkable water to meet and maybe surpass their survival needs.

Investigation 15.3

SKILL
BUILDERS
GRAPHING

1. Figure 15-4 shows the percentage of people in the developing parts of the world that can get safe water. Get an outline map of the world from your teacher. Draw a small pie graph on each part of the world to show this information. In a couple of sentences, compare your map to a map showing world population distribution.

FIG. 15-4 PERCENTAGE OF PEOPLE WITH ACCESS TO SAFE WATER	
Africa (south of the Sahara)	21
North Africa	55
Eastern Mediterranean	33
Southeast Asia (including India)	17
Western Pacific (including China)	40
South and Central America	54

SKILL

BUILDERS

GRAPHING

2. In addition to the water we drink and use to prepare meals, we use fresh water for other purposes.
   (a) Create a bar graph, using Figure 15-5, to show water use in Canada.

FIG. 15-5 WATER USE IN CANADA	
Use	**Water used/day**
Take a bath	90 L
Do the laundry	90 L
Wash dishes	45 L
Flush a toilet	25 L
Total domestic use/person	225 L
Total all uses (domestic, industrial, municipal)/person	560 L

   (b) Suppose your community was facing a serious water shortage. Suggest 5 ways you might reduce your use of water.

Environmental Security

While having good food and water is essential for a high quality of life, people also need an environment where they feel secure. Most people are comfortable with the physical environment in their part of the world. A person raised on a farm near Lethbridge, Alberta, for instance, is accustomed to the landscape and climate of the Prairies. Likewise, a person of the Yanomami tribe is comfortable and confident in the rain forest of the Amazon basin. People usually don't feel threatened by an environment that is familiar and predictable.

On the other hand, hazards in our environment that we can't predict can be very worrisome and can cause much stress. If we have no means to prevent damage that might occur, we are at the mercy of the environment. Floods, earthquakes, and volcanoes are examples of natural events that happen quickly and disrupt the security of our environment. Let's look at each of these to see their impact on people.

Floods

Floods occur when water overflows its normal channels and covers the land. It's the suddenness of floods that leads to death and damage. People simply haven't time to get themselves or their belongings to a safe area.

Fast-flowing flood waters also wash away vegetation and soils and destroy crops. Buildings, roads, and telephone and power lines may be damaged. Water supplies can become polluted and regular activities and services may be seriously disrupted. It often takes days or weeks for things to return to normal.

In North America, most floods are caused by spring flooding or hurricanes. In the spring, heavy rains combine with melting snow to overload streams. Hurricanes, which occur from June to December, produce huge waves that cause flooding in coastal areas. In other parts of the world, **monsoons** (winds blowing constantly from one direction) crossing oceans bring large quantities of moisture and dump it on the land. Low-lying areas, such as flat river valleys and deltas at the mouths of rivers, are most heavily damaged.

FIG. 15-6

This aerial photograph shows Dhaka, the capital of Bangladesh, after 10 days of flooding in September 1988. Seventy-five percent of the country was flooded. (The article on page 317 tells you more about flooding in Bangladesh.)

Factors other than the total amount of rainfall cause floods to occur. A large quantity of rain spread over a few days may not present any threat of flooding at all. But, if the same amount of rain falls in an hour, the results will be disastrous.

Secondly, the conditions in the area before the rain must be considered. Excessively wet soil can lead to flooding because the moisture that falls during a heavy thunderstorm runs off, without soaking into the ground. Or, when streams are already high because of melting snow or are blocked with ice jams, even a small amount of precipitation can be too much and cause flooding.

People who live in river valleys are most affected by floods. In many parts of the world, dams and dykes have been built in an effort to control river floods. The dams are used to slow down water run-off by providing storage areas. Dykes help keep the water within a smaller flood area.

Stations that record water levels are often set up along rivers in highly populated areas. Based on these measurements, officials predict when a flood will be at its worst. This peak occurs at different times along a river as the flood waters move downstream. Being able to predict when the flood will occur and when it will peak helps people to deal with the problem of floods.

However, many parts of the world don't have these warning systems. Therefore, the people don't know when the water will stop rising or how high it is likely to get. For these people, floods reduce their chances of a high quality of life.

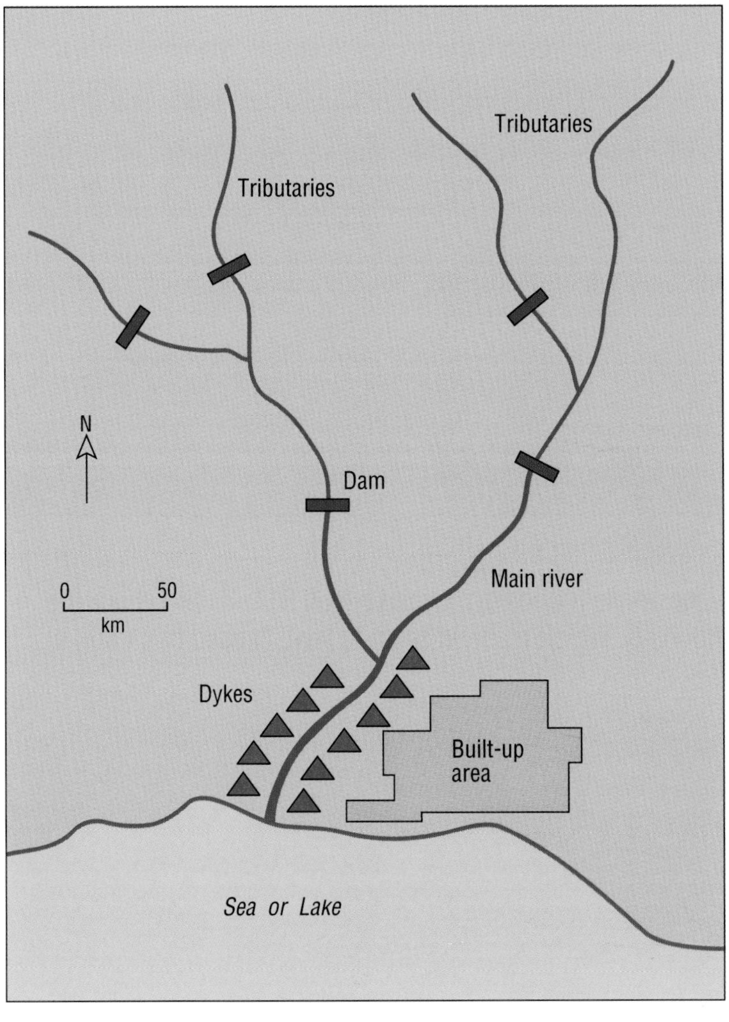

FIG. 15-7

Dams and dykes help to control floods on rivers. Why is it important to protect built-up areas?

Investigation 15.4

1. Besides building dams and dykes, suggest some way people can protect themselves from floods.
2. For the last 6000 years, Egyptians have used the floods of the Nile River to help them produce food. The flood waters bring moisture and a new layer of fertile silt to the lands along the river. Using Figure 15-8, determine the months during which flooding would occur, and the times when farmers could plant their crops.

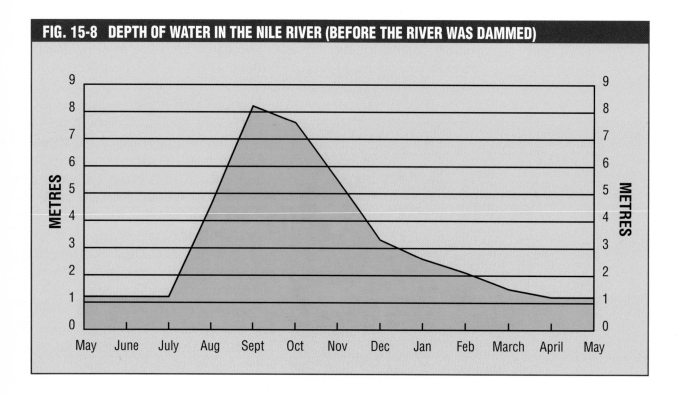

FIG. 15-8 DEPTH OF WATER IN THE NILE RIVER (BEFORE THE RIVER WAS DAMMED)

3. After reading the article (opposite), reread pages 314-15 and check the reasons for flooding. Which reasons seem to have caused this flood in Bangladesh?

Bangladesh
Monsoon Misery in a Troubled Land

Bangladesh sometimes seems to have been twice cursed. It is one of the poorest and most densely populated nations on earth, and it is especially vulnerable to harmful acts of nature. Nearly all of its 105 million people live on the low-lying delta plain formed by the Ganges and Brahmaputra rivers. This area is regularly devastated by floods and tropical storms.

Bangladesh is suffering from its worst floods in 40 years. At the moment, the official death toll from the flooding stands at about 1400, a relatively low number compared with the half million who died in 1970, the estimated 140 000 who were killed by the flood and famine of 1974, or the 11 000 who died in the cyclone of 1985. But at least 4 million people have been left homeless, and millions more have lost their crops and livestock. Total damage from this year's flooding is believed to exceed $1 billion.

Bangladesh's latest tragedy can be traced to a variety of both natural and human-created causes. This year, Bangladesh has been deluged with some of the heaviest monsoon rains in memory. In the Rangpur region of northwestern Bangladesh, for example, the rainfall in July was five times as heavy as last year's. As the swollen rivers have flowed southward toward the Bay of Bengal, the flooding has been made worse by inadequate drainage and flood controls.

Still another factor is the deforestation that has taken place upriver in the hills and mountains of India and Nepal. A recent World Bank report estimated that over 2 billion t of river-borne silt, most of it from neighbouring countries, are flushed through Bangladesh every year.

In the town of Rajbari, 80 km west of Dhaka, more than 12 000 flood victims have sought refuge at government relief centres. Among them are a widow, Saleha Khatoon, 45, and her 4 children, whose mud-and-straw hut was washed away. Said Khatoon: "This is the third time in 4 weeks that I have taken shelter here." When the waters crested the last time, she added, she lost her most prized possession, an egg-laying hen.

The government of Bangladesh has done a fairly effective job of providing emergency food aid. The President has been visiting the flood-stricken areas, promising that "no one will starve." The real crunch will come in a few weeks, however, during the season when, even in the best of years, food is scarce in the Bangladesh countryside.

(Adapted from an article by Wm. E. Smith in *Time*, October 12, 1987)

Volcanoes and Earthquakes

Volcanoes and earthquakes don't occur often in Canada, but in other parts of the world they are serious hazards. Figure 15-9 (p. 318) shows those areas that are most affected.

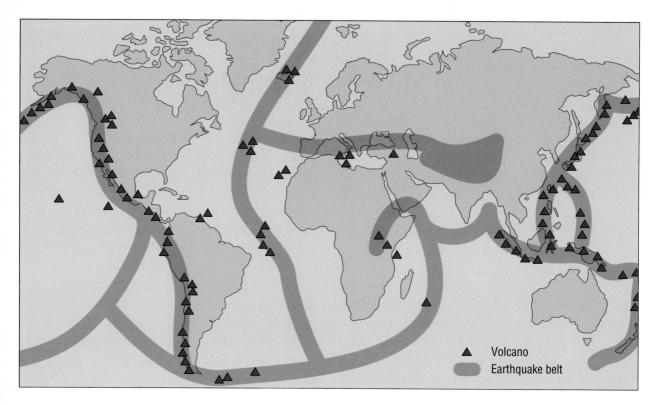

FIG. 15-9 Volcano and earthquake zones

Why do you suppose volcanoes and earthquakes have similar distribution patterns?

Volcanoes are often inactive for hundreds or thousands of years. During this time, people begin to farm on a volcano's fertile slopes and to build settlements nearby. However, the volcano may suddenly become active again, spewing out hot gases, ash, and molten rock. There have been many cases where rivers of lava or clouds of ash have flowed down from a volcano, destroying towns, and killing the people who lived in them.

At other times, a volcano may become active gradually, and people will have time to move away from danger. However, they can't move their homes, businesses, or fields, and these may be destroyed by lava or covered by thick layers of wind-blown ash.

One of the most famous examples of volcanic activity in North America is Mount St. Helens, in Washington State. In the early 1980s, the pressure inside the volcano became so great that the side of the mountain blew apart. In spite of warnings from scientists that the volcano would soon erupt, several people refused to leave their homes and were killed by a huge blast of gas and heat. Thousands of hectares of forest were destroyed. Ash from the explosion was carried by winds over large parts of the continent. With the forest gone, rain washed the soil into the streams, where it killed fish and animals. It was several years before the forest started to regrow and before the streams again ran clear.

FIG. 15-10

The eruption of Mount Saint Helens, Washington State, in May 1980 caused widespread devastation.

The violent shaking of the earth's surface during an earthquake causes damage to people's homes and other buildings. Earthquakes that occur in populated areas are especially serious. Large buildings, like apartment buildings and hospitals, can be knocked flat in seconds. Those people who survive the initial quake and are trapped in collapsed buildings often die before they can be rescued because the ruins are so difficult to clear.

FIG. 15-11

In December 1988, a severe earthquake damaged two cities and destroyed an entire town in Armenia, USSR.

Communication links are usually disrupted by earthquakes: telephone wires are broken, bridges smashed, railway lines destroyed, roads blocked by fallen rocks and buildings. The loss of communication means help can't arrive right away. Disease is another problem in the aftermath of an earthquake. Sewage systems are usually disrupted so that water supplies become contaminated.

Scientists have long recognized that earthquakes and volcanoes aren't random but occur in patterns. Notice that Figure 15-9 (p. 318) shows a close connection between earthquakes and volcanoes. It wasn't until the theory of **continental drift** was developed that scientists had a satisfactory explanation for these patterns. It's now believed that the crust of the earth is made up of a number of **plates** that move about. Scientists think flows of energy inside the earth move upwards and then outwards as they approach the surface. This kind of motion is known as **convection currents**. The outward motion of these convection currents carries the plates along. In certain places around the world, plates push against each other. The areas in which the plates are coming together or moving away from each other are the active zones where earthquakes and volcanoes occur.

FIG. 15-12
Major Continental Plates
What is the name of the plate on which Canada is found?

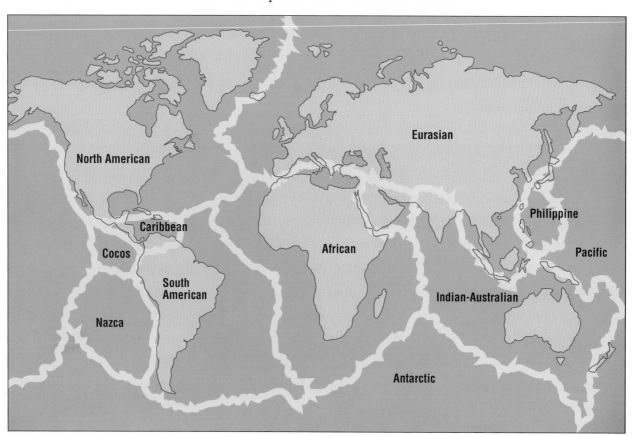

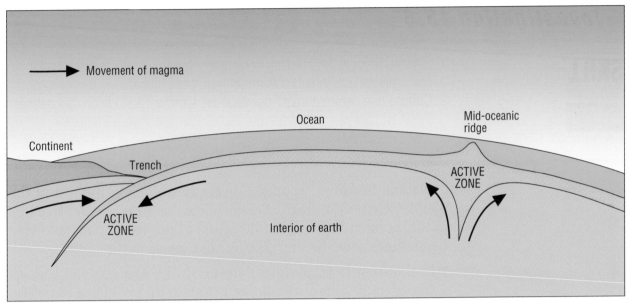

FIG. 15-13   Earth's active zone   *This diagram illustrates the forces in the earth that lead to continental drift. Earthquakes and volcanoes occur in the areas of the active zones.*

Investigation 15.5

SKILL

BUILDERS

RESOURCE
CENTRE

1. (a) Using Figures 15-9, 15-12, and 15-13 describe, in 2 or 3 sentences, the locations of the active areas of the earth's surface.
   (b) Which parts of Canada are near the active zones?
   (c) Using a map showing world cities or populations, name 5 parts of the active zones that are heavily populated.
2. Figure 15-12 shows the major plates.
   (a) List those plates on which the continents are located.
   (b) List those plates that don't include large parts of continents.
3. Using your library or resource centre, identify recent earthquake dates and locations in Canada.

To reduce the effects of earthquakes, buildings have been designed to withstand heavy shocks without falling down. However, not every country in the active zones is wealthy enough that its inhabitants can build such homes.

Like floods, volcanic eruptions and earthquakes occur swiftly and are difficult to predict. Each year people are killed by them because they can't get to safety quickly enough. Environmental threats of this kind affect all people regardless of income or overall quality of life.

Investigation 15.6

SKILL
BUILDERS
RESOURCE
CENTRE

1. Several major natural threats or disasters haven't been discussed here. List other natural threats that might have been included in this chapter.
2. Choose one natural threat from your list. Conduct a study on that natural threat and prepare a 3-to 5-paragraph summary of your findings.

Natural disasters occur in Canada as well as in the rest of the world. Generally, though, disasters here don't cause extensive loss of life, as often happens in other parts of the world. The following list outlines some natural disasters in Canada in the 1980s.

- In February 1982, a violent storm off the east coast of Canada caused the drilling platform *Ocean Ranger* to sink killing 84 people.
- In July 1987, a tornado ripped through Edmonton, Alberta, taking the lives of 26 people and injuring 250 more.
- In December 1987, natural poisons found in Atlantic shellfish caused the death of several people and permanent brain damage in about a dozen others.

Investigation 15.7

SKILL
BUILDERS
BRAINSTORM

1. In a small group, brainstorm a list of things that exist in Canada or things that Canadians could do to prevent the loss of life and property caused by natural disasters. You might want to think about these categories as you are brainstorming: Before Disasters Occur, While Disasters Are Happening, After Disasters Have Taken Place.
2. Investigate the procedure your school follows during a disaster. Find out what takes place if there is a fire; tornado warning; extended power failure; severe winter storm during school hours.
3. How would your community respond to disasters caused by human actions? Research the procedures your community would follow in the event of an accident at a nuclear power station; a large spill of toxic materials; a toxic chemical cloud blowing in your direction; a fire at an explosives factory.
   Try to get information about plans the municipality, police, fire department, and provincial and federal agencies have for these emergencies.
4. How can you protect yourself in an emergency? Write action plans to follow for a fire in your home; a tornado sighting; the announcement of an accident at a nuclear power plant.

Canada's International Role

As you've seen, people's quality of life varies considerably throughout the world. Some people, Canadians included, have a fine quality of life. Other people are constantly struggling to meet their basic needs of food, water, and shelter. For these people, each day is a test for survival.

Canada has a role to play in helping other people around the world. As one of the richer countries, we have more than we need, and we can afford to share with those countries that are still overcoming their problems.

Canada and Canadians give help to other countries in a variety of ways. Government aid giving is co-ordinated by the Canadian International Development Agency (CIDA). This agency decides which countries are to receive help from Canada and in what form the assistance should be. Figure 15-14 shows the proportion of CIDA assistance each part of the world received in 1985-1986. CIDA is especially eager to help countries become self-sufficient. This means that these countries would be able to take care of their own needs and wouldn't rely on other countries for help.

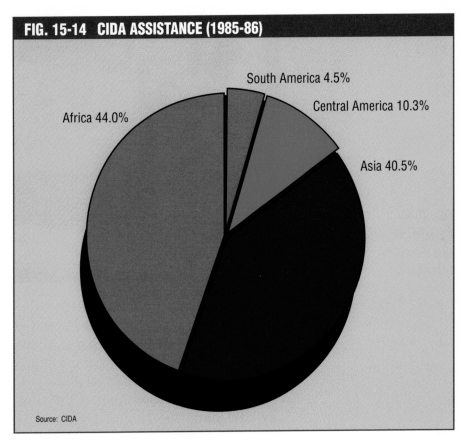

FIG. 15-14 CIDA ASSISTANCE (1985-86)

South America 4.5%

Central America 10.3%

Africa 44.0%

Asia 40.5%

Source: CIDA

A good part of Canada's aid is given directly to projects in developing countries. In 1986-1987, about 38% of CIDA's aid was given in this way. Because it goes directly from one country to another country, this type of aid is termed **bilateral aid**. Canada also makes donations to agencies that distribute aid. For example, CIDA contributes to world food programs and World Bank projects. This **multilateral aid** is distributed to poorer countries by those agencies.

Very little assistance from Canada to other countries is given in the form of money. Often goods are donated. The goods might be tractors for improving agriculture, machines for training mechanics, or hospital equipment. The assistance might also be in the form of skilled personnel — teachers, doctors, scientists, and the like. The Canadian government pays a large part of the expense of sending these people to work with the people of developing countries. Sometimes food is given, in instances where this basic need is most urgent.

FIG. 15-15

Canadian volunteers train health-care workers in developing parts of the world.

The Canadian government isn't the only source of assistance. A great deal of help is given by **non-governmental organizations** (NGOs). These are groups that raise money and provide goods and people to help other countries. The Red Cross and church groups are just some examples of NGOs.

Canada's total assistance is the sum of the contributions made by CIDA and the NGOs. Figure 15-16 shows the total value of

Canadian assistance for the time period 1980-1987. The Canadian government has pledged even higher amounts of assistance, but has been unable to reach those aid goals because of large federal deficits and ongoing economic problems in Canada.

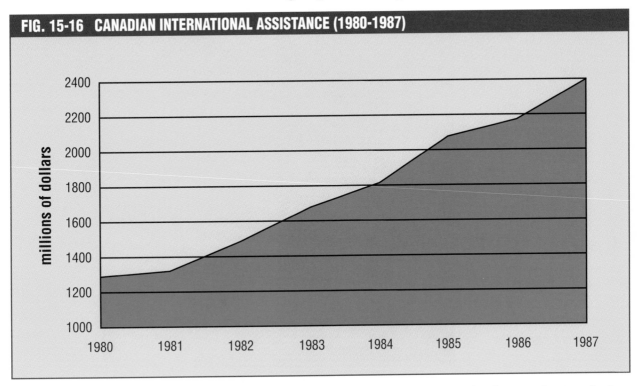

FIG. 15-16 CANADIAN INTERNATIONAL ASSISTANCE (1980-1987)

In 1987, the $2400 million given as aid was only 0.49% of all the wealth earned by Canadians. About what percent of our earnings should be donated to others?

While assistance is usually given in the hope of stimulating future development, sometimes it is given in response to emergency situations.

Canada's emergency assistance to Jamaica after Hurricane Gilbert struck in September 1988 is a good example of this. This devastating hurricane swept across the Caribbean Sea, ripping through the Cayman Islands, Jamaica, and the tip of Mexico's Yucatan Peninsula before coming ashore in northeastern Mexico. At their peak, the hurricane winds measured more than 250 km/h. The American weather office rated Gilbert as a Category 5 hurricane, "capable of doing catastrophic damage." Only two other Category 5 hurricanes have occurred since records have been kept.

On 12 September, Gilbert passed directly over Jamaica. Witnesses reported roofs flying off, houses blown apart by the wind, and trees plucked out of the ground. About 80% of the houses on the island were damaged, a quarter of them beyond repair. Jamaica's banana, coconut, and sugar cane crops were virtually wiped out; its bauxite mines were flooded. All telephone, radio, and satellite communications were knocked out. The nation's prime minister appealed for emergency help from other countries, calling the hurricane the worst disaster in the country's history.

FIG. 15-17

Hurricane Gilbert caused tremendous damage throughout the Caribbean in 1988. This photograph shows the destruction in Kingston, the capital of Jamaica.

The Canadian government responded quickly to the request for help. The federal government pledged $2.6 million in aid. The Ontario government offered $100 000 and chartered a cargo plane to fly supplies to the hurricane-damaged country. In most large Canadian cities, clothing, food, and cash donations poured into collection centres. Volunteers worked frantically packing goods in cartons and preparing them for shipment to Jamaica. Relief activities in Canada continued for several weeks following the hurricane, and then, as often happens, eventually slowed to a halt as people began to forget about the disaster.

Investigation 15.8

1. Suppose you were put in charge of Canada's aid program. List 10 factors you would consider in giving out aid to other countries.
2. Select one of the countries from the following list. Research what types of bilateral aid this country has received from Canada. Try to identify reasons why this country was selected by Canadian officials to receive aid.

- Ethiopia
- Jamaica
- Peru
- Bangladesh
- Nigeria
- Nicaragua
- Colombia
- Indonesia

SKILL
BUILDERS
GRAPHING

3. Figure 15-18 shows the contributions made by the 10 largest donors of assistance to developing countries.
   (a) Where does Canada rank as a contributor of foreign assistance?
   (b) Construct a bar graph to show the information from Figure 15-18.

FIG. 15-18 PER CAPITA ASSISTANCE TO DEVELOPING COUNTRIES (1988)	
(US dollars per person)	
Norway	235.24
Sweden	182.62
Denmark	180.78
Netherlands	151.77
France	125.16
Canada	90.35
Australia	67.35
West Germany	76.80
Switzerland	94.62
Belgium	59.80
United States	49.92

Source: Reprinted with permission from the *World Development Report, 1989*

Canada's aid giving can cause some Canadians to form negative images of other countries. They might look on these countries as poor and dependent on our charity. However, this attitude isn't realistic or useful. Rather, we should view foreign aid as helping our friends to deal with their problems. Canada's aid programs give Canadians opportunities to learn more about other countries, and to participate in the development of other nations — of our friends — around the world.

You and the World

The conclusion to this book is actually a starting point. You have been considering what it is to be a Canadian, and what it is like to live in Canada. Also, you have seen how Canada fits into the rest of the world. Now, let's look at how you fit into the world.

Investigation 15.9

1. This Investigation is to help you see how you fit into the world scene.
   (a) Draw a map of the world on a piece of poster paper.
   (b) Put a symbol to represent where you live in Canada.
   (c) Highlight Canada on your map in some way.
   (d) Find pictures, drawings, or sketches of 5 parts of the world that you find interesting. Fasten them to your map in their proper places.
   (e) Write 5 words that describe how you feel about being a Canadian citizen. Now, on lined paper, write a well-constructed sentence to give a reason for each of these feelings. Tape this to your map.
   (f) On 5 small cards or pieces of paper, write things that could be improved about the world. On the back of each, write one small thing you and people in your community could do to help. Tape these to your map.
2. Create a collage of pictures on a poster and title it **Ways the World Is Getting Better**.

Summing Up

It is our hope that you have enjoyed investigating Canada and the world by using this book. We hope that you will see the ending of this book as a beginning point for you — a beginning of a further investigation of Canada and the world.

SKILL BUILDERS

Contents

The skill builders show you how to get started on assignments, how to cope with tasks, and how to improve your work. What you learn will help you deal with information in other subjects as well.

The first section on thinking skills will help you solve problems and process information. It is followed by three broad groupings of ideas:

1) **Techniques** – ways of processing or working with information;
2) **Gathering data** – ways of gathering information from many resources;
3) **Working with groups** – skills for working with other people and developing your own strengths in group situations.

Developing Thinking Skills

Thinking skills are the mental abilities that you use when solving problems. Like all skills, they can be improved by using better techniques and by practice.

Inductive and Deductive Thinking

These two forms of thinking are often confused, perhaps because they are both processes by which conclusions can be drawn. Also, the words are quite similar. Their meanings can be clarified by using practical situations.

Inductive thinking is the method used by mystery detectives who combine several "clues" to discover who is guilty of the crime.

A practical geographical example is the mystery of acid rain. Scientific detectives noted that the effects of acid rain are more serious (1) close to coal-burning industries, (2) downwind from those industries, and (3) where large amounts of coal were burned for heating. When scientists combined these clues with the fact that the smoke from coal mixes with water in clouds to produce acid rain, they concluded that coal burning was the cause of the acid rain.

Deductive thinking is a skill that is based on looking at what is generally true and making a conclusion that refers to something quite specific. This kind of reasoning is used by urban planners when they determine zoning laws for various land uses. For example, the best location for commercial land use (major stores) is, in almost all cases, on major highways or roads, on the edges of towns, or on large pieces of property. Based on this information, what site would you select for a new Canadian Tire store in your town?

FIG. 1

Inductive and deductive thinking

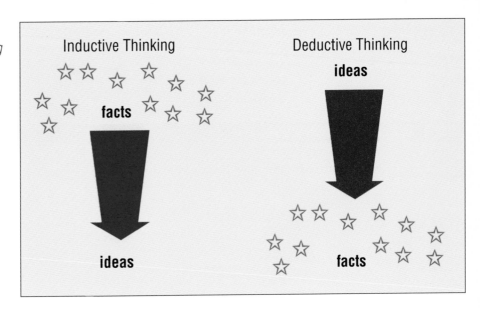

Comparative Thinking

Comparative thinking is the study of two or more different ideas in order to make a decision or reach a conclusion. Comparisons can be simplified if you have a systematic approach that breaks the question into logical parts. This process is called creating a framework. Once a "framework" has been set up, then answering the question is easier.

A geographical example is a comparison between two cities, Québec City and Regina. The framework is intended to solve the problem of organization. Here is a sample framework.

FIG. 2 COMPARISON OF QUEBEC CITY AND REGINA		
Characteristics	**Québec City**	**Regina**
Population		
Location in province		
Site - type of landscape		
Climate - temperature		
- rainfall		
Transportation systems		
Major occupation		
Major industries		
Ethnic composition		
Appearance		

Decision Making

When you are required to make a decision, such as how to increase food supplies in the Third World, you can use a decision-making model.

FIG. 3 DECISION-MAKING MODEL	
Model	**Action taken by student**
A. Question **?**	The question should be thoroughly discussed so that its meaning is fully understood.
B. Developing alternatives 1 2 3 4 etc.	Alternative answers should be suggested. Brainstorm (see p. 333) some ideas and then reduce the list to a workable number, perhaps between three and eight. Other alternatives may be added later when you're researching the choices.
C. Data collection 1 2 3 4	Information is collected about each of the alternatives.
D. Arriving at a conclusion Alternative / A B C D / 1 2 3 4	This is the most important and most difficult stage, because there are two steps involved. The first step is to determine some factors to compare the alternatives. The second step is to set up a framework such as the one on the left.
E. Assessing the conclusion	Once the conclusion has been reached, go back to the original question and determine if it has been adequately answered. Does the answer seem logical? Have better alternatives come up in your research?
F. Expressing your conclusion	Now explain what led you to your conclusion. You might do this in written or oral form and support your reasoning with pictures, slides, or audio items.

Techniques

Techniques are methods used to process information. In this section, you will see a variety of techniques that are useful for studying geography. You'll also find a variety of skills, such as brainstorming, sketching, graphing, and mapping.

Brainstorming Techniques

Brainstorming is a simple and fun way to get innovative ideas on all kinds of problems!

1. Appoint a recording secretary—someone who can jot down key ideas quickly.
2. Make sure everyone knows the topic being brainstormed.
3. When brainstorming, all answers are acceptable. Questions of clarification are allowed.
4. When no more answers are volunteered, the brainstorming is completed.
5. Next, as a group, read over your brainstorming list to (a) eliminate any inappropriate ideas; (b) combine part answers into a unified whole answer.
6. Finally, rank the answers from most to least useful.

Sketching Techniques

Sketching is a useful technique to help you record information quickly and to highlight details in a scene. Each scene has three distinct areas.

Foreground   the area closest to you
Background   the area farthest away from you
Midground   the area between the foreground and background

It will be easier to sketch your scene if you observe the scene carefully and then jot down the key features on a chart like Figure 4. When you start your sketch, rough in the skyline and other major features first, then add the details.

FIG. 4 SKETCHING SUMMARY

Name		Title	
Foreground	Midground		Background

FIG. 5
Field of vision sketching

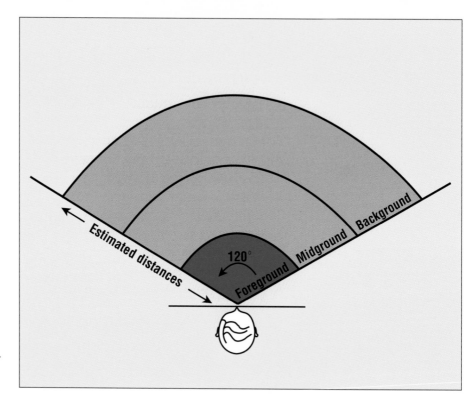

FIG. 6
Skyline silhouette

A silhouette is a dark image against a lighter background (like a). Sketch b shows an outline of the same scene except more details have been added.

Graphing Techniques

Much information is shown in graphs. This method of communication often reveals patterns in the data much better than words, diagrams or maps. Geographers use graphs frequently. The following pages show some common graphing methods.

Line graph – useful for looking at change over a period of time

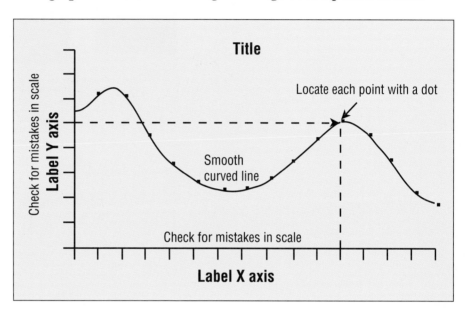

FIG. 7

Bar graph – useful for seeing the differences between things at the same time

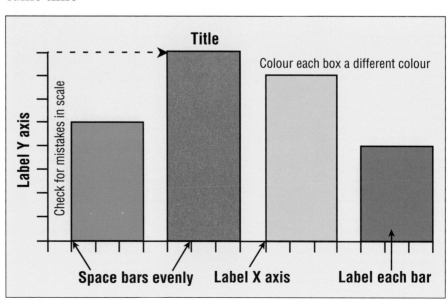

FIG. 8

You can draw variations of bar graphs. Here are three different ways of doing so.

Variation 1 – Compound bar graph

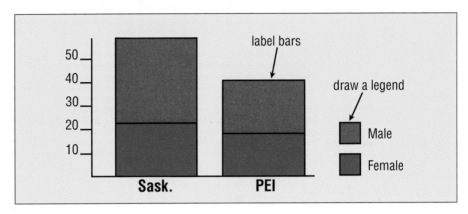

FIG. 9

FIG. 10   ## Variation 2 – Multiple bar graph

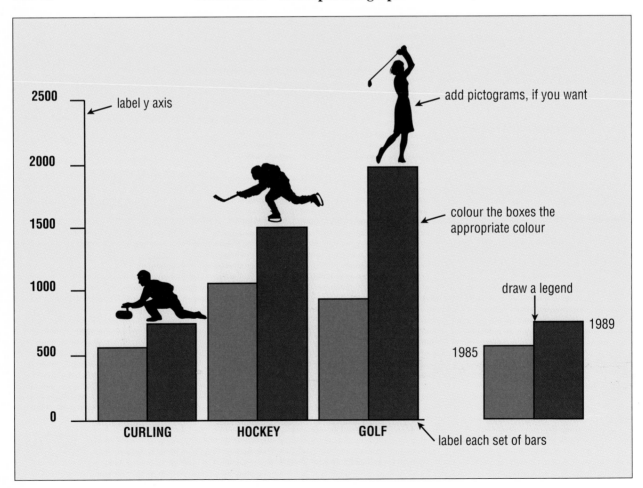

FIG. 11   **Variation 3 – Horizontal bar graph**

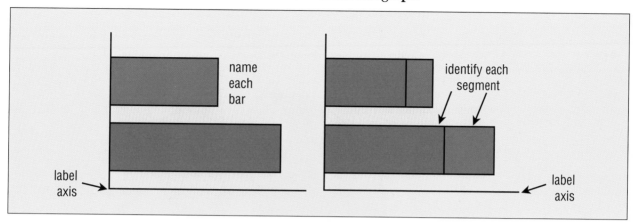

FIG. 12   **Climographs** – show temperature and precipitation for a place

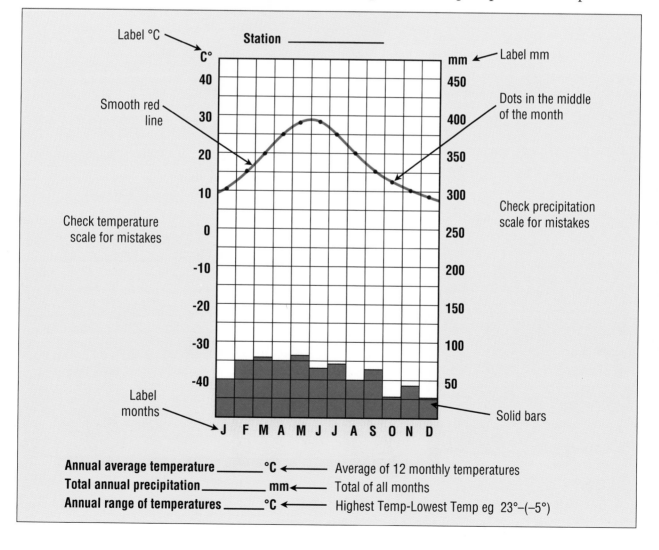

Annual average temperature _____°C ← ——— Average of 12 monthly temperatures

Total annual precipitation _____ mm ← ——— Total of all months

Annual range of temperatures _____°C ← ——— Highest Temp-Lowest Temp eg 23°–(–5°)

Pie graphs – useful for comparing relative size of things or proportions

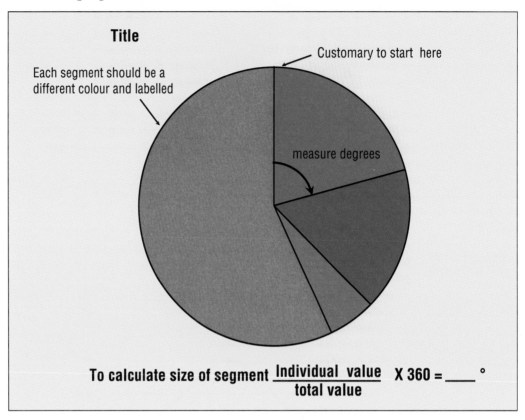

FIG. 13

Pictographs – show symbolic figures as well as numbers

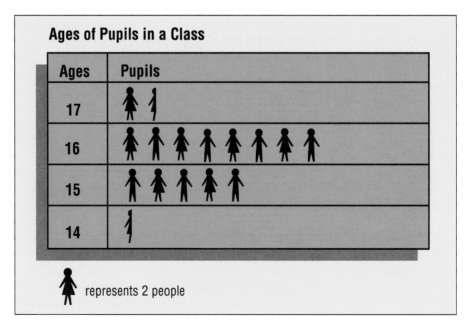

FIG. 14

Measuring Distances

In geography courses, you often need to calculate real distances from maps, models, and photographs. When these items have a "scale," you can do so. Here is how scales work.

There are three ways to express the scale:

1. Statement, e.g., 1 cm = 2 km

2. Line scale, e.g.,

3. Representative fraction, e.g., 1 : 200 000 or $\dfrac{1}{200\,000}$

Therefore, based on this scale, a distance measuring 3 cm on a map would represent an actual distance of 6 km.

1.
$$
\begin{aligned}
1\ \text{cm} &: 2\ \text{km} \\
3\ \text{cm} &: 3 \times 2 \\
&: 6\ \text{km}
\end{aligned}
$$
(The colon is a mapping symbol for "represents.")

2.

3.
$$
\begin{aligned}
&1 : 200\,000 \\
1\ \text{cm} &: 200\,000\ \text{cm} \\
1\ \text{cm} &: \dfrac{200\,000}{100\,000}\ \text{km} \\
&: 2\ \text{km} \\
3\ \text{cm} &: 3 \times 2\ \text{km} \\
&: 6\ \text{km}
\end{aligned}
$$
(In metric system 1 km = 100 000 cm)

Mapping

Maps are one of the most important tools of geographers because they show information about the earth's surface. Every point in the world has a position on the lines of latitude and longitude. Lines of latitude run parallel to the equator in an east-west direction. Lines of longitude run parallel to the prime meridian in a north-south direction. The locations of Charlottetown (1) and Whitehorse (2) are shown on Figure 15 (p. 340).

Many maps, such as contour maps, use grid numbers to determine locations. Figure 16 (p. 340) shows you how to do this. When you're trying to locate squares, it's easier to read the numbers along the bottom first. Next read the numbers along the side. For example, the location of Square I is 2166.

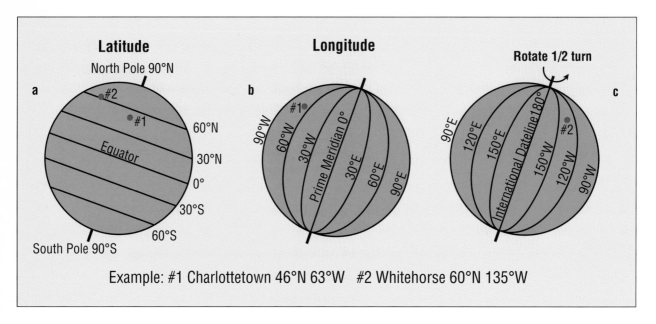

FIG. 15

If you're trying to locate points (not the whole square), you still read the bottom numbers first and then the numbers along the side. But you must divide the square into tenths to find out the last number. See if you can figure out how the grid locations for points A-E were determined.

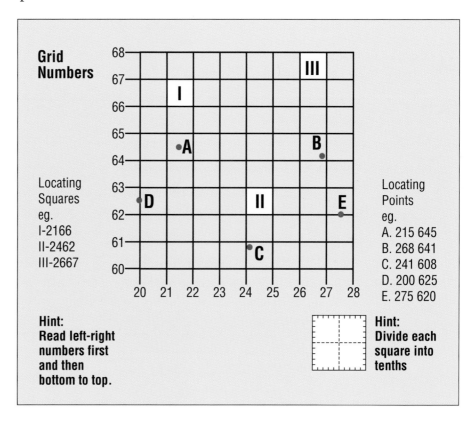

FIG. 16

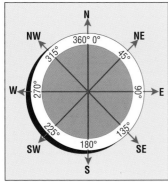

FIG. 17

Direction

The four main map directions, or cardinal points, are North, South, East, and West. Northeast, Northwest, Southeast, and Southwest are called intercardinal points. They are located midway between the cardinal points. Figure 17 shows you these points.

The position of each direction can be stated as a degree of an angle. The angle is measured clockwise from the North, which is numbered zero. For example, Northeast is 45°. This means there are 45° between North and Northeast.

Contour Lines

Drawing rules

1. Contour lines must be drawn with the same interval, e.g., 20 m, 25 m, 30 m, 35 m, etc. The interval doesn't have to be 5 m; it just has to be consistent.
2. Contours must not cross each other.
3. Contours will be cut off by the map's border but they never end.
4. Contours bend in a V-shape when they cross streams and rivers. The open end of the V faces downhill to lower elevations.

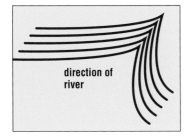

direction of river

FIG. 18

Understanding Contours

1. When they are close together, the land is steep.
2. When they are far apart, the land is flatter.
3. Contours that show the pattern in Figure 18 indicate a river valley.

Gathering Data

In geography you need access to up-to-date information. The key word is "access." You don't have to remember all the information, but you have to know where and how to find it.

Let's examine ways to collect and manage data under three main headings. They are:

1) **Evaluation** how to collect, organize, and record marks on yourself and your classmates;
2) **Surveys** how to collect raw data for use in your geography class;
3) **Resource centres and libraries** an owner's guide and manual for getting the best results from your school resource centre.

Evaluation

You can learn a lot when you and your classmates evaluate your own work. Don't worry about making mistakes (either in your own work or in marking others)—it's a natural part of learning. If you have the opportunity to see where you went wrong, you can learn from your mistakes.

At the beginning, you might feel uneasy about having someone else mark your work. That isn't unusual, but remember the person marking you is probably feeling uneasy also.

The following five questionnaires will help you with your evaluations. They will be most useful after you've completed the Investigations. *Don't put any marks in this textbook.*

A. Evaluating Your Geographic Learning Habits

To analyze how you study and prepare your work, respond to the following statements. There are no wrong answers, but some situations are better than others. Use the following ranking system:

> 4 indicates "most of the time"
> 3 indicates "frequently"
> 2 indicates "occasionally"
> 1 indicates "rarely"

1. I work at most of my tasks a little bit each day.
2. I work best when I have planned and written out a step-by-step procedure.
3. I prefer to study for a short period, take a break, work for a short period, take a break, etc.
4. I work best when I can work out my own time frame.
5. I work well on assignments when I can share the work load and planning with others.
6. When I have homework to do I try to get as much done at school as possible.
7. When I have studying to do at home, I prefer to find a quiet area away from others.
8. I make use of the resource centre when studying and/or doing homework.

Now, describe in three or four sentences your present study habits. Describe one or two good study habits that you're willing to try for the next month.

B. Evaluating Your Performance in a Group

Before you begin your group assignment, read over this evaluation. However, don't complete it until you've finished your group project. Use the following ranking system:

4 indicates "to a very high degree"
3 indicates "most of the time"
2 indicates "occasionally"
1 indicates "never or rarely"

1. I listen attentively while others speak.
2. I present my views on the topic clearly.
3. I help the group plan its activities.
4. I understand and complete my responsibilities.
5. I help others achieve their goals.
6. I help the group prepare and present a finished product.
7. I help group members avoid or settle disagreements.
8. I help the group stay on topic and accomplish its objectives.
9. I use all resources fully in preparing my work.
10. I co-operate with all group members.

C. Group Evaluation

Working together, assign your group a grade from one to ten using the following scale.

Excellent   *Improvement Needed*
10   9   8   7   6   5   4   3   2   1

1. Understood the topic
2. Kept on task
3. Work was evenly shared
4. Work was well organized
5. Work was well researched
6. Ideas were discussed openly
7. All members participated in discussions
8. Learning took place
9. Enjoyed the task

D. Grading Your Group

Using a chart like Figure 19 (p. 344), record what goes on when your group is working. At an agreed upon time, have an observer share the results with the group and think of ways to make the group better. Everyone should have a turn at being the observer.

FIG. 19   GRADING YOUR GROUP

Group _____   Date _____

Names Contribution					
1. Gives suggestions					
2. Gives opinions					
3. Gives directions					
4. Asks for suggestions					
5. Asks for opinions					
6. Asks for directions					
7. Supports the team					
8. Handles pressure					
9. Encourages team					
10. Shows leadership					
Totals					

General Impressions of the Group

1. _____

   _____

2. _____

   _____

3. _____

   _____

E. Evaluating a Group's Finished Project

Complete Figure 20 after you've listened to a group's presentation. The following scale will help you.

Excellent   *Improvement Needed*

10   9   8   7   6   5   4   3   2   1

FIG. 20   PRESENTATION EVALUATION

Topic _____

1. Interested in their topic   _____
2. Made me interested in their topic   _____
3. Expressed their ideas clearly   _____
4. Understood their topic   _____
5. Work was well organized   _____
6. Group worked well together   _____
7. Interesting method of presentation   _____
8. Topic was well researched   _____
9. Discussion was generated by presentation   _____
10. General impression   _____

                                        Total   _____

Surveys

Sometimes you can't locate the information you want in books or magazines—it's just too new or too local. Then, the best way to find information is by conducting a survey. Two methods of conducting a survey are:

a) interviews – develop questions to ask people. This survey is done verbally.

b) questionnaires – develop questions that people write answers to. This survey is written.

Here are some pointers so you can plan a successful survey.

1. Know what information you're looking for before you develop the survey.
2. Make sure your question is answerable. For example, "Where should the new arena be located?" or "Do you think expensive condominiums should be built along the lake shore?"

3. For most surveys, you won't be able to ask everybody or count everything so you will have to choose an appropriate "sample size." Ask your teacher to help you find the best technique for conducting your survey.
4. Be brief: the longer the survey is, the less likely you'll get a good response.
5. Timing is important. Think about the best time to conduct your survey. Remember, it might be harder to get people interested in your survey if you hold it during special events, such as the last game of the Stanley Cup.
6. Introduction: Your survey participants will be more co-operative if you tell them who you are, what school you attend, what subject the survey is for, and the purpose of your survey. Tell them how long the survey will take and who will see the results.

Additional tips
a) Wear something that identifies you as a student from the school.
b) Be careful of strangers who ask too much information about you.
c) Always make sure your parent or guardian knows where you are.
d) Dress to present yourself in the best possible way. The same goes for grooming.
e) Audio and video taping methods are time consuming and not necessarily better than other methods. Also, many people don't like to be taped.
f) Most people don't like to give their names.
g) Any personal questions, such as age or income, will likely be rejected.
h) Prepare a check-off record sheet that you fill in. It will produce the fewest errors, provides the quickest way of conducting your survey, and is the easiest to organize later.
i) Thank the people who participated in your survey.

Resource Centres and Libraries

Available resources in schools vary, but all schools have resource centres or libraries. The following sources contain useful geographic information.

- magazines
- vertical files
- almanacs
- yearbooks
- encyclopedias
- atlases
- base sources
- audio-visual kits
- pictures
- records
- computer software (your computer hardware might hook up to large data bases such as Teledon and Info-Globe.)

Remember, if you need help, the librarian can be a wealth of information.

One of geography's unique characteristics is that it includes elements of many other subjects. *Investigating Canada* includes topics related to Biology (acid rain), History (immigration), Mathematics (graphing), Art (sketching), English (poetry, essay writing), and so on. You could ask other teachers where you might find information on certain topics.

The Card Catalogue

There are three different kinds of cards in the catalogue.

Author card - author's name is on the first line; surname first
Subject card - has the subject in the top corner
Title card - the title appears on the first line

Here is a sample subject card.

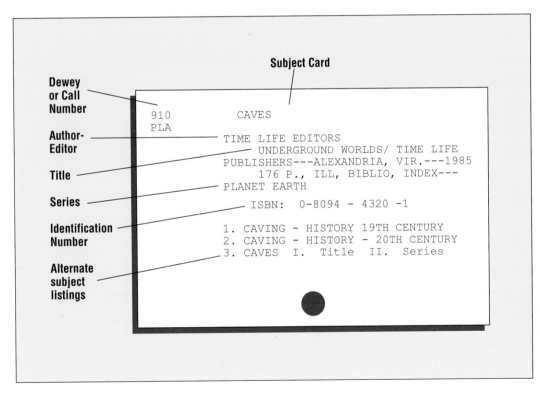

FIG. 21

To find articles you want in magazines (sometimes called periodicals) look in a periodical index. Figure 22 shows how a periodical index is set up.

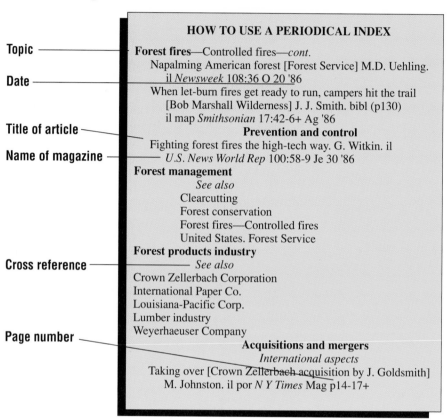

FIG. 22

Classroom Resources

Your geography classroom has many resources. For example, your teacher (and other geography teachers) may have special interests and expertise in specific topics. The geography department may have its own reference sources too.

Working with Groups

Sometimes it may seem easier to do an assignment on your own, but working as part of an effective group has advantages. An effective group:

a) understands clearly the assignment

b) divides the tasks and responsibilities equally among all group members

c) has members who all feel free to express their ideas

d) shares the leadership

e) uses the strength of each member

f) reviews and revises their work

g) maintains a record of work assignments and work achieved on a daily basis

The following pointers (and the section on Evaluation, pp. 342-45) will help you with your next group assignment.

1. Read the Investigation carefully and discuss what is expected.
2. Organize the topic into sub-topics.
3. Assign jobs based on the strengths of each group member.
4. Set deadlines and fill out a Work Plan (Fig. 23) which could be organized like this:

FIG. 23 WORK PLAN			
Task	Person assigned to task	Approx. amount of time needed	Actual time taken to complete the task

5. Fill out a Work Record (Fig. 24) for each person each day. A sample work record could be set up like this:

FIG. 24 WORK RECORD			
Day	Name	Name	Name

6. To produce the final product:
   a) prepare a rough draft of your work
   b) present your rough draft to the group for suggestions
   c) revise the rough draft
   d) prepare the good copy and present the group's final product

Communicating with Others

To improve your discussions, consider the ideas listed here.

Speaking
Develop your speaking skills by doing the following activities.

a) Present a point-of-view on a topic.
b) Support someone else's point-of-view—perhaps by explaining why you support it.

Listening
Keep these pointers in mind.

a) Pay attention to the speaker.
b) Listen for the main idea or point-of-view.
c) Don't make the speaker uncomfortable by staring, making inappropriate noises or gestures, or by moving away.
d) Don't let personal feelings interfere with listening to what the person is saying.

Reaching a Consensus

When you work in a group, other members may have different opinions. Exposure to new ideas is a benefit of working with others, but it can also lead to disagreements or arguments. In order for your group to work effectively, you will have to reach a **consensus**. A consensus is when a majority of the people agree on a course of action or decision. For example, imagine if every group member had a different opinion about the best land use for a river valley. No decision can be made until you all agree upon a plan. Therefore, your group will have to discuss the various options and find something that will make everyone happy. Of course, everyone will have to compromise a bit. Here are some hints to help you work better in group situations.

a) Welcome those who are willing to speak their mind.
b) Review the facts of the discussion.
c) Explore new and different ideas thoroughly before you comment.
d) Make sure that you are having a discussion. Don't just guess at a single correct answer.
e) Don't just identify a problem, propose a solution or compromise to it.
f) Encourage others by praising their ideas or work.
g) Come to an agreement or consensus on the direction for the group.

Glossary

absolute location   the location of a place as described by the intersecting lines of latitude and longitude

acid rain   precipitation that has become acidic due to chemicals, especially sulphur and nitrogen oxides, in the atmosphere

acids   various chemical compounds that can dissolve substances with which they come in contact

air masses   a large body of air that has nearly the same temperature and moisture content throughout it

archipelago   a group of many islands

assets   things that have values (e.g. property like your bike or skills like your computer knowledge)

balance of trade   the difference between the value of a country's imports and exports for a fixed period of time

base   a compound that reacts with an acid to form a salt

biculturalism   federal government policy that supports the existence of two distinct cultures (French and English) in Canada

bilateral aid   financial or human assistance given by one country to another to help deal with the development issues

bilingualism   federal (and sometimes provincial) government policy that supports having two languages with equal status in Canada

biomass   plant and animal life on earth; biomass energy is the energy produced from using this renewable resource (e.g. firewood, gases from decaying manure, etc.)

birth rate   the total number of births in a year for every 1000 people

capital   the amount of money or property that a company or person has access to or owns

cardinal direction   the main or most important directions: north, south, east, and west

Census Metropolitan Areas (CMAs)   cities with more than 100 000 people

Central Business District (CBD)   the downtown area of a town or city that contains most of the commercial activities

central-place functions   services provided by businesses and governments for the people who live in the town or city and its surrounding area (e.g. a large department store)

chain reaction   a process that continues automatically once it has been started

communication skills   abilities that people have to transmit and receive information, especially with other people

community   a group of people with common interests living in the same area or place

consensus   a general agreement; all or most of the people agree on a course of action or an idea

continental drift   a theory that claims that in the last 200 million years the continents have moved by great distances and are still moving today

convection currents   flows of energy inside the earth moving upwards and outwards as they approach the earth's surface

Crown corporations   companies owned by the federal and provincial governments that are set up like private businesses (e.g. Canada Post)

cultural group   people who share the same beliefs, traditions, attitudes, arts, and so on

culture   the beliefs, traditions, attitudes, and way of life shared by a people

death rate   the number of deaths in a year for every 1000 people

density   the number of people living in a given area of land

direct communication   methods of communicating between people that require personal contact (e.g. talking)

distribution   the arrangement or spread of anything over an area

distribution systems   methods used to move goods and people

diversifying   expanding or extending into new and different areas

drainage systems   networks of streams and rivers that drain run-off from the land

duties   a tax that Canadian people and companies pay to the federal government on goods they bring into the country

emigration   to move from one country to another to live

environment   all the conditions and influences that surround a person or thing and affect their growth and development

equator   an imaginary line around the middle of the earth halfway between the north and south poles

ethnic group   people who share the same characteristics, customs, and language

federal government   the people who decide upon and enforce the laws and policies for Canada

first language   the language first understood as a child

food chain   the linkages between life that allow the transfer of energy throughout an ecosystem

fossil fuels   minerals formed from the remains of ancient plants and animals that produce energy. These include coal, natural gas, and petroleum.

franchises   the right to sell the products of a manufacturer or provide a company's services in a given area. This right is purchased from the manufacturer.

free trade   the exchange of goods between countries without the payment of duties or tariffs

function   the normal action, use, or purpose of something

geologist   a person who studies the origins and structures of the earth

goods   products for sale that are manufactured by industries

Gross National Product (GNP)   the value of all the goods and services produced in a country in one year

ground water   water stored beneath the earth's surface

heartland   an area or region that is the centre of, or vital to, a country

high-order services   services found only in large cities; services requiring a large market in order to be profitable (e.g. hospitals, universities, art galleries)

human resources   people, especially the skills and abilities they have

immigration   to move from one country to another country to live

immigration policy   rules, based on the law, that regulate the number and type of people who enter a country

indirect communication   methods of communication that do not require personal contact (e.g. letters, telephone)

Industrial Heartland   part or region that has a strong concentration of manufacturing activity

information age   a period of rapid growth in the amount of information available and in methods used to handle that information

Inuit Native peoples who are geographically located in the Arctic regions

isodemographic map a map that shows the size of countries based on their populations not their land areas

kilojoules a unit that measures the heat or energy produced by food as it is burned by the body

landfill sites places where solid wastes (garbage) are disposed of and covered with soil

liabilities debts or obligations that are a disadvantage to people or companies

life expectancy the number of years a person is expected to live, measured from birth

locations a position or place on the surface of the earth

low-order services services available in a large number of places (e.g. variety stores, gas stations)

map a drawing representing all or part of the earth's surface

map projections a representation of all or part of the earth's surface on a flat piece of paper. There are different kinds of projections.

mechanization the replacement of human and animal labour with machinery

megaproject a very large undertaking, usually involving the extraction or exploitation of natural resources

meridians of longitude imaginary circles passing through points on the earth's surface and the north and south poles. Meridians measure east and west distances.

Metis people descended from North American Indians and Europeans

middle-order services services that are available in towns and cities (e.g. grocery stores, banks)

modes the manner of way in which something is done

monsoons seasonal winds of the Indian Ocean and southern Asia

multiculturalism a federal government policy promoting the existence of a number of distinct cultural groups within Canada

multilateral aid foreign assistance given to an international agency to distribute to developing countries

municipal government governments elected by the people of town, city, or township to run their affairs

municipality a town, city, county, district, or other area having local self-government

Native peoples people who are the traditional inhabitants of Canada

natural increase the rate of increase in a population when the death rate is subtracted from the birth rate

neighbourhood a place or area where people share a sense of community

net migration the difference between immigration and emigration

NIMBY (Not in My Back Yard) an unwillingness to accept necessary services, such as landfill sites and airports, in a neighbourhood or community because of their problem-causing potential

nitrogen oxides chemicals emitted from automobile exhausts and factories that contribute to the acid rain problem

non-governmental organizations (NGOs) private groups that raise funds to help people in other nations

non-porous rock material that does not allow fluids or gases to pass through it

non-renewable resources resources that cannot be replaced once they have been used (e.g. oil)

Non-status Indians Native people who do not qualify for the benefits given to status Indians

nuclear wastes radioactive materials that are produced by the nuclear industry

parallels of latitude imaginary circles around the earth parallel to the equator marking distance north or south of the equator

Parliament of Canada the House of Commons, the Senate, and the Governor General. The Parliament makes the laws for Canada.

physical resources materials and equipment that can be used to help with tasks and solve problems

plates thin, rigid sections of the earth's crust that float on the hot, soft rocks beneath

pollutants something that causes pollution (e.g. by-products from manufacturing, candy wrappers)

porous rock material that allows fluids and gases to move through it

primary industries extractive industries that take natural resources and process them into semi-finished products (e.g. the mining and forestry industries)

prime meridian line of longitude from what east and west is measured. It passes through Greenwich, England.

profit earnings that remain after costs are subtracted from the amount of money taken in from a business

provincial government governments elected by the people of each of the ten provinces to run their affairs

pull factors conditions that attract people to a place, especially a country

push factors conditions that encourage people to leave a place, especially a country

recycling collecting used material, such as newspapers, tins, and glass, to be manufactured into new products thus saving valuable resources

regional disparity differences, usually economic, among various parts of a country or province

regions a part of the earth's surface that has distinctive characteristics

relative location position on the earth's surface as measured from some other position (e.g. Regina's position relative to Montreal's position)

renewable resources resources that can be replenished after they are consumed (e.g. trees)

reserves resources that have not yet been developed

resume a detailed description of a person's education, job experiences, etc.

riding an electoral district, determined by population, that an elected person represents in the House of Commons or a provincial legislature

rural areas parts of a country or province that do not have the characteristics of a town or city

rural having to do with the countryside; not belonging to a town or city

rush periods peak travel periods; in large urban areas usually from 7 a.m. to 10 a.m. and from 3 p.m. to 7 p.m. It used to be called "rush hour," but it now lasts much longer than one hour.

sandspit a long, narrow build up of sand in a water body

secondary industries industries that manufacture the raw materials produced by primary industries and convert them into finished products

sedimentary rock rock formed in layers by materials deposited by wind, water, or ice

self-sufficient self-supporting; able to meet its own needs

services helpful labour done in the service of others

single-family detached dwelling a home that is not attached to another housing unit and is occupied by one family only

single-industry town   a town, often in a remote area, that was developed because of a local resource and depends upon that resource for its survival

site   the spot on which something is located

situation   the general circumstances that are associated with a location

solid waste   materials that are created by municipalities, households, and industries; garbage

standard of living   conditions that contribute to the comfort and happiness of people

Status or Registered Indians   Native people who are officially recognized as Indians by the federal government and therefore receive benefits

sulphur oxides   chemicals released into the atmosphere by the burning of fossil fuels, such as coal or petroleum

tariffs   a tax that Canadian companies pay to the federal government on goods entering the country

technology   scientific knowledge that is applied to practical purposes

tertiary industries   activities that provide services to people

time zones   geographic regions within which the same time is used. There are twenty-four time zones in the world.

townships   part of a province that has certain powers of government; a municipality

transportation systems   networks of transportation modes that complement each other

tributaries   streams that flow into larger bodies of water

unit trains   trains that carry only one cargo from one location to one destination

urban areas   a part of the country having the characteristics of a city or town

urban   having to do with cities or towns

urban sprawl   the process of a city or CMA expanding beyond its borders

urban transit   public transportation methods within built-up areas

urbanization   the process by which an area becomes urban

Credits

1-1 Victor C. Last (hereafter VCL); 1-4 (right) Libra Photographic, (left) EduVision; 1-7 Birgitte Nielsen; 1-9 VCL; 2-0 Ontario Ministry of Tourism and Recreation; 2-1 Courtesy of St. John's; 2-2 Courtesy of St. John's; 2-3 Courtesy of the Government of Newfoundland & Labrador, Department of Cultural Affairs, Tourism & Historic Resources; 2-4 Courtesy of St. John's; 2-8a EduVision; 2-8b EduVision; 2-8c Lorraine C. Parow/First Light; 2-8d Jessie Parker/First Light; 2-8e Janet Dwyer/ First Light; 2-8f Brian Milne/First Light; 2-11 Pat Morrow/First Light; 2-12 Gabrielle Von Gonns/First Light; 3-0 National Archives of Canada/ Karen E Bailey; 4-0 VCL; 4-3 "Eclipse Sound, Bylot Island by Lawren S. Harris (1885-1970). The McMichael Canadian Collection. Reprinted with consent of the artist's family; 4-4 private collection; 4-8a VCL; 4-8b VCL; 4-8c VCL; 4-8d Barry Griffiths/ Network; 4-8e VCL; 4-8f Albert Kuhnigk/ First Light; 4-8g Paul Von Baich/First Light; 4-10 (left) Jessie Parker/First Light, (right) VCL; 4-19 Robert Semenuik/First Light, Brian Milne/First Light, Lorraine C. Parow/First Light, Barry Dursley/First Light; 5-0 Stephen Homer/First Light; 5-18 George Hunter/Miller Comstock; 5-19 Eric Hayes/Miller Comstock; 5-21 M. Beedell/Miller Comstock; 5-22b VCL; 5-23b VCL; 5-24b VCL; 6-0 Brian Leng/First Light; 6-5 Barry Griffths/Network; 6-15 Grant Heilman/Miller Comstock; 6-18 (left) Charles Bisztray/Focus Stock Photo Inc., (right) Noranda Minerals Inc.; 6-23 Tom Tracy/First Light; 6-24 & 6-25 Courtesy of Bombardier Inc.; 6-28 (both) Canadian Tire Corporation, Limited; 7-1 Ontario Ministry of Tourism and Recreation; 7-4 W. Andrew; 7-6 (left) Ontario Ministry of Tourism and Recreation, (right) Miller Comstock #P2135; 7-10 Todd Korol/First Light; 7-14 VCL; 7-15 Birgitte Nielsen; 7-17a Miller Comstock #P1327; 7-17b Miller Comstock; 7-17c Wayne Andrew; 7-18 (clockwise) W. Ian Biggar/Take Stock Inc., Angus McNee/ Take Stock Inc., Public Affairs Alberta, VCL, Angus McNee/Take Stock Inc., L.T. Webster/Take Stock Inc., Public Affairs Alberta; 7-19 VCL; 7-20 Eric Otto/Miller Comstock; 8-0 Chris Bruun/ Focus Stock Photo Inc.; 8-1 Robert Hall/ Miller Comstock; 8-2 George Hunter/Miller Comstock; 8-3 Barry Griffiths/Network; 8-4a Lorraine C. Parow/First Light; 8-4b George Hunter/Miller Comstock; 8-4c William Belsey/Miller Comstock; 8-4d Public Affairs Alberta; 8-7 Patricia Yeomans/Miller Comstock; 8-8 (top to bottom) Brian Milne/First Light, VCL, VCL, Karl Sommeren/Miller Comstock, Robert Hall/Miller Comstock, Wayne Andrew, John Fulker/Miller Comstock; 8-9a (top and bottom) Ontario Ministry of Tourism and Recreation; 8-9b (left and right) Ontario Ministry of Tourism and Recreation; 8-9c (left) George Hunter/Miller Comstock, (right) Ontario Archives; 8-9d (left) Ontario Archives, (right) Barrett & MacKay/Masterfile; 9-0 Ontario Hydro; 9-3a Eric Hayes/Miller Comstock; 9-3b Miller Comstock; 9-3c Jim Russell/First Light; 9-3d Patrick Morrow/First Light; 9-3e EduVision; 9-6 Peter Christopher/Masterfile; 9-11 Ontario Hydro; 9-13 Ontario Hydro; 9-15 Robert Semenuik/First Light; 9-16 Ontario Hydro; 10-0 Ontario Ministry of Tourism and Recreation; 10-5 Ontario Hydro; 10-8 and 10-9 The aerial photographs on pages 212 and 213 © 1953 and 1986 Her Majesty the Queen in Right of Canada. Reproduced from the collection of the National Air Photo Library with permission of Energy, Mines and Resources Canada; 10-12 Canapress; 10-13 Canapress; 11-0 NASA; 11-2 Barry Griffiths/Network; 11-3 City of Toronto Archives, James Collection, #138; 11-7 Tom Grill/Miller Comstock; 11-8 National Archives of Canada, C-57183; 11-11 Royal Ontario Museum, Sigmund Samuel Canadiana Collection; 11-12 Metropolitan Toronto Library Board; 11-14 Kevin Duffy/Focus Stock Photo Inc.; 11-15 Barry Griffiths/ Network; 12-0 Barbara K. Deans/Canapress; 12-3 (left to right) Barry Griffiths/Network, Ontario Ministry of Tourism and Recreation, John de Visser/Masterfile; 12-8 Canapress; 12-9 Robert Semenuik/First Light; 12-11 National Archives of Canada PA 10255, W.J. Topley Collection; 12-15 (clockwise) Gary Archibald/First Light, Canapress; Ontario Ministry of Tourism and Recreation, Gary Archibald/First Light; 12-18 1) Masterfile/Bob Anders; 2) VCL: 3) Lorraine C. Parow/First Light; 4) Grant Black/ First Light; 5) Ronald Weber/ Masterfile; 6) Brian Milne/First Light; 13-0 Jessie Parker/First Light; 13-1 Birgitte Nielsen; 13-4 Royal Bank of Canada; 13-7 Barry Griffiths/Network; 13-11 Courtesy of Canadian Broadcasting Corporation; 13-12 Jessie Parker/First Light; 13-13 Copyright © Terry Mosher. Reprinted with permission — The Toronto Star Syndicate; 14-0 NASA; 14-2 (left to right) Roger Lemoyne/CIDA, Michel Faugere/CIDA, David Barbour/CIDA, Roger Lemoyne/ CIDA, Ron Watts/First Light, 500-06-05/CIDA; 15-0 Pat Morrow/ First Light; 15-2 Canapress; 15-6 Canapress; 15-10 James Mason/First Light; 15-11 Canapress; 15-15 David Barbour/ CIDA; 15-17 Canapress.

Index

Answers to word search puzzle, p. 109:
clerk, mechanic, driver, singer, dentist, nurse, teacher, cook, librarian, minister.